Textile

E.P.G. Gohl
L.D. Vilensky

Longman Cheshire Pty Limited
346 St Kilda Road, Melbourne, Australia, 3004

Offices in Sydney, Brisbane, Adelaide, and Perth.
Associated companies, branches, and representatives
throughout the world.
© 1980 Longman Cheshire

© This edition 1983 Longman Cheshire

First published 1980
Reprinted 1981
Second edition 1983

Printed in Malaysia
by Percetakan Jiwabaru Sdn. Bhd., Kuala Lumpur
Set in 11/13 Plantin (Linotron)

Designed by Joanne Waite

National Library of Australia
Cataloguing-in-Publication data

Gohl, E. P. G. (Erhard Paul Gottlieb).
  Textile science.

  2nd ed.
  Previous ed. : Melbourne : Longman Cheshire, 1980.
  For senior secondary school students.
  Includes index.
  ISBN 0 582 68595 8.

  1. Textile fabrics.   I. Vilensky, L. D.
  (Leo David).   II. Title.

677

Contents

Preface to the first edition

This book is intended to assist senior high school students, technical college students, and all those engaged in the various branches of the textile and clothing industry. It brings together in one volume the explanations which have become generally accepted for the chemical and physical properties, dyeing, printing and chemical finishing of textile fibres. As well, it fills the existing gap between simpler texts and more esoteric texts and learned articles on textile fibres.

It is hoped that the technically and scientifically more sophisticated reader will acknowledge the judicious use of generalisations to which we have had occasionally to resort. These generalisations have kept the book within its intended scope. However, should there be any errors, omissions, or suggestions for improvement of the subject matter presented, we would appreciate hearing of these.

A book of this nature cannot become a reality without the assistance and co-operation of many. For this reason, we would like to express our gratitude to Longman Cheshire Pty Limited for publishing it; to Ms Jane Bohrsmann of Longman Cheshire Pty Ltd for her painstaking interest in what we wrote to ensure that it would be understandable; to Julie Mattick, who typed much of the manuscript, as did Myriam Vilensky; to the many authors of books and scientific papers on textile fibres and related topics which the authors have read over the years and whose accepted theories and postulations are reflected in our explanations; and, finally, to the many firms and organisations, acknowledged elsewhere, who generously and willingly gave their permission to reproduce sundry material.

E.P.G. Gohl
L.D. Vilensky
1979

Preface to the second edition

The necessity to reprint the first edition of *Textile Science* so soon after it was published confirmed that it was realising its aims and objectives, as well as rewarding Longman Cheshire for their interest and material assistance.

Since first publication, we have received many helpful suggestions and useful criticisms to improve the content and presentation of the text. We are therefore grateful to the publishers for bringing out this second edition and thus giving us the opportunity to incorporate most of the suggested improvements. In thanking those named below, we have not forgotten chance remarks, gathered in conversation with others, which have contributed to the revised version.

We thank Vicki Dalla, teacher of Textiles and Design at Wade High School, Griffith, New South Wales, for her helpful criticism of some sections of the revised text. We also thank Les Billingsley (Head Teacher), Ken Boehm, Brian Coleman and Barry Worswick, all teachers at the School of Textiles, Sydney, for advice, information and/or useful discussions; and Peter Carty, Senior Lecturer at the School of Home Economics, Newcastle-upon-Tyne Polytechnic, England.

Mark A. McElroy, a Chief Examiner in Chemistry for the London University School Examination Board, Derby, England, gave freely of his time and provided us with much assistance. In thanking him we also express our appreciation to him for initially accepting the invitation, extended in the first edition, to inform us of any errors, omissions or suggestions for improvement of the book. We hope that future readers will also take up this invitation to ensure that further editions of this book are kept up to date.

Our thanks go also to Barbara Langevad, editor, Myriam Vilensky and last, but not least, to Christa, Christoph and Karl Gohl. Their understanding and patience during the preparation of this edition is gratefully acknowledged.

E.P.G. Gohl
L.D. Vilensky
1983

Acknowledgements

We are grateful to the following for permission to reproduce sundry material as indicated:

Ciba-Geigy Ltd, Switzerland: *pages* 26, 30

Courtaulds Ltd, England: *pages* 34, 35

Fibremakers Ltd, Australia: *pages* 29, 30, 34, 55

International Wool Secretariat, England: *pages* 42, 43

Textile Research Journal, United States of America: *page* 41

Toray Industries Inc., Japan: *pages* 61, 66, 72, 80

Toyo Products Co Ltd, Japan: *page* 61

USA Agricultural Department, United States of America: *page* 17

Note

Various words such as Antron, Blankophor, Dieldrin, Mitin, Eulan, Scotchgard, Fabulon, Remazol, Procion, Zefran, etc. have been used in this book. These words are registered trademarks and should always be spelled with an initial capital.

Acknowledgements

1 Introduction to fibre polymers and fibre properties

. . . I have often thought, that probably there might be a way found out, to make an artificial glutinous composition, much resembling, if not fully as good, nay better, than that excrement, or what ever substance it be out of which, the silkworm wire-draws his clew. . . This hint . . . may give some ingenious inquisitive person an occasion of making some trials, which if successful . . . I suppose he will have no occasion to be displeased.

This speculation on making a filament was written in 1664 by the English physicist Dr Robert Hooke in his book *Micrographica*. His speculation became a reality from 1900 onward. It became a reality because of the continuing scientific investigations being carried out on natural and man-made fibres and similar materials. These investigations have yielded a steadily increasing understanding of fibre composition, structure, properties and behaviour, and have enabled the large-scale manufacture of fibres not found in nature, i.e. man-made fibres. The knowledge and understanding gained from manufacturing fibres, as distinct from growing them, has assisted in increasing the understanding of the very complex molecular or polymer composition of the natural fibres. Even though very much more is now known about fibres, there are still many unanswered questions about their properties and behaviour. Some of the answers will, no doubt, be provided in the years to come.

In the meantime, in order to understand some of the reasons why a fibre possesses certain properties and behaves in a particular manner when in use, it is necessary to acquire a knowledge of the following properties.

Polymerisation

Textile fibres, like most substances, are made up of molecules. Fibre molecules are called **polymers** (derived from the Latin *poly* = many and *mer* = unit). The 'unit' of a polymer is the **monomer**, also derived from the Latin (*mono* = one). At the molecular level the polymer is extremely long and linear, whereas the monomer is very small. Monomers are usually chemically reactive, whereas polymers tend to be unreactive. This is illustrated by the chemical reaction called polymerisation, which causes the monomers to join end-to-end to form a polymer.

Although the polymer tends, in general, to be chemically unreactive, this does not prevent its being subsequently attacked by chemicals and other degrading agents.

The length of the polymer is most important. All fibres, both man-made and natural, have long to extremely long polymers. Measuring the length of a polymer is a complicated, if not impossible, task. Estimates of the length of a polymer can be obtained by determining its **degree of polymerisation**. This is often abbreviated to DP and defined by the following mathematical expression:

$$\text{degree of polymerisation } = \frac{\text{average molecular weight of polymer}}{\text{molecular weight of the repeating unit in the polymer}}$$

Note: Some fibre polymers may have been polymerised from two or more different monomers; thus, the repeating unit is the combination or segment formed by these two or more different monomers which repeat regularly along the length of the polymer.

In determining the degree of polymerisation of cotton, for instance, a figure of 5000 is obtained. This means that, on average, each cotton polymer consists of about 5000 repeating units. With cotton the repeating unit is **cellobiose**, which may also be taken as its monomer. Cotton provides an example to illustrate the size relationship between polymer and monomer. Imagine the cotton polymer to be as thick as an ordinary 8 mm pencil; the polymer would then be about 50 m long. As it consists on average of about 5000 repeating units or monomers, then each one of these would be about 10 mm long — a ratio of 5000:1.

A polymer is often described as having a **backbone**, consisting of the atoms which are bonded to each other in a linear configuration and which are responsible for the length of the polymer. This is illustrated in Table 1.2.

Although it is not yet known how cellulose and keratin are polymerised in nature, the polymerisation of man-made, synthetic monomers to polymers is quite well understood. The manufacture of the synthetic, polymeric material which will be extruded to form the synthetic, man-made filament is categorised into two types of polymerisation: addition and condensation polymerisation.

Addition polymerisation

With this type of polymerisation the monomers add or join end-to-end without liberating any by-product on polymerisation. Some fibres consisting of addition polymers are acrylic, modacrylic, polyethylene or polyethene, polypropylene or polypropene, polyvinyl alcohol and the chlorofibres, namely polyvinyl chloride and polyvinylidene chloride.

Condensation polymerisation

With this type of polymerisation the monomers join end-to-end and liberate a by-product. This by-product is usually a simple compound — generally water — but it may alternatively be hydrogen chloride or ammonia, depending upon the specific monomers involved. Some fibres consisting of condensation polymers are elastomeric, nylon and polyester.

Note: The polymers of acetate, cotton, flax, silk, triacetate, viscose and other regenerated cellulose fibres, and wool, do not fit readily into the above classification, because not enough is known as yet about the way their polymers are synthesised in nature.

A knowledge of addition and condensation polymerisation is of importance in the synthesis and large-scale manufacture of the textile polymeric substances and their extrusion as textile filaments. Such knowledge belongs more to chemical engineering technology than to textile technology. Similarly, a knowledge of the propagation, growth, nurturing and harvesting of natural fibres belongs more to the specialised agricultural sciences of animal husbandry and crop cultivation. The textile technologist recognises such knowledge as being peripheral and to be used for rounding off explanations and understanding of fibre properties and behaviour. Synthetic fibre polymers and their respective fibres are at times referred to by the appropriate name found in the categorisation below. It will be noted that the natural, regenerated and ester-cellulose fibres are not included. The reason is that insufficient is known about the growth, formation and/or synthesis of their polymers.

Types of polymer

Homopolymer

Such a polymer is polymerised from the same (= *homos* in Greek) or only one kind of monomer. Some homopolymer fibres are: nylon 6, nylon 11, polyethylene, polypropylene, polyvinyl chloride, polyvinylidene chloride, polyacrylonitrile as distinct from acrylic and modacrylic. See also Tables 1.1 and 1.2.

Copolymer

Such a polymer is polymerised from two or more different monomers. There are four sub-categories of copolymers, as follows.

Alternating copolymer

Usually two monomers polymerise in an alternating sequence, as shown in Table 1.2. Some alternating copolymer fibres are: nylon 6.6 and polyester; see also Table 1.1.

Block copolymer

Two or more different monomers polymerise in blocks or segments before linking up to form the polymer; see Table 1.2. Block copolymers are still largely experimental.

Graft copolymer

The polymer is polymerised in such a manner that a segment, polymerised from the two or more different monomers used, attaches itself as a side-chain or forms a branch of the polymer; see Table 1.2. Sometimes the side-chain may be polymerised only from one of the three monomers. Then the other two monomers form the backbone of the polymer, usually as an altering or random copolymer. In general, graft copolymer

Table 1.1 Chemical composition and structure of the most commonly used textile fibres.

Fibre	Basic unit or monomer	Polymer
Acetate	The hydroxyl groups on the cellulose polymer are acetylated to the degree that the **acetate** or **secondary cellulose acetate polymer** has less than 92 per cent but at least 74 per cent of its hydroxyl groups acetylated; that is, 2.3 to 2.4 of the OH-groups per glucose unit are acetylated. This is usually shown as 4 acetate groups per cellobiose unit. The **triacetate** or **primary cellulose acetate polymer** has at least 92 per cent of its hydroxyl groups acetylated. In general, this is shown as 6 acetate groups per cellubiose unit.	 The **acetate** or **secondary cellulose acetate polymer**, which has a degree of polymerisation of about 130 units (i.e. $n = 130$). The **triacetate** or **primary cellulose acetate polymer**, which has a degree of polymerisation of about 225 units (i.e. $n = 225$).
Acrylic	*Acrylic* At least 85 per cent of the mass of the acrylic fibre must be composed of **acrylonitrile monomers**; that is, and no more than 15 per cent is complosed of the **copolymer**; that is, where X is usually an anionic radical, e.g. —Cl, —OOCCH$_3$, —CONH$_2$, etc. *Modacrylic* At least 35 per cent but no more than 85 per cent of the mass of the modacrylic fibre polymer must be composed of **acrylonitrile monomers**, and the remainder is composed of the **copolymer**.	 The **acrylic polymer**. The values of m and p depend upon the mass of copolymer present; hence, whether it will be an acrylic or a modacrylic polymer fibre. The degree of polymerisation is about 2000 units (i.e. $n = 2000$).

Table 1.1 (continued)

Fibre	Basic unit or monomer	Polymer
Cotton	**Cellobiose**, the basic unit of cellulose.	Cellulose, the polymer of cotton, with a degree of polymerisation of about 5000 celloboise units (i.e. n = 5000).
Cuprammonium or **cupro, polynosic** or **modal**, and **viscose**	**Cellobiose** is the basic unit of the cuprammonium, polynosic and viscose polymer. See **cotton** for chemical formula details. *Note*: The name rayon is no longer preferred for these three fibres; see page 54.	Cellulose, in regenerated form, is the polymer of these three regenerated cellulose fibres; their degree of polymerisation is about: 250 cellobiose units (i.e. n = 250) for cuprammonium; 300 cellobiose units (i.e. n = 300) for polynosic; 175 cellobiose units (i.e. n = 175) for viscose.
Elastomeric	The complexity and length of the elastomeric monomers and the repeating units of their polymers makes it impossible to reproduce them satisfactorily within the confines of this table. Refer, therefore, to the section on elastomeric fibres in Chapter 5, 'The Synthetic Fibres' for the two types of elastomeric monomers and polymers; that is, the polyester and polyether types.	
Flax	Cellobiose — see **cotton** for chemical formula details.	Cellulose is also the polymer of flax, with a degree of polymerisation of 18 000 cellobiose units; that is, n = 18 000. See **cotton** for chemical formula details.
Nylon	For **nylon 6,6** the monomers are **adipic acid**: $HOOC(CH_2)_4COOH$ and **hexamethylene diamine**: $H_2N(CH_2)_6NH_2$. for **nylon 6** the monomer is *caprolactam*:	$[-OC(CH_2)_4CONH(CH_2)_6NH-]_n$ Polyhexamethylene diamino adipate, the repeating unit of the **nylon 6,6 polymer**, with a degree of polymerisation of 50 to 80 units (i.e. n = 50 to 80) $[-(CH_2)_5CONH-]_n$ Polycaprolactam, the repeating unit of the **nylon 6 polymer**, with a degree of polymerisation of 200 units (i.e. n = 200).

Table 1.1 (continued)

Fibre	Basic unit or monomer	Polymer
Polyester	The monomers of the most common polyester are **ethylene glycol**, $HOCH_2CH_2OH$ and **terephthalic acid**: $HOOC$ —⟨O⟩— $COOH$	$[-OOC$ ⟨O⟩ $- COO-(CH_2)_2-]_n$ Polyethylene terephthalate, the repeating unit of the **polyester polymer**, with a degree of polymerisation of 115 to 140 units (i.e. $n = 115$ to 140).
Rayon	*Note*: the name rayon is no longer preferred (see page 54).	

Silk and wool	The **silk fibroin polymer** is composed of 16 different amino acids, whilst the **wool keratin polymer** is composed of 20 different amino acids.
	
	    Amino acids have this general formula:
	
	$$H_2N-\underset{\underset{H}{\mid}}{\overset{\overset{R}{\mid}}{C}}-COOH$$
	
	where R = a radical, which is different for each of the 20 known amino acids.
		$$H-[-NH-\underset{}{\overset{\overset{R}{\mid}}{CH}}-CO-NH-\underset{}{\overset{\overset{R'}{\mid}}{CH}}-CO-NH-\underset{}{\overset{\overset{R''}{\mid}}{CH}}-CO-]_n-OH$$
		
		The general formula for the **polypetide polymer**.
		    Depending upon the type of radicals R, R', R'', etc. the polypeptide polymer would be identified either as being a **silk fibroin polymer** or a **wool keratin polymer**.
		    The degrees of polymerisation for silk and wool are not known.

fibres tend to have softening points which are too low for apparel and household textile use. However, Zefran, an acrylic graft copolymer fibre, has become successful. Its manufacturer describes Zefran as 'a graft copolymer of dye-receptive groups on a backbone of heat-resistant polyacrylonitrile'.

Random copolymer

The monomers are polymerised in no particular order or in a random fashion as shown in Table 1.2. Random copolymers tend to be polymerised mainly from only two different monomers. Some random copolymer fibres are acrylic and modacrylic; see also Table 1.1.

The term comonomer is also used. It refers to the monomer which is added to the polymerisation reaction to impart the special properties desired in the copolymer, e.g. greater affinity for dyes as in the case of acrylic and modacrylic fibres. For instance, the comonomer of acrylic and modacrylic polymers, which incidentally gave rise to the term copolymer, is the 'monomer other than acrylonitrile' as defined and described on pages 91 to 94.

Table 1.1 summarises the chemical composition and gives an indication of the structure for the polymers of the more commonly used textile fibres. Explanations of the chemical terms used can be found in the text and in the Glossary. Should further information be required, reference should be made to *The Penguin Dictionary of Science* by E.B. Uvarov et al., Penguin Books.

Table 1.2 Categories of fibre polymers
(Let △, □ and ◯ be the symbols to represent three different monomers)

Fibre polymer category	Symbolic representation of fibre polymer category	Monomer example(s)	Extended polymer formula	Contracted polymer formula
Homopolymer	—△—△—△—△—△—△— All polymers of the fibre are polymerised from only one kind of monomer.	acrylonitrile	polyacrylonitrile polymer	polyacrylonitrile polymer
Copolymers **a alternating copolymer**	—△—□—△—□—△—□— All copolymers of the fibre are polymerised, usually from only two monomers which alternate along the backbone of each copolymer.	hexamethylene diamine; adipic acid	nylon 6, 6, or polyhexamethylene diamino adipate	nylon 6, 6
b block copolymer	—△—◯—◯—◯—◯—◯—◯—◯—△—□—□—□—□—□—□—□—□—△— block or segment of polymerised monomer of one particular kind; block or segment of polymerised monomer of another kind	block or segment of polymerised monomer of another kind		block copolymers are as yet only experimental and no practical application has been found for them to date
c graft copolymer	theoretically this could be —△—□—□—△—□—□—△— polymer backbone; grafted polymerised segment. A random, alternating or homopolymer backbone from two or more monomers with a side-chain, branch or polymerised segment again consisting of one or more monomer; in practice, a successful graft copolymer, namely Zefran, is a homopolymer onto which has been grafted a polymerised segment consisting of only one kind of monomer, i.e.	acrylonitrile; vinylpyrrolidone	polyacrylonitrile backbone; grafted segment of polymerised polyvinylpyrrolidone; polyacrylonitrile-polyvinylpyrrolidone	n_1 = degree of polymerisation for the polyacrylonitrile backbone; n_2 = degree of polymerisation for the grafted polymerised segment of polyvinyl-pyrrolidone
d random copolymer	△—□—△—□—□—△—△—□—△—□— Random copolymers are usually polymerised from two different monomers which occur in a random fashion along the backbone of the copolymer; it is probable that some copolymers are random molecules i.e. those which form copolymers from three monomers; it is more likely for addition monomers. i.e. those which form polymers by addition	polymerisation, to cause the formation of random copolymers; addition monomers can join to each other in any order as may be seen from the example given at right; however, condensation monomers, i.e., those which may form copolymers by condensation polymerisation, tend to form alternating copolymers due to their specific reactive end or terminal groups; this may be seen from the example given for a alternating copolymer above.	acrylonitrile; vinylidene chloride	polyacrylonitrilevinylidene chloride	polyacrylonitrile vinylidene chloride e.g. Teklan

7

Intrapolymer bonding

Intrapolymer bonding means the bonds holding the atoms together to make up the fibre polymer. The fibre polymer is equivalent to a molecule — the smallest portion of a substance capable of existing independently and retaining the properties of the original substance.

Textile fibre polymers are organic compounds; the exceptions being the molecules comprising the man-made inorganic fibres and the natural mineral fibres. Describing

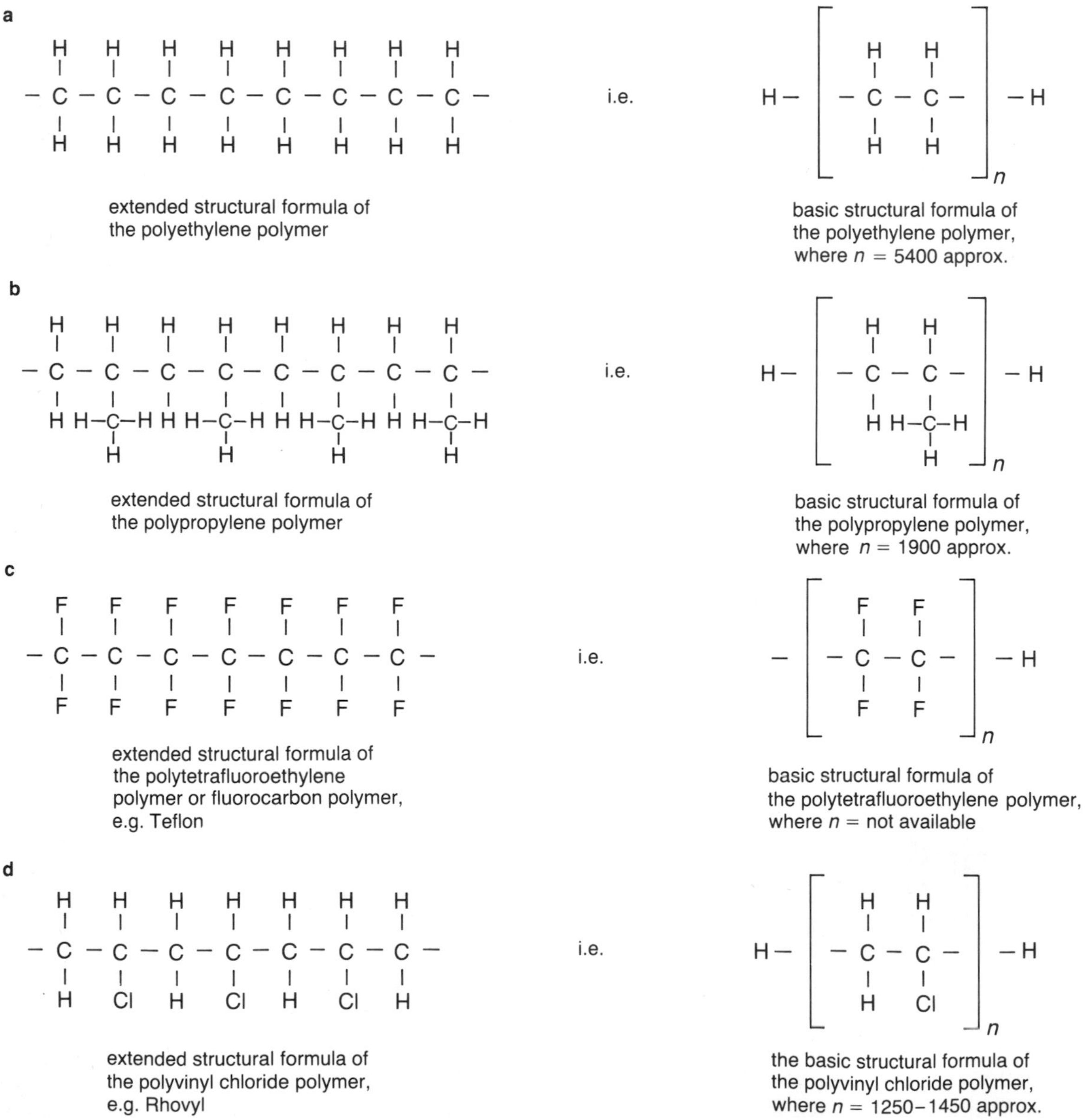

a

i.e.

extended structural formula of
the polyethylene polymer

basic structural formula of
the polyethylene polymer,
where $n = 5400$ approx.

b

i.e.

extended structural formula of
the polypropylene polymer

basic structural formula of
the polypropylene polymer,
where $n = 1900$ approx.

c

i.e.

extended structural formula of
the polytetrafluoroethylene
polymer or fluorocarbon polymer,
e.g. Teflon

basic structural formula of
the polytetrafluoroethylene polymer,
where n = not available

d

i.e.

extended structural formula of
the polyvinyl chloride polymer,
e.g. Rhovyl

the basic structural formula of
the polyvinyl chloride polymer,
where $n = 1250-1450$ approx.

Figure 1.1 Four examples of fibre polymers to illustrate the fact that they are organic compounds predominantly composed of carbon and hydrogen atoms; other examples of fibre polymers are given in Tables 1.1 and 1.2.

fibre polymers as organic compounds signifies that they are predominantly composed of carbon and hydrogen atoms, with some oxygen, nitrogen, chlorine and/or fluorine atoms. This may be seen from the polymer formulae given in Tables 1.1 and 1.2 and Fig. 1.1.

The bonds between atoms in polymers

In general, single covalent bonds join the atoms forming the polymer. The single covalent bond is represented by a single short line drawn between the letters or symbols used to represent the atoms of each polymer; see Tables 1.1 and 1.2. Single covalent bonds, defined and explained on page 21, are chemically very stable and unreactive. In fact this type of bond is practically indestructible when it occurs between carbon and carbon atoms, carbon and hydrogen, carbon and oxygen, carbon and chlorine, and carbon and fluorine atoms:

$$-\overset{|}{\underset{|}{C}}-\overset{|}{\underset{|}{C}}-; \quad -\overset{|}{\underset{|}{C}}-\overset{|}{\underset{|}{H}}-; \quad -\overset{|}{\underset{|}{C}}-\overset{|}{\underset{|}{O}}-\overset{|}{\underset{|}{C}}-; \quad -\overset{|}{\underset{|}{C}}-\overset{|}{\underset{|}{Cl}}; \quad -\overset{|}{\underset{|}{C}}-F.$$

It will be noticed (Tables 1.1 and 1.2) that much of the backbone of any fibre polymer consists of carbon segments of varying length, i.e. $-\overset{|}{\underset{|}{C}}-\overset{|}{\underset{|}{C}}-\overset{|}{\underset{|}{C}}-\overset{|}{\underset{|}{C}}-\overset{|}{\underset{|}{C}}-\overset{|}{\underset{|}{C}}-$.

The reason for this is the ready formation of such segments which, owing to their single covalent bonding, contribute significantly to the chemical stability of the polymer and hence of the fibre.

The stability and unreactive nature of the single covalent bond joining the atoms of fibre polymers may also be expressed objectively. It has been estimated that the bond energy or bond strength is between 330 and 420 kilojoules for these single covalent bonds. This indicates a magnitude of bond strengths in excess of any other intra- or inter-polymer forces of attraction. It is for this reason also that it usually requires severe and prolonged exposure to chemicals and/or heat before fibre polymer breakdown occurs.

There are, of course, segments of the polymer backbone that are composed of other atoms, which influence the properties of the polymer as follows.

The amide or peptide group

This group is given in Fig. 1.2. When present in nylon polymers it is called the **amide group**; it is also present in silk, wool, mohair and all other animal or protein fibres, and is then called the **peptide group**. Figure 1.2 also shows the acid and alkaline hydrolysis of the amide or peptide group. This hydrolysis represents the most common chemical destructive attack upon the amide or peptide group during the life of the polymer, and hence of the fibre. Such hydrolysis (see Fig. 1.2) breaks the amide or peptide bonds, i.e. the single covalent bond between the carbon and nitrogen atoms. It is also important to note that the carbonyl oxygen of the amide or peptide group is strongly electronegative. This means it will develop a slight negative charge and give rise to hydrogen bonds. These hydrogen bonds will occur between the carbonyl oxygen and hydrogen atoms on closely aligned and adjacent polymers. An explanation of hydrogen bonds is given on page 16.

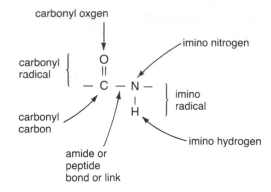

Figure 1.2a The amide or peptide group

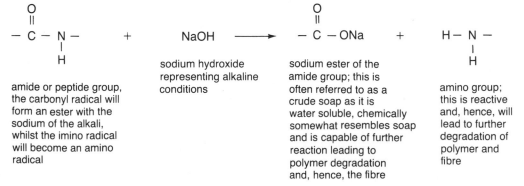

Figure 1.2b Acid hydrolysis of the amide or peptide group; the hydrolysis occurs at the single covalent bond which exists between the carbon and nitrogen atoms.

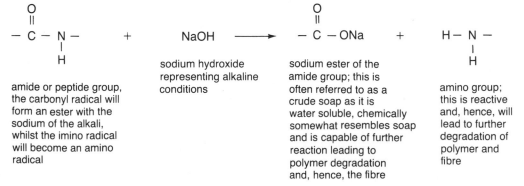

carbonyl radical {
$$-\overset{O}{\underset{}{\overset{\|}{C}}} - \underset{\underset{H}{|}}{N} -$$
} imino radical

amide or peptide group, the carbonyl radical will form an ester with the sodium of the alkali, whilst the imino radical will become an amino radical

$+$ NaOH $\longrightarrow$

sodium hydroxide representing alkaline conditions

$$-\overset{O}{\underset{}{\overset{\|}{C}}} - ONa$$

sodium ester of the amide group; this is often referred to as a crude soap as it is water soluble, chemically somewhat resembles soap and is capable of further reaction leading to polymer degradation and, hence, the fibre

$+$

$$H - \underset{\underset{H}{|}}{N} -$$

amino group; this is reactive and, hence, will lead to further degradation of polymer and fibre

Figure 1.2c Alkaline hydrolysis or spaonification of the amide or peptide group; the hydrolysis occurs at the single covalent bond which exists between the carbon and nitrogen atoms.

The benzene ring

Benzene rings occur at regular intervals along the backbone of the common textile polyester polymer polyethylene terephthalate, e.g. Dacron, Terylene, Tetoron, Tre-

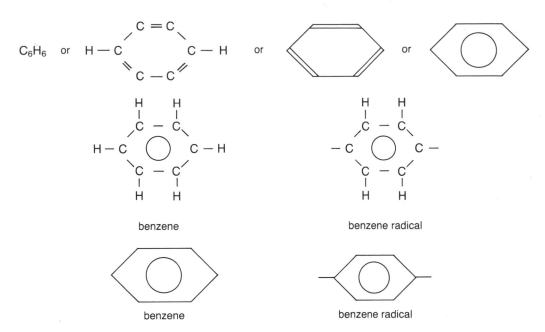

Figure 1.3 Benzene, its molecular and structural formula and symbolic representation. See text below for explanation

vira, etc. Invariably the benzene ring is a constituent of dye molecules (see Chapter 6, Figs 6.1 and 6.15 for example). The benzene ring is sometimes referred to as the **aromatic radical**. This term came about from the pleasant and/or distinctive odours of many naturally occurring substances, such as balsams, resins and by-products from coal tar, which once were the main source of benzene.

The benzene molecule is a hexagon, often referred to as a **ring structure**, composed of carbon and hydrogen atoms as shown in Fig. 1.3. The accepted symbol for benzene in chemical formulae is a hexagon containing a circle; the circle indicates the resonance or orbiting electrons of the benzene molecular structure. It is the unique manner in which the carbon atoms of the benzene molecule adhere to their electrons which makes the benzene molecular structure relatively unreactive. Thus the presence of benzene in fibre polymers and dye molecules may be taken as an indication of chemical stability and resistance to degradation. Of course, this may not have been the primary intention when the fibre polymer or dye molecule was synthesised. Rather, it may have been more the ability of the benzene-containing compound to react in a certain way (i.e. to provide a particular hue, etc.) which prompted its initial use. Its contribution to greater stability of the resultant fibre polymer or dye molecule is of distinct advantage.

Ether linkage

The ether linkage may be found in such polymers as cellulose, elastomeric, ester-cellulose and polyesters. It exists between carbon and oxygen atoms thus:

$$-\overset{|}{\underset{|}{C}}-\overset{|}{\underset{|}{O}}-\overset{|}{\underset{|}{C}}-.$$

The linkage obtains its name from the family of organic compounds in which it is found, namely the ethers — diethyl ether being the well known anaesthetic ether.

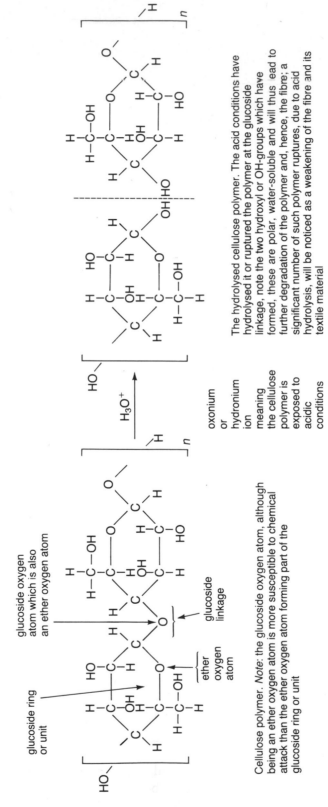

Figure 1.4 Acid hydrolysis of the cellulose polymer

Ethers are chemically quite unreactive. One reason for this is the great chemical stability of the carbon–oxygen linkage found in every ether molecule. In general, an ether linkage in a fibre polymer tends to be the most durable and least affected by degrading agents.

There is, however, one exception to the above. This is the ether linkage in cellulose known as the **glucoside link**. It links the glucose units (see Fig. 2.4). Under acidic conditions the glucoside link will undergo hydrolysis as shown in Fig. 1.4. This is the reason for the destructive effect with acids have upon cellulosic fibres.

Ester group

Esters may be regarded as organic salts: they correspond to the inorganic salts. They are formed by replacing the hydrogen of an acid with an organic radical. In fibre polymers this is usually the reaction between:

a **a carboxyl group**, i.e. –COOH, the characteristic group of the commonly occurring organic acids called carboxylic acids; e.g. acetic acid, formic acid, citric acid, etc.

and

b **a hydroxyl group**, i.e. –OH, the characteristic group of alcohols, such as the monohydric alcohols (e.g. ethanol) as found in alcoholic drinks, which only have one –OH group per molecule; and the polyhydric alcohols such as cellulose (see Table 1.2 and Fig. 1.5) which have more than one –OH group per molecule.

Figure 1.5 shows the formula of the ester group. The group is not resistant to alkalis — it is subject to saponification or alkaline hydrolysis, as shown in Fig. 1.5b. The saponification of the ester group produces water-soluble and reactive end-groups, leading to further degradation of the polymer and hence of the fibre.

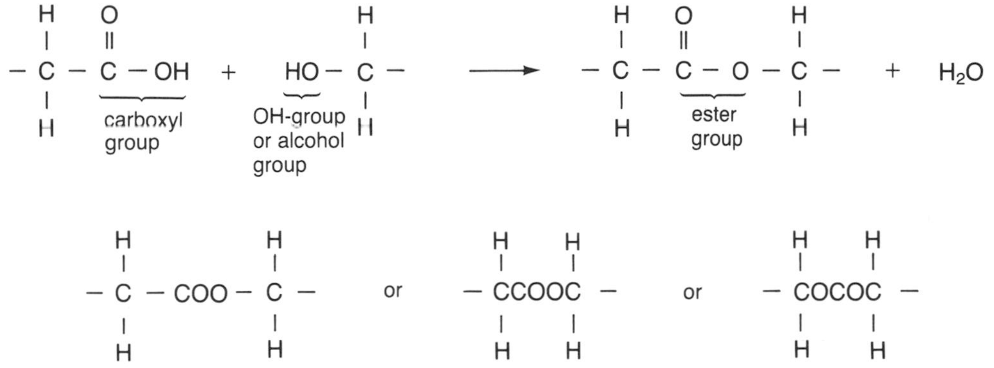

Figure 1.5a Formation of an ester group, generally as shown, from a carboxyl group and a hydroxyl group, –OH group, or alcohol group. The ester group is often also shown as depicted below.

Hydroxyl group or –OH group

By definition, the hydroxyl group is the univalent –OH group, pronounced O-H-group. It is attached by a single covalent bond as a side-group to fibre polymers (e.g. cellulose polymers; see Figs 1.4 and 2.4). This distinguishes it from the *free* hydroxyl

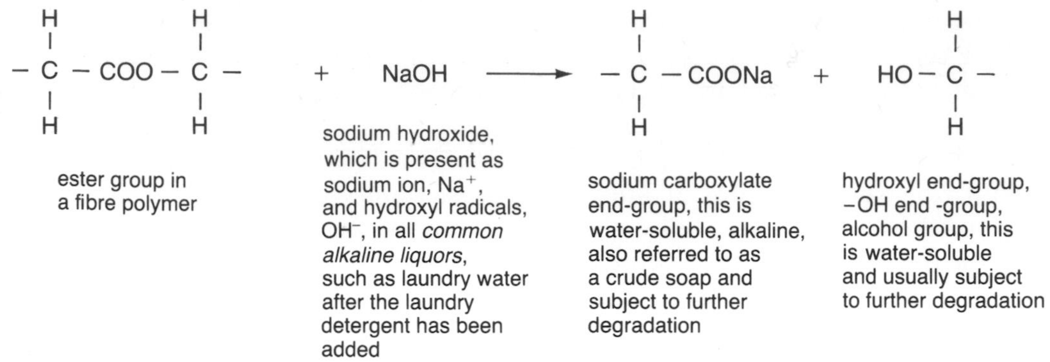

Figure 1.5b Alkaline hydrolysis or saponification of an ester group in a fibre polymer. *Note*: saponification means soap-making and the sodium carboxylate group is the typical water-soluble end-group of all soaps made from natural oils or fats with sodium hydroxide.

group which is the cation, ion or negative radical OH^-.

The presence of –OH groups on fibre polymers is of two-fold significance:

a The –OH groups are polar and will therefore attract water molecules, which are also polar. Thus –OH groups are mainly responsible for the moisture absorbency of a fibre, and hence its comfort when worn.

b The polarity of –OH groups will give rise to the formation of hydrogen bonds (see page 16 for explanation). The formation of such hydrogen bonds will contribute significantly towards the coherence of the fibre's polymer system.

The presence of –OH groups on fibre polymers should not be underestimated. Their importance is illustrated by the fact that constant efforts are being made to have –OH groups introduced onto the hydrophobic, synthetic fibre polymers. The presence of –OH groups on these polymers would significantly enhance the hygroscopic nature and comfort of these fibres.

In general, the –OH group is chemically reactive and may contribute to the degradation of the polymer of which it is a constituent.

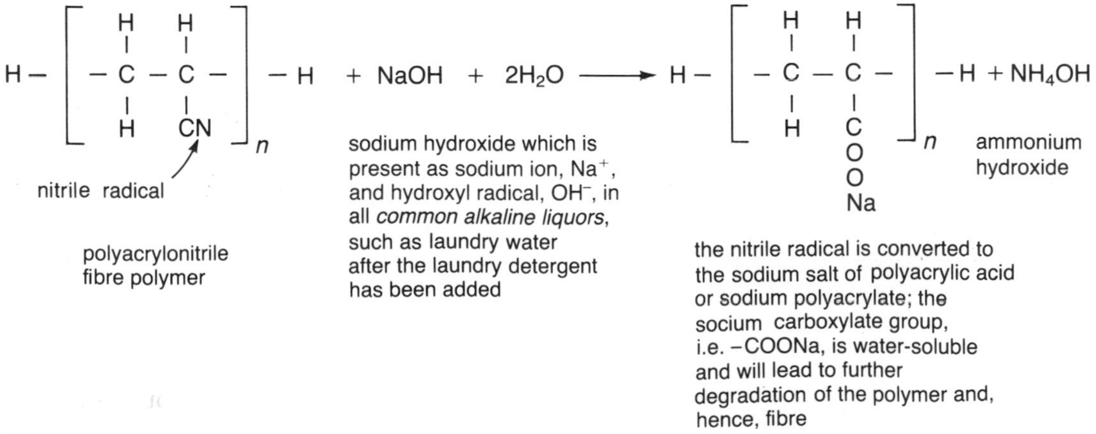

Figure 1.6 Alkaline hydrolysis or saponification of the polyacrylonitrile fibre polymer; the above indicates how polyacrylonitrile segments in acrylic and modacrylic fibres can become degraded by alkalis.

Nitrile group

This is the characteristic polymer side-group of acrylic and modacrylic fibres, i.e. –CN (see also Tables 1.1 and 1.2). In general, the nitrile group does not react with acids or break down in acidic conditions. It is, however, subject to alkaline hydrolysis or saponification, as would occur during normal laundering. Under normal circumstances this is not very noticeable, because the crytallinity or good orientation of the polymer system of the acrylic fibre allows such hydrolysis to occur only on the surface of the fibre.

Inter-polymer forces of attraction

It is stated on pages 1, 8 that textile fibres are composed of polymers; polymers being the equivalent of molecules of other substances. This statement of fact requires the development of some sort of abstract or real picture of a coherent mass of polymers forming the fibre, which may be called the polymer system of the fibre.

The coherence of the polymer system of a fibre is due to the four inter-polymer forces of attraction: **van der Waals' forces, hydrogen bonds, salt linkages,** and **cross-links** (see Table 1.3 for a detailed summary of these forces).

A more detailed description of the four inter-polymer forces follows.

Van der Waals' forces

These are very weak inter-polymer forces of attraction, named after the Dutch physicist Johannes Diederik van der Waals who first postulated their existence.

Van der Waals' forces may be defined as very weak electrostatic forces which attract neutral molecules to each other in gases, liquefied and solidified gases, organic liquids, and, most importantly in this context, **organic solids such as textile fibres.** They become an inter-polymer force of attraction as a result of electrons of very closely adjacent atoms *moving in sympathy with one another.* A more detailed explanation of the formation of van der Waals' forces requires the use of quantum mechanics, which is beyond the scope of this book.

Provided any two or more atoms and/or molecules are close enough together, then van der Waals' forces will come into existence between them. Fibre polymers need to be about 0.2 nm apart for van der Waals' forces to occur along their length. Such very close alignment of polymers occurs in the crystalline regions of the polymer system of any fibre. Thus, it may be assumed that van der Waals' forces exist between the polymers of the crystalline regions of any fibre'e polymer system.

It is important to remember that the diameter or size of the atoms which give rise to van der Waals' forces influences the relative strangth of this very weak inter-polymer force of attraction. This means that larger atoms give rise to stronger van der Waals' forces than smaller atoms. For instance, the hydrogen atom is the smallest, being about 0.06 nm in diameter. By comparison, the chlorine atom is about 0.2 nm, i.e. more than three times as large in diameter. Consider now the polymer system of polyethylene and polyvinylidene chloride fibres. The polymer systems of both fibres are held together by only van der Waals' forces. However, because of the presence of

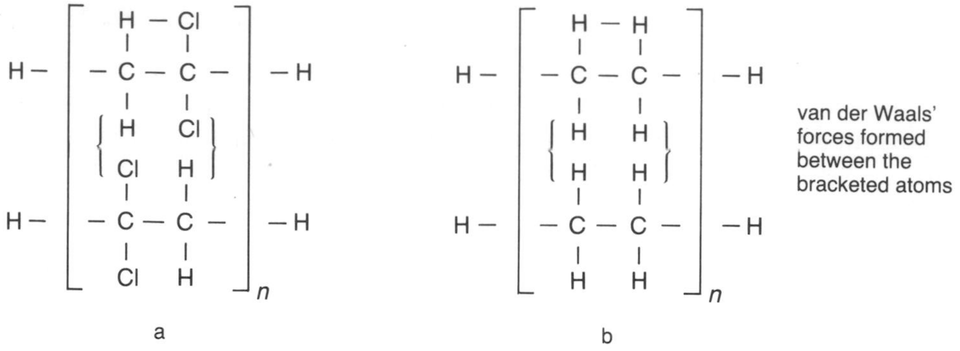

$$
\text{H}-\begin{bmatrix} \begin{array}{cc} \text{H} & - & \text{Cl} \\ | & & | \\ -\text{C} & - & \text{C}- \\ | & & | \\ \{\text{H} & & \text{Cl}\} \\ \{\text{Cl} & & \text{H}\} \\ | & & | \\ -\text{C} & - & \text{C}- \\ | & & | \\ \text{Cl} & & \text{H} \end{array} \end{bmatrix}_n -\text{H}
\qquad
\text{H}-\begin{bmatrix} \begin{array}{cc} \text{H} & - & \text{H} \\ | & & | \\ -\text{C} & - & \text{C}- \\ | & & | \\ \{\text{H} & & \text{H}\} \\ \{\text{H} & & \text{H}\} \\ | & & | \\ -\text{C} & - & \text{C}- \\ | & & | \\ \text{H} & & \text{H} \end{array} \end{bmatrix}_n -\text{H}
$$

van der Waals'
forces formed
between the
bracketed atoms

a

b

Figure 1.7
a Two adjacent or very closely aligned polyvinylidene chloride polymers; owing to the presence of the chlorine atoms, stronger van der Waals' forces will be formed.
b Two adjacent or very closely aligned polyethylene polymers; owing to the presence of only hydrogen atoms, weaker van der Waals' forces will be formed.

chlorine atoms on the polyvinylidene chloride polymers, the van der Waals' forces formed in the polymer system of this fibre will be stronger than those formed in polyethylene (see also Fig. 1.7).

Van der Waals' forces become of utmost importance when none of the other forces of inter-polymer forces of attraction is present to a significant degree. This is the case with such fibres as acrylic, polyester, polyethylene, polypropylene, and the chlorofibres. Their polymer systems need to be made highly crystalline. Only then will sufficient van der Waals' forces occur along the lengths of their polymers to make them useful fibres.

The influence of the difference in strength of the van der Waals' forces in the above two fibres is illustrated by their melting points. In general, the stronger the inter-polymer forces of attraction, the higher the melting point of the polymer system and, hence, of the fibre:

Fibre	Melting point range
polyethylene	110–140°C
polyvinyl chloride	170–200°C

Van der Waals' forces are also formed between fibre polymers and dye molecules, when these come close enough together. In this way, van der Waals' forces contribute towards the colour-fastness of dyed or printed textile fibres.

Hydrogen bonds

These may be written as H-bonds. Hydrogen bonds are weak electrostatic bonds which occur between covalently bonded hydrogen atoms and the strongly electronegative atoms: oxygen, nitrogen, fluorine and chlorine. The formation of a hydrogen bond requires that:

a the hydrogen atom assumes a very slight positive charge or polarity, shown as δ^+ in Fig. 1.8, and pronounced delta positive;

b the oxygen, nitrogen, fluorine or chlorine atoms, i.e. the strongly electronegative

16

atoms, assume a very slight negative charge or polarity, shown as δ^- in Fig. 1.8 and pronounced delta negative;

and

c the distance is less than about 0.5 nm between the two very slightly polar, but oppositely charged atoms of **a** and **b** above.

The most common hydrogen bond in the polymer system of textile fibres is that formed between hydrogen and oxygen atoms. This means that the hydrogen bond may be formed between:

the –OH groups on closely adjacent cellulose polymers;

the amide groups of nylon polymers; and

the peptide groups of the polymers of the protein fibres (see also Fig. 1.8).

It is now considered doubtful that significant hydrogen bonding occurs between the nitrile nitrogen of acrylic polymers and hydrogen atoms on adjacent polymers (see also Table 1.2). It is necessary to point out that hydrogen bonds formed between hydrogen and nitrogen atoms are weaker than those formed between hydrogen and oxygen atoms, because nitrogen becomes less electronegative than oxygen.

Before a hydrogen bond can form, the two participating atoms, say hydrogen and oxygen, must develop or assume very slight, but opposite, charges or polarity. The development of this polarity may be explained by considering the hydrogen bond which can come into existence between the **imino hydrogen** of an amide or peptide group on one polymer, and the **carbonyl oxygen** on an amide or peptide group on a

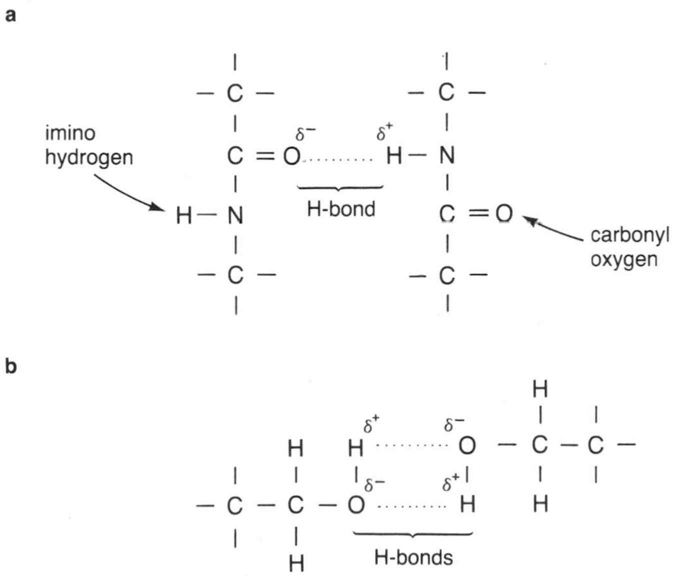

Figure 1.8
a The existence of a hydrogen bond between the carbonyl oxygen and imino hydrogen of two very closely adjacent amide or peptide groups. Note how the very slight polarity or partial charge, as it is sometimes called, is shown against the relevant atoms.
b The existence of a hydrogen bond between two hydroxyl groups on very closely adjacent cellulose polymers. Note that two hydrogen bonds are formed between any two –OH groups.

very closely adjacent polymer (see also Fig. 1.8). The nitrogen atom, to which the imino hydrogen atom is bonded, is a strongly electronegative atom. This means that the nitrogen atom will disproportionately concentrate its own electrons and the one electron of the hydrogen atom about itself. This tends to give the nitrogen atom an excess of electrons and thus cause it to assume a very slight negative polarity. This is shown as δ^- in Fig. 1.8. The lopsided concentration of electrons towards the nitrogen atoms leaves the hydrogen atom with a deficiency of electrons. This will cause it to assume a very slight positive polarity, shown as δ^+ in Fig. 1.8. In the carbonyl group of the amide or peptide group a similar electron displacement occurs. The oxygen, which is linked by a double covalent bond to the carbonyl carbon atom, is also a very strongly electronegative atom. It will therefore tend to concentrate its own electrons and those of the carbon atom about itself. This gives a disproportionate concentration of electrons about the oxygen atom, causing it to assume a very slightly negative polarity. The carbonyl carbon atom will, of course, assume a very slightly positive polarity. These polarities are shown as δ^- and δ^+ respectively in Fig. 1.8. Thus, as the carbonyl oxygen and the imino hydrogen assume opposite polarities, a force of attraction known as the hydrogen bond will form between them.

With regard to the hydrogen bond formed between two –OH groups on adjacent cellulose polymers, the oxygen atom will assume a very slight negative polarity as explained above. This causes the hydrogen atom of the –OH group to assume a very slight positive polarity, resulting in the formation of a hydrogen bond as shown in Fig. 1.8.

It is also possible for hydrogen bonds to form within the one polymer as depicted in Chapter 4, Fig. 4.7b.

The presence of a predominant number of hydrogen bonds in any polymer system will advantageously influence the tenacity, elastic-plastic nature, durability, and heat-setting properties of the fibre.

The presence of hydrogen bonds also indicates, of course, the existence of polar sites along the polymer lengths. These polar sites will attract water molecules, which are also polar (see page 22). Thus, if the polymers attract water molecules, the polymer system will tend to be moisture absorbent or hydrophilic, which will tend to make the fibre more comfortable to wear.

Salt linkages

These are also called **salt links** or **salt bridges**, and are **electrovalent** or **ionic bonds**. Salt linkages occur between negatively and positively charged radicals on very closely adjacent fibre polymers, as shown in Table 1.3. The formation of a negatively charged radical occurs when it gains one or more electrons over its normal electron complement.

Electrons are negative and, being in excess, cause the radical to become negatively charged. This negative charge is shown on the radical with a small negative sign. The number of negative signs shown against a radical indicates the number of electrons the radical has gained over its normal complement of electrons. In the formation of a positively charged radical, electrons are lost by the radical. Losing electrons causes the

Table 1.3

Inter-polymer force of attraction and its formation	Bond energy or bond strength in kilojoules★	Relative strength	Occurs between the polymers of	Relative importance
van der Waals' forces formed between atoms along the length of adjacent polymers when these are less than 0.3 nm apart but no closer than about 0.2 nm	8.4	very weak	all fibres	they are the only inter-polymer force of attraction existing in the polymer system of polyethylene, polypropylene, polyvinylchloride, polyvinylidene chloride, primary cellulose acetate and 100 per cent polyacrylonitrile fibres; they are considered to be the predominant inter-polymer force of attraction in the polymer system of acrylic, modacrylic and polyester fibres
hydrogen bonds formed between hydrogen and oxygen atoms, and, hydrogen and nitrogen atoms on adjacent polymers when these are less than 0.5 nm apart; note, the hydrogen–oxygen bond is stronger than the hydrogen–nitrogen bond	20.9	weak	natural, regenerated cellulose, nylon, polyvinyl alcohol, polyester, protein and secondary cellulose acetate fibres	they are mainly reponsible for the tenacity and the elastic-plastic nature of the natural, regenerated cellulose, nylon, polyvinyl alcohol and protein fibres; they contribute significantly towards the heat setting property of nylon and protein fibres; hydrogen bonds occurring in the polymer system of polyester fibres are very weak and not consider to be important; insignificant hydrogen bonds are formed in the polymer system of secondary cellulose fibres; there is doubt about hydrogen bond formation in the polymer system of acrylic and modacrylic fibres
salt linkages formed between the carboxyl radical on one polymer and the positively charged or protonated amino group on an adjacent polymer, i.e. $-C-O^{-}$ $^{+}H_3N-$ less than 0.1 nm	54.4	strong	protein and nylon fibres	they contribute towards the tenacity of the fibre; attract water molecules, hence, enhance the hygroscopic nature of the fibre; attract the anion of acid dyes, i.e. they are very good dye sites; may make the fibre's polymer system liable to chemical degradation.

Table 1.3 (continued)

Inter-polymer force of attraction and its formation	Bond energy or bond strength in kilojoules*	Relative strength	Occurs between the polymers of	Relative importance
cross-links formed as a single covalent bond between adjacent polymers of wool due to the disulphide bond or cross-link, i.e.	245.3	very strong	all protein fibres, except silk, and elastomeric fibres	they contribute significantly to the elastic nature of elastomerics; contribute towards the tenacity of wool; are broken and re-formed under controlled conditions for heat and chemical setting of wool and other protein fibres, but not silk.

$$
\begin{array}{c}
\overset{|}{-}\ \overset{|}{N}\ \ \overset{|}{H}\qquad\ \overset{|}{H}\ \ \overset{|}{H}\ \ \overset{|}{C}= \\
-\overset{|}{C}-\overset{|}{C}-S-S-\overset{|}{C}-\overset{|}{C}-\overset{|}{C}- \\
=\overset{|}{C}\ \ \overset{|}{H}\ \underbrace{\qquad\qquad}_{\text{less than}}\ \overset{|}{H}\ \ \overset{|}{H}\ \ \overset{|}{N}- \\
\overset{|}{}\ \ \overset{|}{}\ \ \ 0.1\ \text{nm}\qquad\qquad\ \overset{|}{}
\end{array}
$$

also formed in elastomeric, but details not known.

* from 'Dyeing and Chemical Technology of Textile Fibres' by E.R. Trotman, 5th Edition, Griffin, United Kingdom.

radical to become positively charged. The number of small positive signs shown on the radical indicates not only its positive charge but also the number of electrons it has lost.

Atoms may also gain or lose electrons. Such a gain or loss alters the normal complement of electrons of the atom. It is then called an ion, i.e. it is either a positively or negatively charged atom. This is the reason why salt linkages are also called ionic bonds, or **electrovalent bonds** (**electro-** = electric, from the strongly positive and negative charges which must always be present; and **valent** from valence). Valence is the combining power of an atom, which means the number of hydrogen atoms with which the atom can combine or which it can displace. It is thus also the number of electrovalent or ionic bonds the atom or radical can form. If the radicals of the fibre polymers carry only one charge, i.e. one negative and one positive sign as shown in Table 1.3, then they will form only one electrovalent bond or salt linkage.

These inter-polymer forces of attraction are described as salt linkages (or salt links, or salt bridges) because ionic or electrovalent bonds are formed between the ions and/or radicals of the chemical compounds called **salts**. Table or common salt, which is sodium chloride, is the best known example of a salt.

Salt linkages occur between the polymers of protein fibres and at the ends or terminals of nylon polymers (see Table 1.3). They are a strong inter-polymer force of attraction and, therefore, contribute to the cohesion of the appropriate fibre's polymer system. In this way, salt linkages enhance the tenacity, elastic-plastic nature, and durability of the fibre and its textile materials. The strong polarity of salt linkages makes them the prime site to which the anion of (acid) dyes attaches itself (see also pages 132 and 133). Furthermore, their polarity will attract water molecules. This contributes to the hydrophilic nature of the fibre's polymer system, making the fibre more absorbent and, hence, more comfortable to wear.

In general, it will also be found that fibres, whose polymer systems contain salt linkages, will be more reactive than those without these inter-polymer forces of attraction.

Cross-links

These occur between the polymers of elastomeric and protein fibres, except silk. Cross-links are covalent or valence bonds and, more specifically, single covalent bonds. Single covalent bonds are formed when two atoms share one pair of electrons. The sharing of a pair of electrons by two atoms (i.e. the single covalent bond) is represented in the structural formulae of organic compounds such as fibre polymers by a single, short line drawn between the letters representing the atoms. The carbons atoms, occasionally joined by oxygen and/or nitrogen atoms, in the backbone of fibre polymers are linked by single covalent bonds thus:

$$-\overset{|}{\underset{|}{C}}-\overset{|}{\underset{|}{C}}-\overset{|}{\underset{|}{C}}-\overset{|}{\underset{|}{N}}-\overset{|}{\underset{|}{C}}-\overset{|}{\underset{|}{C}}-\overset{|}{\underset{|}{C}}-\overset{|}{\underset{|}{O}}-$$

Single covalent bonds occur not only *within* fibre polymers, but also at selected points *between* the polymers in such fibres as elastomeric, wool, mohair, but not in silk. When single covalent bonds link adjacent polymers, they are called **cross-links** (see also Table 1.3, page 20).

The number of cross-links or the amount of cross-linking between polymers in a polymer system is spoken of as the **degree of cross-linking**. Thus the degree of cross-linking in the polymer system of a fibre significantly influences that fibre's elastic-plastic nature and tenacity. In general, the greater the degree of cross-linking or the more cross-links between polymers, the stiffer, less flexible, more rigid will be the fibre. Fibres such as wool, which have relatively few cross-links or a low degree of cross-linking, will have good to very good elastic properties. When the degree of cross-linking is even lower, such as in elastomerics, then the elastic property will be very good to excellent.

Synthetic resins applied to textile materials to make them easy-care have very highly cross-linked polymers. Such a very high degree of cross-linking makes these resins, when set, very rigid and thereby imparts the necessary stiffness to the textile to achieve the easy-care property. The considerable stiffness and rigidity of these resins is considered to be due to the **three-dimensional cross-linking** of their polymers; this means that these polymers are able to form cross-links in three directions — length, breadth and depth — within their polymer system (see also page 167).

The water molecule and textile fibres

The comfort of textile materials depends very much upon the moisture absorbency, hygroscopic or hydrophilic nature of such material. The comfort derived from textile

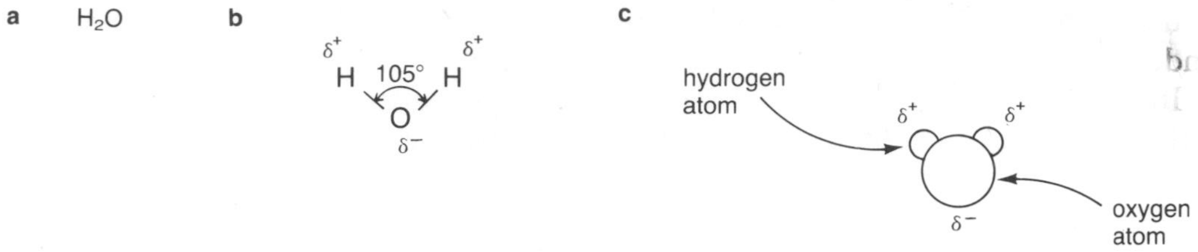

a H_2O **b** **c**

b

hydrogen atom

oxygen atom

Figure 1.9
a The conventional molecular formula of the water molecule
b The structural formula of the water molecule. The angle between the two hydrogen atoms is about 105°. Note the dipolarity of the structure: two poles, one negative and one positive.
c Simplified representation of the structural formula for water, retaining the angle between the hydrogen atoms as well as the proportion in size between the hydrogen and oxygen atoms.

fibres is critically dependent upon the ability of the fibre to absorb moisture or the ability of its polymer system to take up or attract water molecules. Water plays a very important role in textiles and clothing, hence it is important to become familiar with the water molecule and its polarity.

Each water molecule consists of two atoms of hydrogen and one atom of oxygen. This gives the familiar chemical formula for water: H_2O, which is convenient to write, but does not give the important structural formula of the water molecule. The structure is shown in Fig. 1.9. As may be seen, the two hydrogen atoms are more to one side of the molecule, while the oxygen atom is on the opposite side. This arrangement of atoms in the water molecule permits the ready development of its **dipolar nature**. Dipole means two poles, which implies a positive and a negative pole. The dipolar nature of the water molecule is due to the very electronegative oxygen atom (see also hydrogen bonding, page 16). The oxygen atom, because of its strong electronegativity, will disproportionately concentrate its own electrons, and the one electron from each of the hydrogen atoms, about itself. This tends to give the oxygen atom an excess of electrons, causing it to assume a very slight negative charge or polarity. On the other

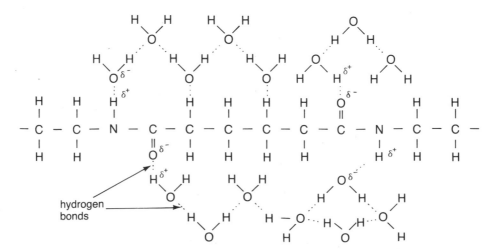

Figure 1.10 An indication of how water molecules, because of their dipolarity, are attracted to each other and to polar sites on the fibre polymer; in this example the polar sites on the fibre polymer are due to an amide group.

22

side of the water molecule, the two hydrogen atoms tend to be disproportionately deficient in electrons and therefore to assume a very slight positive charge or polarity. It is for this reason that water molecules are always dipolar (i.e. very slightly positively charged at their hydrogen end and very slightly negatively charged at their oxygen end). This is indicated by delta-negative and delta-positive in Fig. 1.10. The polarity of water molecules causes them to be attracted to one another and partly linked together by hydrogen bonding. For the same reason, they will also be attracted to any polar sites on fibre polymers, as shown in Fig. 1.10.

Requirements of fibre-forming polymers

Fibre-forming polymers of apparel fibres should be:

1 hydrophilic
2 chemically resistant
3 linear
4 long
5 capable of being oriented, and
6 able to form high-melting-point polymer systems.

This does not necessarily mean that the various polymers, which constitute the polymer systems of the different fibres, meet *all* these requirements. However, the polymer systems of such commonly used apparel fibres as the acetates, acrylics, cotton, flax, nylon, polyester, silk, viscose and wool consist of polymers which do, to a very large extent, meet the above requirements.

On the other hand, man-made fibres such as the chloro-fibres, polyethylene and polypropylene fibres are restricted in their apparel use because they do not satisfactorily meet the first, fifth and sixth requirements listed above. On the other hand, polyvinyl alcohol is not so commonly used, although it has similar properties to nylon. It is probably this similarity to nylon which makes it very difficult for polyvinyl alcohol to compete against the longer established, successful nylon.

Natural cellulose fibres such as abaca, coir, hemp, jute, kenaf, ramie and sisal have very restricted apparel use because they are very stiff. These fibres are examples of the fifth requirement, which has, so to speak, been 'overdone'. Their polymers are far too well oriented, and this imparts stiffness to the fibres. The polymers of the natural fibres angora, cashmere and mohair largely meet the above requirements, but because the fibres are relatively scarce, they are expensive and therefore infrequently used.

Leaving economic considerations aside, the usefulness of a fibre for apparel purposes is generally dependent upon the extent to which its polymers meet the requirements of fibre-forming polymers listed above.

An explanation of these requirements is now given.

1 Hydrophilic properties

Fibre polymers should be hydrophilic. This means that the polymers should be polar, enabling them to attract water molecules. A fibre is comfortable to wear if its polymer system consists of hydrophilic polymers, and the system itself permits the entry of water molecules. The latter is explained under 5 below.

There are, of course, fibres whose polymers are *not* hydrophilic (i.e. their polymers are hydrophobic) and yet these fibres are used for the manufacture of apparel. In order to make the textile materials of these fibres more absorbent and, hence, more or less comfortable, hydrophilic-polymer fibres need to be blended with the hydrophobic-polymer fibres. Nylon and polyester, for example, are hydrophobic-polymer fibres and are often blended with cotton, viscose or wool (e.g. two-thirds polyester/one-third cotton blend). Such blending improves the absorbency and comfort of their textile materials. Acrylics are also hydrophobic-polymer fibres. Knitted outerwear made of acrylics is very popular; but it will be found that it is usual to wear this non-absorbent knitwear over an absorbent or hydrophilic-polymer fibre garment to counter or reduce the potential discomfort which might otherwise be experienced.

A fibre consisting of hydrophilic polymers attracts water molecules which prevent, or enable, the discharge of any static electricity accumulating on the fibre. The static electricity is discharged by the water molecules, because of their polarity, to the surrounding atmosphere. A build-up of static electricity on a fibre is undesirable because it will cause the fibre to attract dirt particles more readily and thus to soil more quickly. Garments that become charged with static electricity may cling together to such an extent as to create discomfort during wear.

2 Chemical resistance

Fibre polymers should be chemically resistant for a reasonable length of time against the common degrading agents such as sunlight and weather, common types of soiling, body exudations, laundry liquors and dry cleaning solvents. Chemically resistant polymers should also not be toxic or hazardous to wear against human skin; this is a most important requirement which is usually taken for granted.

Although fibre polymers should be chemically resistant, they should not be inert (i.e. totally unreactive). Chemical inertness of fibre polymers tends to have a detrimental effect on other fibre-forming requirements. For instance, the polymers of chlorofibres, fluorocarbon, polyethylene and polypropylene may be regarded as chemically inert from a practical point of view. For this reason the polymers are non-polar and hence hydrophobic, making the textiles of these fibres non-absorbent, with a greasy, slippery, aesthetically displeasing handle.

The degree of chemical resistance desirable from the common fibre polymers may be deduced from the section on intra-polymer bonding (pages 8–15).

3 Linearity

Fibre polymers should be linear (i.e. the polymers should not be branched; see also Fig. 1.11). As explained in 5 below, only linear polymers allow adequate polymer alignment to bring into effect sufficient inter-polymer forces of attraction to give a cohesive polymer system and, hence, useful textile fibre.

It is, however, a normal occurrence for many fibre polymers, which need to be linear, to have side groups, as distinct from branches. Side groups may be thought of as causing 'bulges' along the polymer backbone, rather than the distinct projection of a branch. Thus the nitrile group of acrylics, the hydroxyl and methylol groups of the cellulose fibres, and the hydroxyl and acetyl groups of ester-cellulose fibres are some examples of side groups. By examining Tables 1.1 and 1.2 other fibre polymers with side groups will be found. Note that the Zefran polymer given in Table 1.2 is a branched polymer: seemingly the only one which gives a useful fibre.

The importance of considering side groups on polymers is the fact that they give rise to three types of linear polymer configurations, better referred to as three types of **stereo-polymers. Stereo**, from the Greek, is used here in the sense of spatial or three-dimensional arrangements of the side groups on the polymer backbone. In man-made fibre manufacture it is important to have the right stereo-polymer for the extrusion of useful filaments. The three types of stereo-polymers are described below.

The atactic polymer

This is a **stereo-irregular** polymer. It has its side groups arranged at random (i.e. in no particular order) above and below the plain of the polymer backbone. Two-dimensionally this may be represented thus:

polymer backbone   side group

Atactic polymers are usually not found in the polymer systems of fibres. This is because they do not allow close enough alignment or orientation of polymers for the formation of effective inter-polymer forces of attraction. If atactic polymers were used they would give an insufficiently cohesive polymer system, as indicated by the wax-like substance formed.

The syndyotactic polymer

This is a **stereo-regular** polymer. It has its side groups arranged in a regular alternating fashion above and below the plane of the polymer backbone. Two-dimensionally this may be represented thus:

Such a regular polymer structure permits close enough alignment or orientation of polymers to form effective inter-polymer forces of attraction, giving a cohesive enough polymer system to form a useful fibre. The polymers of cellulose and some chlorofibres are thought to be syndyotactic polymers.

The isotactic polymer

This is also a **stereo-regular polymer**. It has, however, all its side groups arranged on the same side or plane of the polymer backbone. Two dimensionally this may be shown thus:

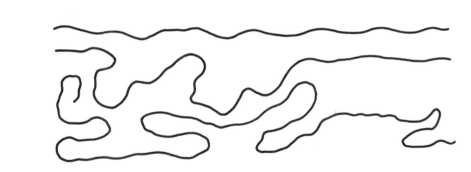

Isotactic polymers orient themselves readily and very closely. This permits effective formation of inter-polymer forces of attraction to give a cohesive polymer system and, thus, a useful fibre. Polypropylene and pure acrylonitrile fibres are known to have their polymer system constituted of isotactic polymers.

4   Length

Fibre polymers should be long. It has been found that the length of the polymers constituting the commonly used apparel fibres is in excess of one hundred nanometres.

Polymers of such length can readily be oriented. This is explained under 5 below. Having the polymers oriented can give rise to sufficiently effective inter-polymer forces of attraction to form a cohesive polymer system and, hence, a useful fibre.

In general, the longer the polymers the more cohesive will be the polymer system and the stronger will be the fibre. For this to occur the polymers have to be closely aligned or well oriented so that the maximum formation of inter-polymer forces of attraction can take place. (See also Figs 1.11 and 1.12.)

a

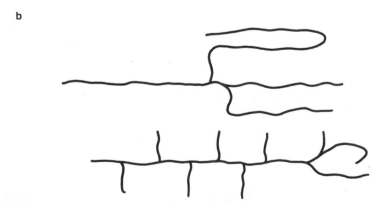

Figure 1.11a   Linear polymers: they can assume various configurations as shown; however, they can be oriented or aligned to form a cohesive polymer system suitable for useful fibre formation.

b

Figure 1.11b   Branched polymers: they can assume various configurations as shown; however, they cannot be sufficiently oriented to form a polymer of adequate cohesion; therefore, they are unsuitable for fibre formation.

a

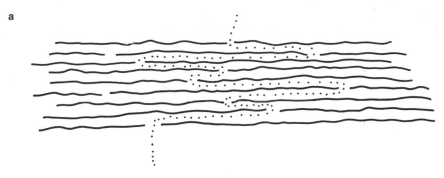

Figure 1.12a A strong fibre because it has long polymers which are well aligned or oriented, giving it a long 'path of break'

path of break

b

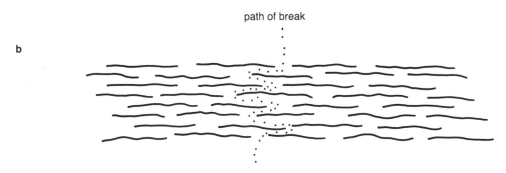

Figure 1.12b A weak fibre because it has short polymers; although they are well oriented, the shortness of its path of break tends to make it weak.

5 Orientation

Fibre polymers should be capable of being oriented, as foreshadowed under **4** above. This means that the polymers are or can be arranged or aligned (i.e. oriented) into more or less parallel order in the direction of the longitudinal axis of the fibre or filament.

It is not known how the orientation of polymers occurs during the growth of natural fibres. With man-made fibres, the operation called **drawing**, which stretches the extruded and coagulated filament, causes the polymers to orient themselves longitudinally into a more or less parallel order. The extent of this drawing markedly influences the properties of the filament and those of the staple fibre which may be cut from it.

Perfect orientation of polymers is usually not obtained, nor is it desirable, as explained in Table 1.4. The orientation of polymers in the polymer system of any fibre consists of two distinct, yet integrated forms. The two forms of polymer orientation are called the amorphous and the crystalline regions. (See Table 1.4 for definition, explanation, comparison and influence upon fibre properties of the amorphous and crystalline regions.)

6 Formation of high-melting-point polymer systems

A fibre consisting of a high-melting-point polymer system tends to have adequate heat resistance to enable it to withstand the various heat treatments of textile finishing,

Table 1.4 Polymer orientation in the polymer system of fibres

1 **Amorphous polymer orientation**	1 **Crystalline polymer orientation**
a amorphous orientation of polymers within the polymer system of any fibre is called the *amorphous region*	**a** crystalline orientation of polymers within the polymer system of any fibre is called the *crystalline region*
b in amorphous regions the polymers are oriented or aligned at *random*, i.e. display no particular order of arrangement, see Fig. 1.13	**b** in crystalline regions the polymers are oriented or aligned *longitudinally into more or less parallel* order, see Fig. 1.13

c the polymer system of any man-made and natural fibre
  (i) consists of *randomly arranged* amorphous and crystalline regions, see Fig. 1.13;
  (ii) may be predominantly constituted of
   – *more amorphous* than crystalline regions; if this is the case then the particular fibre or filament is spoken of as being a *more amorphous fibre* or *filament*;
    or
   – *more crystalline* than amorphous regions, if this is the case then the particular fibre or filament is spoken of as being a *more crystalline fibre* or *filament*.

d owing to their length, most polymers pass through several amorphous and crystalline regions (see Fig. 1.13).

e The presence of either more or less amorphous or crystalline regions determine the specific properties of the fibre (see below).

f owing to the random orientation, the polymers are further apart, hence, – formation of inter-polymer forces of attraction will be *less effective* – *permits easier entry* of water and dye molecules as well as molecules, ions and/or radicals of degrading agents – allows the polymers to be more readily displaced when the fibre is subject to stresses and strains during wearing	**f** owing to the more or less parallel orientation, the polymers are often closer together, hence, – formation of inter-polymer forces of attraction will be *more effective* – *restricts the entry* of water and dye molecules as well as molecules, ions and/or radicals of degrading agents – does not allow the polymers to be displaced when the fibre is subject to stresses and strains during wearing

2 **In general, more amorphous fibres are**	2 **In general, more crystalline fibres are**
a more absorbent	**a** less absorbent
b weaker	**b** stronger
c less durable	**c** more durable
d more easily degraded by chemicals	**d** less easily degraded by chemicals
e more easily dyed	**e** less easily dyed
f more pliable, softer handling	**f** less pliable, stiffer handling
g plastic, more easily distorted	**g** less plastic, resist being distorted

Reasons for the above may be deduced by considering **1f** above.

Note The amorphous and crystalline regions constituting any fibre's polymer system are too minute to be seen under an optical microscope

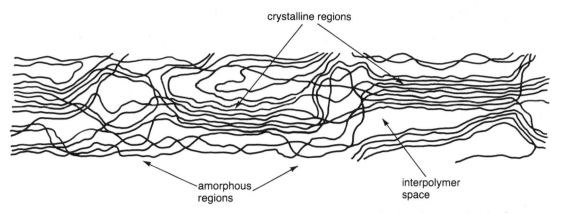

Figure 1.13a A simplified and exaggerated representation of a segment of a fibre's polymer system to show amorphous and crystalline regions. Each polymer tends to form part of several amorphous and crystalline regions. This assists in the cohesion of the polymer system. Whenever several polymers are aligned or oriented in more or less parallel order they form a crystalline region. Amorphous regions occur wherever polymers are not oriented or are aligned at random. Amorphous and crystalline regions do not occur in any particular order, i.e. they occur at random throughout the polymer system of the fibre.

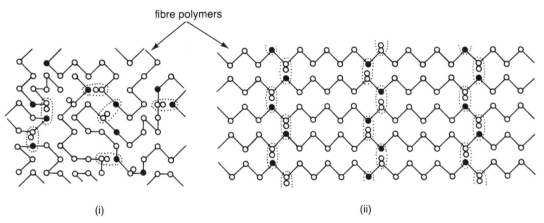

Figure 1.13b An attempt to show (i) an amorphous region, and (ii) crystalline orientation by using symbolic chemical formulae; note the angular bonding which exists between carbon atoms and tends to impart a zigzag configuration to the backbone of fibre polymers.

○   = carbon atom
●   = atom of another element
● ∞ = hydrogen bond

apparel manufacture, and the heat subsequently applied to it during laundering and pressing or ironing during its useful life as a garment.

It appears that a fibre's melting point needs to be above 225°C if it is to be useful for textile manufacture and apparel use. Insufficient is known about the influence of polymer orientation and polymer composition upon the melting point and heat resistance of polymer systems and, hence, fibre. In general, however, the longer the polymers and the better their orientation, the more inter-polymer forces of attraction will be formed, giving a more cohesive polymer system with a higher melting point. This means more heat or kinetic energy will be required to break the inter-polymer forces of attraction and free the polymers from each other. Once this has occurred, the polymers are free to move independently of each other, and gravity tends to cause them to flow to the lowest point of the plane on which they are situated. This flowing or moving of the polymers in a mass is seen and recognised as melting of the fibre.

When heat is applied to a fibre it *may* melt. Continued heating may lead to the fibre's ignition and burning. Heat is a form of energy; the heat energy possessed by a substance, polymer system or polymer is in the form of kinetic energy which is due to the atomic or molecular translation, rotation or vibration. In other words, at any temperature above absolute zero (–273.15°C = 0°Kelvin), the atoms, molecules or polymers of any substance constantly vibrate or are in a constant state of excitement. This rate of vibration or the state of excitement may be *increased* by applying heat, that is by increasing the temperature of the polymer system or polymer; or *decreased* by removing heat, that is by cooling, which decreases the temperature. Exposure to a heat source such as a naked flame can increase the kinetic energy of a polymer system and its polymers to such a degree that most of the interpolymer forces of attraction are broken. This will tend to free the polymers and is seen, as described above, as melting of the fibre. Further exposure to the heat source may provide so much kinetic energy as to raise the state of excitement of the individual polymers to such a level that their intra-polymer bonding is broken. This would free individual atoms of the polymer from each other. As soon as this occurs, the atoms would react immediately and violently with the oxygen of the atmosphere. This is seen and recognised as combustion of the fibre.

The **heat resistance** and **heat conductivity** of any fibre are directly related. From a textile viewpoint, a fibre resistant to heat, such as cotton or viscose, will also conduct heat. On the other hand, a fibre of poor heat resistance, such as wool or nylon, will be a non-conductor or insulator of heat. It seems that the ability of a fibre to conduct heat, which means passing it along its polymers and through its polymer system, depends upon the degree of polarity of its polymers. Polar sites along the lengths of the polymers may provide the necessary free electrons to convey the heat or kinetic energy along. This is not unlike the conduction of an electric current travelling through a copper wire.

The **thermoplastic nature** of a fibre is largely a question of whether or not most of the inter-polymer forces of attraction can be broken at the one time, under controlled conditions of heating (i.e. increasing the kinetic energy of the polymers and polymer system). In the very brief time when the polymers are more or less free of each other, they can be induced, by manipulation of the fibre, to assume new positions in the polymer system of the fibre. These new positions are retained by the polymers when they cool because the inter-polymer forces of attraction reform. The fibre is then said to be **heat-set**. It will be realised from the above that, if a fibre can be melted, then it is thermoplastic and can be heat-set, and vice versa. A thermoplastic fibre does not lost its heat-setting property. However, this is not the case with thermo-setting materials, which lose their plasticity once they have been heat-set, and usually become hard, stiff and even brittle. For this reason no thermo-setting fibres are used in textile and apparel manufacture. (See also *Thermoplasticity*, page 116.)

General definition of a textile fibre and a textile filament

A **fibre** or **staple fibre** is a unit of matter which is usually at least 100 times longer than it is thick.

Usually, fibres are several thousand times longer than they are thick. Most apparel fibres range in length from about 15 mm to 150 mm, with exceptions: for example, flax ranges up to 500 mm and sometimes even longer. The thickness of these fibres tends to range from about 10 μm to 50 μm.

A **filament** is a very long fibre. The length of filaments may range from a few hundred metres, as in the case of silk, to several kilometres in the case of man-made fibres. The thickness of filaments tends to be similar to that of fibres.

General considerations with regard to fibre properties

The general considerations given below provide the background information upon which the explanations of a fibre's properties are based. An awareness of these considerations will improve one's understanding of fibre properties.

Fibre morphology

Morphology is the study of the size, shape, and structure of a material or textile fibre, and the relationship between these properties. The morphology of textile fibres and filaments may be divided into the following.

The macro-structure of a textile fibre and filament

Fibre length

(See also 'general definition of a textile fibre and textile filament', above.) Fibres shorter than about 15 mm tend to have insufficient length to permit them to be twisted into a strand of adequate cohesion, regularity and evenness to make it a useful yarn structure. Fibres longer than about 150 mm tend to require specialised spinning machinery which adds to the cost of converting them into yarn.

Filaments, of course, are so long that they need, in principle, only to be gathered together to form a suitable yarn structure.

Fibre thickness

(See also 'general definition of a textile fibre and textile filament, above.) Fibres or filaments finer than about 10 μm tend to become too delicate or fragile for ready conversion into a yarn structure. Fibres or filaments exceeding about 50 μm in thickness tend to give a yarn structure which is too coarse and too thick for comfort when used as apparel.

Fibre length to fibre breadth (thickness) ratio

This ratio determines whether or not a fibre is suitable for spinning into yarn, provided it first meets the fibre length and thickness requirements given above. The smallest suitable ratio of fibre length to fibre breadth (thickness) is about 350:1. Anything less than this — say about 200:1 — indicates a fibre which probably will not permit twisting into a yarn structure. But a ratio of 1000:1 or more indicates a fibre which should readily spin into a useful yarn.

Colour

White or colourless fibres and filaments are preferred. Natural fibres and delustred man-made fibres are white to off-white in colour. Bright-lustre man-made fibres and filaments are colourless because they are translucent. White or colourless fibres and filaments are preferred because they can be dyed or printed with any hue of colour.

Translucency

A translucent fibre will transmit light but is *not* transparent. In general silk and man-made fibres, when bright-lustred, are translucent. Cotton, flax and wool, and also delustred man-made fibres, tend to be opaque; but if these fibres are made into light- to very light-weight fabrics, then their fineness tends to make them somewhat translucent. The acceptability of translucent fibres, their translucent textile materials, and apparel items depends upon the prevailing *mores* of the particular community or peer group(s). With the increasing use of man-made fibres over the years, problems have been encountered in the manufacturing of textiles that are sufficiently opaque to satisfy the requirements of modesty.

Lustre

This is a subjective measure of the reflection of incident light from a fibre, filament or textile material. The more lustrous a fibre, the more evenly does it reflect the incident light. The less lustrous or duller a fibre or filament, the less evenly does it reflect or the more does it scatter the incident light.

Cotton has a convoluted fibre structure and wool a serrated surface structure; the result is that these fibres scatter the incident light, and are thus dull fibres. The more regular and even surface structure of flax, mercerised cotton and silk gives these fibres a distinct lustre, due to the even reflection of incident light. Table 1.5 shows the reflection of incident light by various man-made fibres.

The irregular specks of delustring agent contained within delustred man-made fibres scatter sufficient of the incident light to make these fibres or filaments duller than their bright-lustre equivalents. A preference for non-lustrous or dull textile fibres and filaments exists. This is evident in the predominance of dull-lustred or non-lustrous apparel and household textiles normally purchased and used by consumers.

Table 1.5 The general effect of fibre cross-sectional upon lustre and other physical fibre properties

Generalised shape of fibre cross-section	General effect of cross-sectional shape upon fibre lustre	General effect of cross-sectional shape upon other physical fibre properties
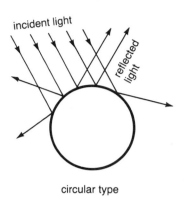 circular type	Theoretically this cross-sectional shape should impart only a soft lustre to the fibre or filament because the incident light is reflected so unevenly; in fact it tends to impart a rather harsh, strong lustre; this is because, no matter how the fibre or filament may be twisted in the yarn or fabric, its circular shape always permits it to reflect the same amount of incident light despite the unevenness of its reflection.	This cross-sectional shape imparts the greatest bending stiffness, is the most rigid, least flexible and least pliable because it is so regular in diameter; its smooth regularity of surface imparts a waxy, slippery handle and causes the fibre or filament to make maximum contact with the skin; this may be aesthetically displeasing
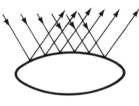 oval type 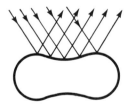 dog-bone or bean type 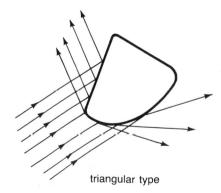 triangular type	Theoretically these cross-sectional shapes should be the most lustrous because they can reflect the incident light most evenly; in fact though, because the fibre or filament would be twisted upon itself in the yarn and fabric, the incident light is not reflected as evenly as expected and a softer lustre results.	These cross-sectional shapes tend to impart the least bending stiffness, are the most pliable, most flexible, most supple and even limp because they are so readily deformed across the shorter of their two diameters; the smooth regularity of their surfaces may impart a waxy, slippery handle and causes the fibre or filament to make maximum contact with the skin; this may be aesthetically displeasing. The distinct edges of the more triangular cross-sectional shape create more friction between fibre or filament and the skin giving it a crisper, less waxy, less slippery handle.

Table 1.5 (continued)

Generalised shape of fibre cross-section	General effect of cross-sectional shape upon fibre lustre	General effect of cross-sectional shape upon other physical fibre properties
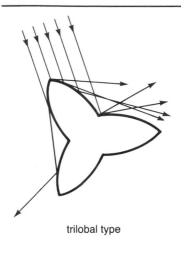 trilobal type 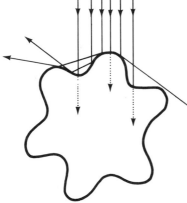 multi-lobal type	These cross-sectional shapes reflect the incident light quite unevenly; theoretically they should therefore impart to the fibre or filament a very dull lustre; in fact they impart a distinct and very bright sparkle or glitter; the reason for this is that when the fibre or filament is twisted upon itself in the yarn and fabric the already irregular reflection of incident light is further reduced; thus only 'bursts' of evenly reflected incident light from the less curved surfaces of the cross-sectional shape are seen along the length of the fibre, filament, yarn and/or fabric; the tri-lobal cross-section plossess the sparkling lustre to the greatest degree; as the number of lobes in the cross-sectional shape are increased (i.e. it becomes multi-lobal), the incident light is scattered to such an extent on reflection that no sparkle and only a very dull lustre can be seen.	These cross-sectional shapes are not stiff, easy to bend, pliable, flexible with a soft to firm handle; the handle may also be crisp because the lobes may create increased friction between the fibre or filament and the skin; the regularity and evenness of the lobes may still, however, give a somewhat smooth and slippery handle.
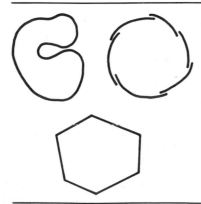	The irregular cross-sectional shapes and uneven longitudinal surfaces of such fibres as cotton, flax and wool makes them dull or non-lustrous fibres; however, flax with its polygonal or many sided cross-section and relatively flat, regular longitudinal surfaces tends to display a slight lustre.	for the general effect of the cross-sectional shape upon the other physical fibre properties see the individual Chapters on these fibres.

Table 1.5 (continued)

Generalised shape of fibre cross-section	General effect of cross-sectional shape upon fibre lustre	General effect of cross-sectional shape upon other physical fibre properties
Titanium dioxide	Titanium dioxide is a white substance. It is ground to a very fine powder so as to have a particle size of less than one micrometre. It is added to the spinning solution of man-made fibres as a delustring agent. The many different shapes of the titanium dioxide particles (see left) reflect the light at random or in no particular order. Thus when they are within the extruded filament, it will display a reduced lustre. Filaments or staple fibres containing no titanium dioxide have a **bright lustre**. To manufacture filaments with a **semi-lustre** about half a per cent of titanium dioxide has to be added to the spinning solution. For the manufacture of delustred or **dull lustre** filaments and staple fibre up to two per cent of titanium dioxide may have to be added to the spinning solution.	

The micro-structure of a textile fibre and filament

Microscopic longitudinal and cross-sectional structure and appearance

The microscopic structure is of importance for two main reasons:

1 conclusive identification
2 influence on skin contact comfort.

With, for example, cotton, flax, viscose or wool it is possible to make a conclusive identification by examination under the microscope of the longitudinal and cross-sectional structure of the fibre or filament.

The individual characteristics of the textile micro-structure have a decisive influence on its skin contact comfort. For instance, the minute surface irregularities of the otherwise regular and even fibre structure of cotton and silk make them comfortable and pleasant to wear against the skin. In contrast, the extremely smooth, even, regular surface structure of such fibres as nylon and polyester tends to feel aesthetically unpleasant and uncomfortable against the skin. (See also 'hygroscopic nature', page 39.)

Figure 1.14 shows that manufacturers can determine the longitudinal and cross-sectional structure and appearance of man-made fibres. However, most of these modifications have not been very successful (see also Fig. 1.15). The conventional structure of the man-made fibres used for apparel is the result of their extrusion through circular orifices in the spinnerets. The only intentionally modified man-made fibres are the tri-lobal nylon and polyester, which are extruded through T-shaped orifices to give the three-lobed cross-section (see Figs 1.15 and 5.10).

The only natural fibres on which significant surface modifications are carried out are cotton and wool. The modifications are usually made during the conversion of the fibres into fabric. Cotton may be mercerised; this is a process by which the fibres are swollen (see also page 47). Wool may be made shrink-resistant, by altering the frictional properties of the wool fibre surface; the process is described on page 176.

Profiled fibres

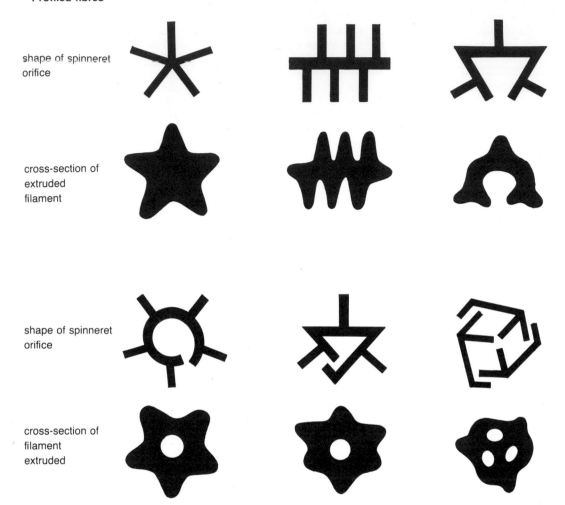

shape of spinneret orifice

cross-section of extruded filament

shape of spinneret orifice

cross-section of filament extruded

Figure 1.14 Modifying the morphology of man-made fibres. These diagrams show how solid and hollow **profiled** filaments can be produced. From them, profiled staple fibres may be made.

Profiling filaments reduces the contact they make with the skin, thus making them aesthetically more pleasing to handle. Profiling also increases the friction that develops between filament surface and skin, giving a more pleasant handle than the non-profiled equivalent.

Hollow filaments are lighter in weight, more insulating and possible more absorbent than their solid core equivalents.

The disadvantage of profiling is that it adversely affects extensibility, tenacity, permanent flexing and resistance to abrasion. This adverse effect becomes worse, the more pronounced the profiling. However, profiled solid and hollow filaments and their staple fibres have the following advantages: better cover factor, greater bulk, better handle, greater crimp effect, greatly increased permeability to air, better absorption of perspiration, higher water absorbency, considerably less tendency to pill, reduced slippage, better dimensional stability of knitted fabrics.

Nevertheless, the only profiled filaments which have been successfully utilised are the nylon and polyester trilobal filaments as shown in Fig. 1.15.

Sub-microscopic fibre features

These are the morphological features of the fibre which are more readily seen under the electron microscope than under the optical microscope. Most of the natural fibres tend

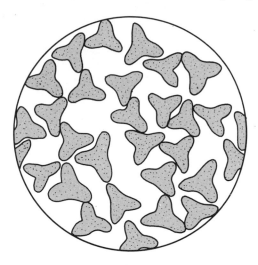

Figure 1.15 Cross-section of profiled tri-lobal nylon filaments, magnified 200 times. Tri-lobal polyester is also manufactured. These two are so far the only profiled man-made fibres which have become established. They tend to be used mainly as fashion fibres for specialised knitted outerwear for women, and in the pile of certain carpets.

to have distinct sub-microscopic features: for example, the fibre walls of cotton; or the variety of cells found in wool fibres. At this level, silk appears more like a man-made fibre, and tends to lack readily identifiable sub-microscopic features.

Man-made fibres, though mainly lacking distinguishable sub-microscopic features, are considered to have a distinct surface skin. This skin is considered to be more crystalline in its polymer orientation than the core of the fibre. Its existence appears to be of no particular relevance.

Natural fibres, more than man-made fibres, tend to consist of fibrils (exceedingly small fibres). These may be considered as strands of polymers, which vary considerably in diameter and length. The fibrils found in natural fibres vary in thickness from about 4 to 10 nm; no estimate of their length has been reported.

While some fibrillar features of certain fibres might be seen using an optical microscope, only the electron microscope will reveal any details of a fibre's polymer system. The polymer system is the coherent mass of polymers which determines to a very large extent the physical properties, and to a somewhat lesser extent the chemical properties, of the fibre. The polymer system consists of randomly arranged amorphous and crystalline polymer regions. Table 1.4 shows how these randomly arranged polymer regions may influence fibre properties.

Amorphous and crystalline regions consist of polymers which tend to influence fibre properties according to:

1 how well or otherwise they fulfil the requirements of fibre-forming polymers given from page 23 onwards;
2 the number and types of inter-polymer forces of attraction formed between the polymers (see also page 15 onwards);
3 their intra-polymer bonding (see also page 8 onwards).

Table 1.6 Dimensional relationships between some fibre features

Fibre feature	Approximate range of its dimensions
Visual	
filament length	from several hundred metres to several kilometres
fibre length	from shorter than 15 mm to longer than 150 mm
length of crimp waves in man-made and natural fibres	from just less than 1 mm to more than 25 mm
Microscopic	
spacings of convolutions of cotton fibres	0.1 mm or 100 μm
fineness or diameter of filaments and fibres	from finer than 10 μm to thicker than 75 μm
cortical cells of wool	
length	100 μm to 200 μm
maximum thickness	2 μm to 5 μm
Sub-microscopic	
fibrils of natural fibres	
length	not known
thickness	2 nm to 5 nm
fibre polymers	
length	from not much less than 75 nm to 5000 nm and longer
thickness	1 nm to 10 nm

Fibre tenacity

The tenacity or strength of a fibre is in general directly related to the length of its polymers, degree of polymer orientation, and strength and types of inter-polymer forces of attraction formed between polymers. Thus, the longer the polymers, the more crystalline can be their orientation, and the stronger may be the inter-polymer forces of attraction formed, the stronger and more inflexible may then be the fibre (see also Table 1.4).

Elastic-plastic nature of fibres

It has already been stated that a fibre with a rather crystalline polymer system tends to be stiff and inflexible, owing to restricted polymer movement. Excessive bending or stretching of such a fibre tends to cause polymer rupture, resulting in irreparable damage to the polymer system, which will now be weak where polymer rupture has occurred. This will cause undesirable fibre wrinkling and creasing due to these weakened regions of the polymer system.

A more amorphous polymer system has sufficiently large interpolymer spaces into which polymers can be displaced when the fibre is bent or stretched, giving fibres with this characteristic a softer handle. Should the fibre's polymer system be held together only by weak interpolymer forces of attraction, fibre polymer displacement will occur readily from bending or stretching, because these weak forces can be easily broken.

Such polymer displacement will be seen as wrinkling and distortion of the textile material produced from the fibre.

An elastic fibre is one whose polymers can be strained with subsequent recovery following the removal of the strain or applied load. The interpolymer forces are such that they aid the recovery of the strained polymer system (see also Table 1.4).

Hygroscopic nature

The hygroscopic nature of a fibre is directly related to the polarity of its polymers and the ratio of its amorphous and crystalline regions.

A hygroscopic or absorbent fibre tends to have a predominantly amorphous polymer system consisting of polar polymers. These attract water molecules, while the amorphous nature allows entry of the water molecules into the polymer system. Highly crystalline polymer systems do not permit ready entry of water molecules even if the polymers are distinctly polar, as is the case with nylon.

The hydrophobic nature of the highly oriented or crystalline synthetic fibres gives rise to static electricity. This can be a considerable nuisance during yarn and fabric manufacture, as well as during garment making and subsequent wearing of the apparel item. The absence of static electricity in the more amorphous fibres is usually due to their moisture absorbency. It is for this reason that the amorphous fibres are blended with the more crystalline fibres to make the latter more comfortable to wear.

Thermal properties

The most important thermal property of a textile fibre or filament is the temperature at which it may soften and begin to melt. This temperature is a relative measure of the fibre's heat resistance. It indicates to what temperature the fibre may be safely heat-processed during finishing, pressed during garment manufacture, hot laundered, ironed and/or pressed after dry cleaning.

The softening and melting point temperatures of a fibre are related to the crystallinity of its polymer system, the length of its polymers, and the type and number of interpolymer forces of attraction holding its polymer system together. The greater the crystallinity of the polymer system, the longer (usually) are the polymers and the stronger tend to be its interpolymer forces of attraction. Hence more heat or kinetic energy will be required to free the polymers from each other. This would result in the fibre having a greater resistance to heat, as well as to softening and melting at a higher temperature (see also pages 27–30).

It should be noted that the above considerations, and those given elsewhere, do not provide a complete explanation for the effect of heat upon fibres. This applies especially to the natural fibres and the regenerated cellulose fibres, neither of which soften or melt when heated, for example by ironing.

Chemical properties

The general chemical reactivity of individual fibre polymer compositions is given under 'Intra-polymer bonding' on pages 8–15. This gives an indication of the extent to which the polymers of a fibre may react with the common degrading agents such as the alkalis of laudering liquors, atmospheric pollution, normal soiling of textiles, sunlight, etc.

A fibre's chemical properties are directly influenced by the ratio of amorphous to crytalline regions in its polymer system. In general, fibres with a more crystalline or more highly oriented polymer system tend to be chemically more resistant than fibres with a more amorphous polymer system. The more amorphous polymer system, with its greater inter-polymer spaces, can be more readily penetrated by the ions, molecules and/or radicals of degrading agent. Not only can the more crystalline fibres keep out the molecules etc. of degrading agents, but they also make it very difficult for dye molecules to enter their polymer sytem to colour the fibre.

2 The cellulosic fibres

Textile fibres composed of pure cellulose are:

1 *Natural cellulosic fibres*: abaca, coir, cotton, flax, hemp, henequin, jute, kenaf, sisal, etc.
2 *Man-made cellulosic fibres*: cuprammonium, polynosic, and viscose.

Of the very many cellulosic textile fibres, only the commonly used ones — cotton, flax and viscose — will be considered here.

Cotton

Textile classification

The word *cotton* is derived from the Arabic. Depending upon the arabian dialect, it is pronounced *kutan, qutn, qutun*, etc. As the cotton fibre is obtained from a plant it is classified as a natural, cellulose, seed, mono-cellular, staple fibre. The density of the fibre (referred to from now on as fibre density) is 1.52 g/cm^3, which makes cotton a rather heavy fibre.

Fibre morphology

The macro-structure of cotton

Under a microscope, a cotton fibre appears as a very fine, regular fibre. It ranges in length from about 10 mm to 65 mm, depending upon the quality of the fibre. The length of a textile fibre is an important factor in spinning yarn. This is particularly so with cotton, which is a relatively short staple fibre. The longer the cotton fibre, the easier it is to spin into a smoother, stronger yarn. In turn, this results in a more comfortable, more durable, more attractive fabric and garments.

Cotton fibres are amongst the finest in common use. They range in fibre diameter from about 11 μm to 22 μm. Such very fine fibres permit the manufacture of fine, light-weight cotton fabrics and garments, despite the fact that it is a dense fibre.

Cotton is a very fine fibre with little variation in fibre diameter; compared with wool for instance, its fibre diameter is not considered as critical a fibre dimension as its length. The fibre length to breadth ratio of cotton ranges from about 6000:1 for the longest and best types, to about 350:1 for the shortest and coarsest cotton types. The greater this ratio, the more readily can the cotton fibres be spun into yarn. Cotton fibres vary in colour from near white to light tan. The colour of cotton fibres depends on its type, environment, soil and climatic conditions under which it is grown. These factors influence the amounts of protein and minerals which will occur in the fibre and, thus, its colour.

Sea Island and Egyptian cotton types have a subdued lustre due to their greater fibre length which causes more even reflection of incident light. However, the lustre of these two cotton types is of little significance when compared with lustrous man-made fibres.

The microscopic appearance of cotton

Under the microscope, the cotton fibre looks like a twisted ribbon or a collapsed and twisted tube. These twists or **convolutions** identify the cotton fibre under the microscope (see Figs 2.1 and 2.2).

The seed end of the fibre is quite irregular, having been torn, during ginning, from the epidermis or skin of the cotton seed. The main part of the fibre, about three-quarters to fifteen-sixteenths of its length, is quite regular, with a thick fibre wall, a canal along the centre of the fibre called the **lumen**, and about sixty convolutions per centimetre. The fibre tip is less than one-quarter of the fibre length. At this end, the fibre tapers to a cylindrical, pointed tip, and has no convolutions. The convolutions are

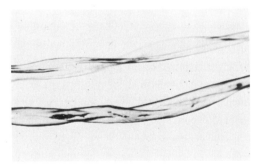

Figure 2.1a A longitudinal section of raw cotton, magnified 500 times. Note the convolutions or twist in the fibres.

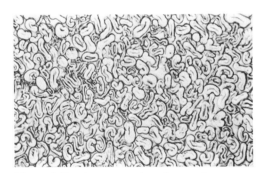

Figure 2.1b A cross-section of raw cotton magnified 500 times. Note the kidney shape of the cross-section of the fibres.

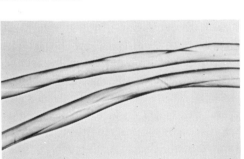

Figure 2.2a A longitudinal section of mercerised cotton, magnified 500 times. Note the much reduced prominence of the convolutions compared with raw cotton.

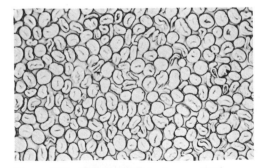

Figure 2.2b A cross-section of mercerised cotton, magnified 500 times. Note the oval to round shape of the cross-section of the fibres.

formed after the cotton boll bursts open. When this happens, the limp, sap-filled cotton seed hairs begin to dry out, their cell walls collapse inward, decreasing the size of the lumen. When the cotton seed hairs cease shrinking, twisting and collapsing inward, they become the valuable, convoluted cotton fibres.

The convolutions give cotton an uneven fibre surface, which increases inter-fibre friction and enables fine cotton yarns of adequate strength to be spun.

The appearance of the cotton fibre's cross-section under the microscope is referred to as being kidney-shaped, see Fig. 2.1(b). This shape occurs from the inward collapse of the cotton fibre when it dries out, while still attached to its seed. The cross-section varies in its kidney-shape according to where it was cut from the fibre's length. The cross-section tends to provide an indication of the relative dimensions of the lumen and fibre walls.

The convolutions and kidney-shaped cross-section of the cotton fibre enable it to make only random contact with the skin. This type of contact is more compatible with human skin physiology and therefore more comfortable. The countless minute air spaces which exist because of the convolutions and kidney-shaped cross-section of cotton fibres increase the moisture absorbency of cotton textile materials thus making them more comfortable to wear. It is for these reasons that manufacturers crimp and texture man-made filaments and staple fibres in order to increase fibre moisture absorbency and minimise fibre contact with the skin.

The micro-structure of the cotton fibre

The cotton fibre is a single plant cell. Its cross-section is oval, compared with the normal hexagonal plant cell. However, like all plant cells, cotton has a distinct **cuticle**, well developed **primary** and **secondary walls**, and a **lumen** (see Fig. 2.3).

The **cuticle** is the 'very outside' or 'skin' of the cotton fibre. It is composed of a waxy layer (cotton wax) only a few molecules thick. The waxy nature of the cuticle enables it to adhere tenaciously to the primary wall of the fibre. The inert nature of this cotton wax protects the rest of the fibre against chemical and other degrading agents. Kier boiling and bleaching during cotton finishing removes much of the cuticle or wax.

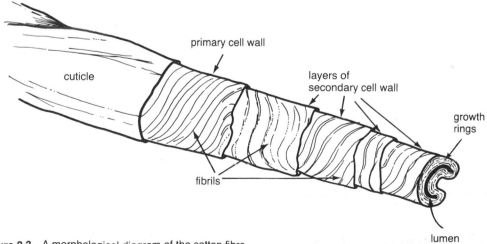

Figure 2.3 A morphological diagram of the cotton fibre.

This enables cotton to absorb moisture more quickly. Subsequent laundering will gradually remove most of the remaining cuticle. As the extent of the cuticle is decreased further, deterioration of the cotton textile material increases.

The **primary cell wall**, which is immediately underneath the cuticle, is about 200 nm thick. It is composed of very fine threads of cellulose, called **fibrils**. These fibrils are about 20 nm thick, but their length is as yet unknown. The fibrils spiral at about 70° to the fibre axis. This spiralling imparts strength to the primary cell wall and, hence, to the fibre. The primary cell wall can be visualised as a sheath of spiralling fibrils.

Beneath the primary cell wall lies the **secondary cell wall**, which forms the bulk of the fibre. Concentric layers of spiralling, cellulosic fibrils, not unlike the growth rings of trees, make up the secondary wall. Its fibrils are about 10 nm thick, but of undefined length. Near the primary cell wall, the fibrils of the secondary wall spiral at about 20° to 30° to the fibre axis. This spiral angle widens to about 20° to 45° for the fibrillar layers nearer the lumen. Much of the strength and stability of the cotton fibre and, hence, of the yarns and fabrics may be attributed to these spiralling fibrils. Whenever the fibrils change the direction of their spirals, a weak area exists in the secondary wall structure. It is at these weak areas that the convolutions of the fibre also alter the direction of their twist.

The hollow canal, running the length of the fibre, is called the **lumen**. Its walls are the innermost, concentric layers of spirals of the secondary cell wall. The lumen was once the central vacuole of the growing cotton fibre. It was full of cell sap, which was composed of a dilute, aqueous solution of proteins, sugars, minerals and cell-waste products. When the sap evaporated, its constituents remained behind to contribute to the colour of the cotton fibre. Further, as the sap evaporated, the pressure inside the fibre became less than the atmospheric pressure on the outside. This caused the fibre to collapse inward resulting in the characteristic kidney-shaped cross-section of the cotton fibre.

The polymer system

The cotton polymer

The cotton polymer is a linear, cellulose polymer. The repeating unit in the cotton polymer is **cellobiose** which consists of two glucose units (see Fig. 2.4). It is not fully understood how cellulose is formed or polymerised by plants. It is therefore better to refer to cellobiose as the repeating unit of the cotton polymer rather than as its monomer.

The cotton polymer consists of about 5000 cellobiose units, that is, its degree of polymerisation is about 5000. It is a very long, linear polymer, about 5000 nm in length and about 0.8 nm thick. (See also page 2.)

The most important chemical groupings on the cotton polymer are the hydroxyl groups or $-OH$ groups. These are also present as methylol groups or $-CH_2OH$. Their polarity gives rise to hydrogen bonds between the OH-groups of adjacent cotton polymers. Van der Waals' forces also occur but compared with the hydrogen bonds, the van der Waals' forces are of little significance.

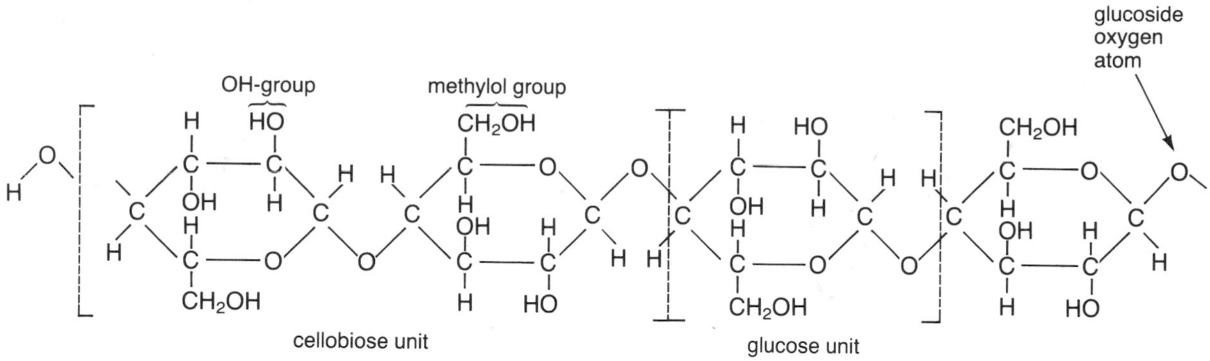

Figure 2.4 The chemical formula of the cellulose polymer. It is thought that the cotton cellulose polymer is composed of 5000 cellobiose units, while the flax cellulose polymer is thought to contain 18 000 cellobiose units.

The polymer system of cotton

Cotton is a crystalline fibre. Its polymer system is about 65 to 70 per cent crystalline and, correspondingly, about 35–30 per cent amorphous. Therefore, the cotton polymers are, in the main, well oriented and probably no further apart than 0.5 nm, in the crystalline regions. This is the maximum distance across which hydrogen bonds can form between polymers. Hydrogen bonds are the dominant and most important forces of attraction present in the polymer system of cotton. For this reason, van der Waals' forces which are also present have little relevance. Because the appearance of the cellulose polymer is not unlike a chain of hexagonal units, the polymer system of cotton can be imagined as a roll of wire netting. The crystalline regions are therefore the well ordered lines and rows of hexagonal holes of the wire netting. The amorphous regions are a disarrangement of these orderly lines and rows of hexagons.

Physical properties

Tenacity

The strength of cotton fibres is attributed to the good alignment of its long polymers (that is, its polymer system is about 70 per cent crystalline), the countless, regular, hydrogen bond formations between adjacent polymers, and the spiralling fibrils in the primary and secondary cell walls.

It is one of the few fibres which gains strength when wet. It is thought this occurs because of a temporary improvement in polymer alignment in the amorphous regions of the polymer system. The improved alignment when wet results in an increase in the number of hydrogen bonds, with an approximate 5 per cent increase in fibre tenacity.

Elastic-plastic nature

The cotton fibre is relatively inelastic because of its crystalline polymer system, and for this reason cotton textiles wrinkle and crease readily. Only under considerable strain will cotton polymers give and slide past one another. They are usually prevented from doing so by their extreme length and countless hydrogen bonds, which tend to hold them within their polymer system. Bending or crushing of cotton textile materials places considerable strain on the fibres' polymer systems. It will probably cause polymer fracture since the crystallinity of the polymer system makes it difficult for cotton polymer to be displaced by bending or crushing forces. Polymer fracture results in polymer disarrangements. These become weak points in the polymer system, and hence weak areas in the cotton fibre structure. Such weakening of the polymer system, and therefore fibre structure, causes cotton textile materials to crease and wrinkle readily.

Hygroscopic nature

The cotton fibre is very absorbent, owing to the countless polar −OH groups in its polymers; these attract water molecules, which are also polar. However, the latter can only enter the polymer system in its amorphous regions, as the inter-polymer spaces in the crystalline regions are too small for the water molecules. Aqueous swelling of the cotton fibre is due to a separation or forcing apart of polymers by the water molecules in the amorphous regions only.

The general crispness of dry cotton textile materials may be attributed to the rapidity with which the fibres can absorb moisture from the skin of the fingers. This rapid absorption imparts a sensation of dryness which, in association with the fibres' inelasticity or stiffness, creates the sensation of crispness.

The hygroscopic nature ordinarily prevents cotton textile materials from developing static electricity. The polarity of the water molecules, attracted to the hydroxyl groups on the polymers, dissipates any static charge which might develop.

Thermal properties

Cotton fibres have the ability to conduct heat energy, minimising any destructive heat accumulation. Thus they can withstand hot ironing temperatures. There is no satisfactory explanation for this.

Excessive application of heat energy causes the cotton fibre to char and burn, without any prior melting. This is an indication that cotton is not thermoplastic, which may be attributable to the extremely long fibre polymers and the countless hydrogen bonds they form. These prevent the polymers from assuming new positions when heat is applied, as would be the case with the shorter polymers of thermoplastic fibres. When sufficient heat, that is, kinetic energy, is applied to the cotton fibre, its polymers will begin to vibrate or become so excited as to disintegrate. This in conjunction with the large quantity of kinetic energy present results in violent chemical reactions observed as fibre combustion.

Chemical properties

Effect of acids

Cotton fibres are weakened and destroyed by acids. Acidic conditions hydrolyse the cotton polymer at the glucoside oxygen atom, which links the two glucose units to form the cellobiose unit (see Fig. 2.4 and page 12). Mineral or inorganic acids, being stronger than organic acids, will hydrolyse the cotton polymer more rapidly.

Effect of alkalis

Cotton fibres are resistant to alkalis and are relatively unaffected by normal laundering. The resistance is attributed to the lack of attraction between the cotton polymers and alkalis. **Mercerising without tension**, or slack mercerising, causes the cotton fibres to swell; that is, increase in thickness and contract in length. The swelling is thought to be due to alkali molecules, or radicals, entering the amorphous regions of the fibres' polymer system. In so doing, they force the cotton polymers further apart, which can be seen as swelling of the fibres. This results in somewhat greater inter-polymer spaces, permitting poorly aligned polymers to orient themselves more satisfactorily, as well as forming additional hydrogen bonds. This explains the increase in fibre strength on mercerising. There is no satisfactory explanation for the contraction of the fibre.

With **mercerising under tension**, which can only be carried out on cotton yarn or fabric, little swelling or fibre contraction occurs. The fibre emerges with increased tenacity and with a distinct, though subdued lustre. Tensioning the cotton yarn or fabric in the aqueous, alkaline liquor assists the fibre polymers to align themselves further, leading to an increase in hydrogen bond formation. This explains the increase in tenacity achieved during mercerising under tension. Mercerising under tension also causes the fibre surface to become smooth and more regular, enabling it to reflect incident light more evenly. This is responsible for the subdued lustre that is associated with tension mercerised cotton textile materials. (See Fig. 2.2.)

Either type of mercerising swells the fibres sufficiently to alter their normal kidney-shaped cross-section to a more circular one. In addition, mercerising improves the dye-uptake of the cotton. This means that mercerised cotton fibres dye and print a deeper hue, that is a hue with more chroma, than equivalent unmercerised fibres, when using the same quantity of dye. No satisfactory explanation for this is currently available.

Effect of bleaches

The most common bleaches used on cotton textile materials arc sodium hypochlorite and sodium perborate.

Sodium hypochlorite ($NaOCl$) is a yellowish liquid, smelling of chlorine. Sodium perborate ($NaBO_2H_2O_2,3H_2O$) is a white powder, contained in most commonly available domestic laundry detergents. Sodium hypochlorite bleaches cotton textile materials at prevailing room temperatures. However, bleaching with sodium perborate is more effective when the laundry solution exceeds 50°C in temperature.

These two bleaches are examples of oxidising bleaches, which is the class of bleaches used most frequently on cotton textile materials. They bleach most effectively in alkaline conditions to which cotton textile materials are resistant.

Oxidising bleaches are so called because they liberate oxygen which does the actual bleaching. The reactions between the oxygen liberated by the bleach and the molecules on the fibre surface responsible for the cotton's discolouration are not known in any detail. In general it is considered that the oxygen forms water-soluble compounds with the molecules of the fibre surface contaminants. These water-soluble products are rinsed off the fibre during bleaching.

Careful bleaching leaves the fibre polymer system largely intact. Careful bleaching will restrict the chemical attack of bleaches to the fibre surface polymers of cotton.

Effect of sunlight and weather

The ultraviolet rays of sunlight provide photochemical energy whilst the infrared rays provide heat energy necessary to degrade the cotton polymers in the presence of atmospheric oxygen, moisture and air pollutants.

Atmospheric moisture (humidity) significantly contributes to the breakdown of the polymers on the surface of the cotton fibres through various hydrolytic reactions. Initially, such degradation, or polymer hydrolysis, is noticed as a slight fibre discolouration. In due course, the reactive nature of the hydrolytic compounds formed accelerates the breakdown of the fibre. The weakening of the fibre and breakdown of the cotton textile material is, of course, a clear indication that the polymer system of the fibre has broken down completely.

In general, air pollutants are acidic and may rapidly accelerate fibre breakdown through acid hydrolyis to which cotton polymers are not resistant.

Fading of coloured cotton textiles is partly due to a breakdown of the dye molecules in the fibres' polymer systems. This is explained in Chapter 6, 'Dyeing and printing'.

Colour-fastness

Cotton is considered to be a relatively easy fibre to dye and print. The classes of dye which may be used to colour cotton are azoic, direct, reactive, sulphur and vat dyes.

The ease with which cotton takes up dyes, and other colouring matter, is due to the polarity of its polymers and polymer system. This polarity will readily attract any polar dye molecules into the polymer system. In fact, dye molecules which can be dispersed in water will be absorbed by the polymer system of cotton.

However, as with all other textile fibres, the dye molecules can only enter the amorphous regions of the polymer system of cotton. The small inter-polymer spaces in the crystalline regions of the polymer system prevent the entry of the relatively large and bulky dye molecules.

Azoic dyes

Azoic dyeing or printing occurs when two relatively small, water-soluble molecules are made to react within the amorphous regions of the polymer system to form the comparatively much larger, water-insoluble azoic dye molecules. (See also pages 137–139.)

The very good to excellent light-fastness of azoic dyed and printed cotton textile materials is due to the resistance of the azoic dye molecules to the potential photochemical degradation of the ultraviolet radiation of sunlight.

The very good to excellent wash-fastness of azoic dyed and printed cotton textile materials is due to the relatively large azoic dye molecules. These are trapped and entangled in the amorphous regions of the polymer systems of the cotton fibres. The azoic dye molecules are attracted to the fibre polymer by van der Waals' forces. As these forces of attraction are very weak, it is the water-insolubility, relatively large size and entanglement in the polymer system of the azoic dye molecules which account for the very good to excellent wash-fastness properties.

Direct dyes

The attraction between fibre polymers and dye molecules is called **substantivity**. Because of the very great substantivity direct dyes have for cotton, they have also been given the name of cotton colours.

Direct coloured cotton textile materials have only a moderate light-fastness. This may be attributed to the fact that direct dye molecules are affected by the photochemical degradation due to the ultraviolet radiation of sunlight, as well as by atmospheric pollutants.

The poor wash-fastness of direct dyed and printed cotton textile materials is attributed to the good water-solubility of direct dye molecules. As the direct dye molecules are only attached to the cotton polymers by hydrogen bonds and van der Waals' forces, any aqueous solution will break these forces of attraction. The cotton fibre will swell in water, enabling some of the direct dye molecules to be removed from the amorphous regions of the cotton polymer system.

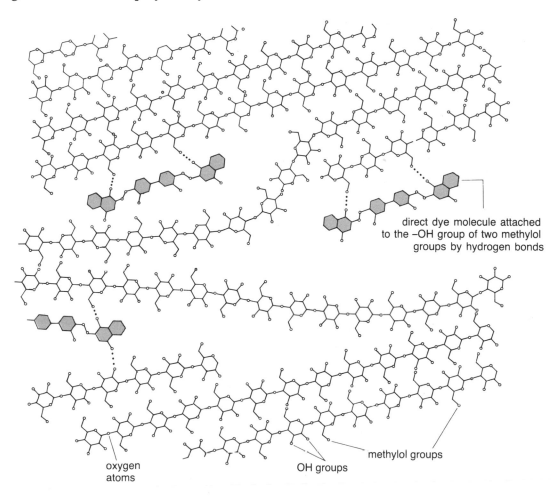

direct dye molecule attached
to the –OH group of two methylol
groups by hydrogen bonds

oxygen
atoms

OH groups

methylol groups

Figure 2.5 A possible arrangement of cellulose polymers in the polymer system of a cotton fibre. Note that the dye molecules, represented by shading, occur only in amorphous regions.

Increasing the molecular size of direct dye molecules, as described on pages 143, 144 results in a slight improvement in wash-fastness.

Reactive dyes

As their name implies, these dyes react chemically with the fibre polymer. The reactive dye molecules form a covalent bond with the hydroxyl groups on the cotton polymers.

The great strength and relative inertness of the covalent bond to most common degrading agents securely anchors the reactive dye molecules to the polymers of the cotton fibres. It is for this reason that cotton textile materials which have been dyed or printed with reactive dyes have good wash-fastness properties.

The molecules of reactive dyes are also very resistant to the degradative effects of the ultraviolet radiation of sunlight and air pollutants. This means that cotton textile materials coloured with reactive dyes have very good light-fastness.

However, some reactive dyes are degraded by chlorine bleaches and chlorinated water, such as in swimming pools. The presence of chlorine may result in a breakdown of the covalent bond which is formed between the dye molecule and the cotton polymer, resulting in a removal of colour from the fibre. It must be emphasised that only some reactive dyes are affected by chlorine.

Sulphur dyes

Cotton textile materials coloured with sulphur dyes have good wash-fastness. This is attributed to the relatively large sulphur dye molecules which become entangled and trapped within the amorphous regions of the polymer system of the cotton fibres. In conjunction with this is the dye molecules' water-insolubility. This makes it difficult for aqueous solutions to remove the sulphur dye molecules from the fibre. Sulphur dye molecules tend to form only van der Waals' forces with cotton polymers. It is thought, however, that these forces of attraction contribute little towards the good wash-fastness properties of sulphur dyed cotton goods.

Sulphur dyed cotton textile materials have only fair light-fastness. This is attributed to the lack of resistance by the sulphur dye molecules to the degrading photo-chemical effects of the sunlight's ultraviolet radiation. After-treatments, as explained in Chapter 6, improve somewhat the light-fastness of sulphur dyed cotton textile materials.

Vat dyes

Excellent wash-fastness is achieved with vat dyed and printed cotton textile materials. This is because of the comparatively large vat dye molecules. Their physical size causes them to become trapped and entangled within the amorphous regions of the polymer system of the cotton fibres. This and the water-insolubility of vat dye molecules make it extremely difficult for any aqueous solutions to remove the dye molecules from the fibres' polymer systems. The vat dyes, being non-polar, can only form van der Waals' forces. These are not considered to contribute significantly towards the wash-fastness properties.

Vat dyed and printed cotton textile materials have excellent light-fastness. The chemical composition of the vat dye molecules provides them with the excellent resistance against the degrading photo-chemical effects of the ultraviolet radiation of sunlight and air pollutants. There are, however, some exceptions to this, e.g. indigo.

Flax

Textile classification

The word flax is derived from the Old English *fleax*. The Teutons referred to it as *flakso*, coming from the teutonic root *fleh*, to plait. Linen is the term applied to the yarn spun from the flax fibres, and to the cloth or fabric woven from this yarn.

The flax fibre is classified as a natural, cellulose, bast, multi-cellular fibre. It has a fibre density of 1.50 g/cm³, and is considered to be a heavy fibre. It is for this reason that most linen textile materials are of light construction. Thick linen textile materials would be uncomfortably heavy to wear.

Fibre morphology

The macro-structure of flax

The flax fibre is a thick, regular fibre with a subdued lustre. It ranges in length from about 10 cm to 100 cm, averaging about 50 cm in length. As the flax fibre is a strand of cells, it thickness depends upon the number of these cells in any one fibre cross-section. It seems that about 3 to 6 cells constitute a fibre cross-section. The flax cells are about 25 mm long and 10 μm to 20 μm thick. This would give an average fibre thickness ranging from about 40 μm to 80 μm.

The value of flax is directly proportional to its fibre length. Its fibre length to breadth ratio is, therefore, of considerable significance. For the longest and the best flax this tends to about 15 000:1. Short flax fibres may have a fibre length to breadth radio of 1500:1, or less.

The colour of flax varies from light blond to grey blond, the particular shade resulting from the agricultural and climatic conditions under which it was grown and the quality of retting.

The subdued lustre of flax is due to its long regular fibre surface, which is coated with a film of wax. This enables a significant amount of the incident light to be reflected, resulting in the subdued lustre. However, when compared with that of the lustrous man-made fibres the subdued lustre of flax is insignificant.

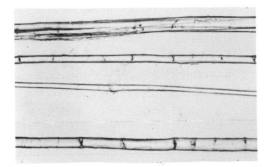

Figure 2.6a A longitudinal section of bleached flax or linen fibre, magnified 200 times. Note the cross-markings or nodes.

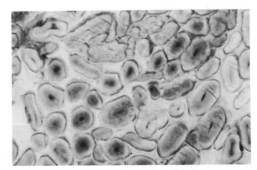

Figure 2.6b A cross-section of bleached flax or linen fibres, magnified 200 times. Note the polygonal or many-sided cross-section of the fibres.

Microscopic appearance of flax

The cross markings, known as **nodes,** on flax fibres give them their characteristic microscopic appearance. There may be up to 800 nodes in a single flax fibre cell. The length of the node indicates the width or thickness of the fibre cell. The nodes are thought to be fissures in the cell walls. Wherever a node occurs, it indicates a change in the spiral direction of the fibrils which constitute the cell walls. As with the cotton fibres, such spiralling imparts strength to the cell and, hence, to the flax fibre.

The polygonal cross-section of the flax fibre cell is typical of most plant cells. (See Fig. 2.6.)

The micro-structure of flax

Although the flax fibre cell is covered with a wax film, this does not constitute as distinct a cuticle as in the case of cotton. The cell walls of flax are constructed of spiralling fibrils composed of cellulose polymers. On the whole, the flax cell is more sturdily constructed that the cotton cell, as indicated by the former's thicker cell walls. This explains, in part, the greater tenacity of flax compared with cotton.

The polymer system

The flax polymer and its polymer system

Chemically, the flax polymer is the same as the cotton polymer; both are celluose polymers.

Physically, the flax polymer differs from the cotton polymer, in that it has a degree of polymerisation of about 18 000. This means the flax polymer is made up of about 18 000 cellobiose units (see Fig. 2.4). The flax polymer is about 18 000 nm long, and about 0.8 nm thick. This makes it the longest known, linear textile polymer. The polymer system of flax is more crystalline than that of cotton, because of its longer polymers. These spiral about each other at approximately 6° to the fibre axis, thereby contributing towards the tenacity and durability of the fibre. The greater crystallinity of flax fibres is demonstrated by the fact that they are stronger, crisper and stiffer to handle, and textile materials wrinkle more readily than those of cotton fibres.

Physical properties

Tenacity

Flax is a very strong fibre because its very crystalline polymer system permits its extremely long polymers to form more hydrogen bonds than cotton polymers.

The reasons given to explain the increase in wet tenacity of cotton fibres apply also to flax fibres.

Elastic-plastic nature

The very inelastic nature of flax is due to its very crystalline polymer system. It tends to lock its polymers into position with the aid of the countless hydrogen bonds which form between the polymers. Hence, the polymers cannot yield, and they resist being displaced from their positions in the polymer system.

The unyielding nature of the very crystalline polymer system gives the flax fibre its stiff handle. Flax will resist being flexed or bent. As with cotton the crispness of its handle is due to its ability to absorb moisture rapidly.

The ready wrinkling and creasing which occurs with linen textile materials is also due to the very crystalline polymer systems of the flax fibres. When these are bent or flexed, their polymers are liable to break leading to fractures in the polymer system. These fractures become weak areas on the fibre structure, leading to wrinkling and creasing in the linen textile material.

Hygroscopic nature

The reasons given above to explain the hygroscopic nature of cotton apply also to flax.

Thermal properties

Flax has the best heat resistance and conductivity of all the commonly used textile fibres. No satisfactory explanation can be offered for this.

With regard to other thermal properties of flax, the reasons given for cotton apply equally to flax.

Chemical properties

Owing to the similar chemical constitution of cotton and flax, the explanations offered for the chemical properties of cotton may also be applied to flax.

However, it needs to be remembered that linen textile materials are *not* mercerised. Normal laundering will result in alkaline hydrolysis of the waxes and gums bonding the cells forming the flax fibre together. This results in cell ends projecting above the surface of the linen textile material, and is referred to as *cottonising* of linen. Severe cottonising will cause a noticeable weakening of the linen textile material.

Viscose
Textile classification

Viscose is a man-made, natural polymer, cellulosic or regenerated cellulose filament or staple fibre. There are two other man-made regenerated cellulose fibres, namely **cuprammonium** or **cupro** and **polynosic** or **modal**.

The International Organisation for Standardisation, in its standard ISO 2076–1977 (E), defines these three man-made, regenerated cellulose fibres as follows:

Cuprammonium or **cupro**   regenerated cellulose obtained by the cuprammonium process. The name **cuprammonium** is obtained from the aqueous cuprammonium hydroxide solvent in which the cellulose is dissolved to form the spinning solution. The International Organisation for Standardisation prefers the name **cupro**.

Polynosic or **modal**   regenerated cellulose obtained by processes giving a high tenacity and a high wet modulus. In other words, polynosic or modal is a regenerated cellulose fibre which, when wet, remains stronger and distorts less than either cuprammonium or viscose. **Polynosic** means many fibrils, whilst **modal** is derived from *modulus*. The International Organisation for Standardisation prefers the name **modal**.

Viscose   regenerated cellulose obtained by the viscose process. The name **viscose** was derived from the word *viscous*, which describes the liquid state of the spinning solution. A viscous solution is as thick as, and/or flows like, honey.

The above three regenerated cellulose fibres are sometimes still referred to collectively by the generic name **rayon**. The International Organisation for Standardisation does not use the name rayon because, as it states in ISO 2076–1977(E), 'this name, used generically for regenerated cellulose fibres in some countries, does not have the same meaning everywhere.'

The Organisation also suggests that each country should determine whether or not to use the name 'rayon'. If it finds such use desirable, then it should define 'rayon' in one of its national standards.

In the case of Australia, the name 'rayon' is not defined in a national standard; but the name is written into all textile labelling legislation. In this legislation, rayon is used generically for the above three regenerated cellulose fibres. The names 'cuprammonium' and 'polynosic' are used instead of 'cupro' and 'modal', respectively.

The fibre density of viscose is 1.49 g/cm^3, which makes it a heavy fibre, similar to cotton and flax. However, its availability as fine filament yarns enables the manufacture of light weight viscose textile materials.

Fibre morphology

The macro-structure of viscose

Viscose is a fine, regular filament or staple fibre. The staple fibre is usually manufactured in a crimped configuration. This overcomes to a large extent the very regular, even, smooth and slippery nature of the uncrimped equivalent.

Crimping viscose staple fibre increases the inter-fibre friction, resulting in better fibre cohesion during and after spinning of its yarns. On the whole, crimped viscose staple fibre spins into yarns of slightly improved texture and bulk, with sufficient irregularity to make the crimped staple fibre yarn aesthetically more pleasing compared with its uncrimped equivalent.

The length of staple fibre cut from viscose filaments depends upon the required end-use. Usually they are cut to lengths similar to those of cotton, flax and wool fibres. In contrast, the length of the viscose filament is only restricted to the number of kilometres which can be wound upon the particular yarn package being used.

Viscose is extruded in fibre diameters ranging from 12 μm to 22 μm, depending upon end-use requirements. These give a fibre length to breadth ratio in excess of 2000:1, ensuring that even the shorter staple fibres will spin satisfactorily into yarn.

The colour of the extruded viscose filaments tends to be slightly off-white. This is attributed to their translucency which permits some light to pass through the filaments before it is reflected. Therefore some of the incident light is absorbed, with the effect that the light reflected is off-white in colour.

Most of the incident light upon viscose is reflected with considerable intensity from the filaments' or staple fibres' smooth and regular surface. This results in a harsh and bright lustre. Hence, a delustring agent, usually titanium dioxide, may be added to the spinning solution. Titanium dioxide is a white powder, with a particle size of about 0.8 μm. When these are present in the filaments, they make the viscose appear white. As the titanium dioxide particles also scatter the reflected light, it will be less intense and make the viscose filaments appear to have a subdued lustre. The degree to which the lustre is subdued depends upon how much titanium dioxide is added to the spinning solution of viscose. (See also Table 1.5.)

Man-made fibres, more so than natural fibres, tend to be translucent. Translucency of a fibre means that it is partially transparent; that is, that its fibre structure and polymer system permit some incident light to pass completely through the fibre. It also means that translucent fibres are more uniform in their micro-structure. Fibres, such as cotton, wool and flax, which are not translucent but are opaque have quite an intricate fibre microstructure, as well as more involved polymer configurations in their polymer systems. These fibres tend to contain more impurities, even after thorough cleaning, compared with the man-made fibres and silk. Thus, the fibre micro-structure of cotton, flax and wool is more likely to absorb any light entering the fibre. On the other hand, viscose, the other man-made fibres and silk lack a discernible fibre micro-structure and impurities, thus permitting some light to pass through the fibre, which makes them translucent.

Microscopic appearance of viscose

Viscose filaments and staple fibres have many **longitudinal striations** (tiny grooves) which give them their characteristic microscopic appearance. These are responsible for the irregularly serrated perimeter of their nearly round to oval cross-section. See Fig. 2.7. The striations are formed by irregular contractions of the freshly extruded viscose filaments as they solidify in the coagulation bath.

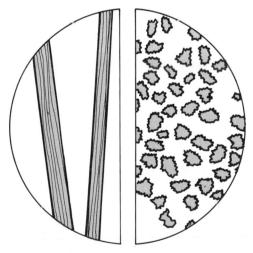

Figure 2.7 Bright lustre viscose. Note the characteristic striations on the filament at the left. These striations are due to the irregularly serrated cross-section of the filament, or staple fibre, shown at the right. Both sections are magnified 400 times.

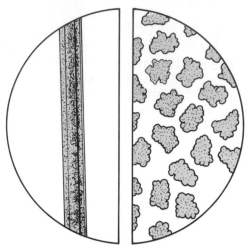

Figure 2.8 Delustred viscose. Note the specks of delustring agent. These are white but appear black in the photograph. Both sections are magnified 400 times.

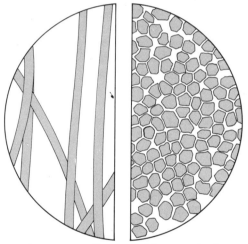

Figure 2.9 Bright lustre cuprammonium or cupro. Because of the near-circular cross-section of the fibre, there are no characteristic longitudinal features. Both sections are magnified 400 times.

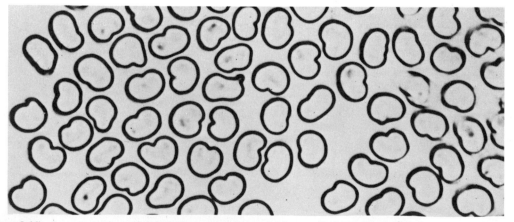

Figure 2.10 A cross-section of bright-lustre polynosic or modal, magnified 500 times. The near-circular or very swollen kidney shape of the cross-section provides a featureless longitudinal section.

A speckled longitudinal appearance identifies viscose, and all other man-made fibres of similar appearance, as delustred man-made fibres (see Fig. 2.8).

As cuprammonium and polynosic are coagulated much more slowly during extrusion, their filaments and staple fibres do not develop any striations (see Figs 2.9 and 2.10).

The minute striations are countless tiny grooves which cause the filaments or staple fibres to make random contact with the skin. Such skin contact feels more comfortable than the much more intimate contact of the non-striated fibres.

The micro-structure of viscose

The viscose filament is a fine, coagulated stream of regenerated cellulosic solution, which displays no discernible micro-structure. However, as its name implies, polynosic does show, under the electron microscope, a distinct fibrillar structure. This fibrillar structure is a distinct remnant of its natural cellulosic origins, and of significance with regard to its properties, which are somewhat superior to those of the other two regenerated cellulose fibres.

The polymer system

The viscose polymer

It is a linear, cellulose polymer, similar to that of cotton (see Fig. 2.4). However, the viscose polymer does not have the spiral configuration of the cotton polymer. The significant physical differences between the regenerated cellulose and cotton polymers are listed in Table 2.1.

As the chemical groupings and forces of attraction of the viscose and other regenerated cellulose polymers are very similar to those of the cotton polymer, reference should be made to the section on cotton for further details.

The polymer system of viscose

The polymer system of viscose is rather similar to that of cotton. However, there are some differences. The viscose polymer system is very amorphous, being about 35–40 per cent crystalline and about 65–60 per cent amorphous. Its relatively short polymers make it difficult to achieve a more crystalline polymer system without producing disadvantageous fibre properties.

Table 2.1 Significant physical difference between regenerated cellulose and cotton polymers

Polymer	Approx. number of cellobiose units	Approx. polymer length (nm)	Approx. polymer thickness (nm)	Approx. degree of polymerisation
Viscose	175	180	0.8	175
Polynosic or modal	300	310	0.8	300
Cuprammonium or cupro	250	260	0.8	250
Cotton	5000	5000	0.8	5000

The polymer system of polynosic is considered to be somewhat more crystalline than that of viscose, as borne out by the former's physical and chemical properties.

Physical properties

Tenacity

Because the polymer system of viscose is very amorphous, its filaments or staple fibres are weaker than cotton and have only a fair tenacity. The shorter, more poorly aligned viscose polymers give rise to fewer hydrogen bonds than would otherwise be possible. When wet, viscose is only half as strong as when dry. The reason for this is again the very amorphous nature of its polymer system which readily permits the entry of water molecules. These push the polymers apart, breaking a significant number of hydrogen bonds, resulting in the weaker fibre when wet.

The somewhat more crystalline nature of polynosic or modal permits fewer water molecules to enter its polymer system. Therefore, fewer hydrogen bonds are broken, and polynosic will not weaken as much when wet as its viscose equivalent.

Elastic-plastic nature

Viscose is a limp handling fibre because its polymer system is so very amorphous. Its polymers are not sufficiently long for a more satisfactory alignment, and so do not allow the formation of more hydrogen bonds which would result in a more rigid polymer system and thus a crisper handle to the viscose fibre and its textile materials.

The very amorphous nature and fewer hydrogen bonds of viscose, when compared with cotton, enable the polymers to slide past each other when the filament, or staple fibre, is put under strain. When the strain is removed, the polymers do not return to the original position they occupied in the polymer system. Thus, the polymer systems of the filaments will be disarranged and the viscose textile material will become distorted, stretched, wrinkled and/or creased.

By comparison, the handle of polynosic is somewhat less limp, and is somewhat less plastic than viscose. This is because its polymers are slightly longer and better aligned within the polymer system.

Viscose, and the other regenerated cellulose fibres, become more plastic when wet, for reasons similar to those given to explain its reduced wet tenacity.

Hygroscopic nature

The very amorphous polymer system of viscose, as well as its polar polymers, make viscose the most absorbent fibre in common use. The slightly more crystalline polynosic rayon is somewhat less absorbent than viscose.

With regard to other hygroscopic properties (that is, static electricity and crispness), the explanations given for cotton apply also to viscose and the other two regenerated cellulose fibres.

Thermal properties

Viscose and the other two regenerated cellulose fibres have somewhat similar thermal properties to cotton. The explanations offered for the thermal properties of cotton, therefore, also apply to these fibres. However, no satisfactory explanation can be given for the fact that the regenerated cellulose fibres have a lower heat resistance and poorer heat conductivity than cotton. Viscose is the most common man-made fibre which is *not* thermoplastic. The reason for this is its hygroscopic nature, which enables it to absorb water molecules very readily. Thus the polymer system of viscose always tends to contain a considerable number of water molecules, which tend to break a significant number of hydrogen bonds. (See also 'Tenacity' of viscose.) Broken hydrogen bonds prevent the retention of any heat-set. (See also pages 109 and 116.

Chemical properties

The chemical properties of cotton and the regenerated cellulose fibres are similar, so the explanations given for the chemical properties of the former apply also to viscose and the other two regenerated cellulose fibres. However, the shorter polymers and the very amorphous nature of the regenerated cellulose fibres are responsible for the much greater sensitivity of these fibres to acids, alkalis, bleaches, sunlight and weather, when compared with cotton.

With regard to dyeing and printing, the regenerated cellulose fibres will generally colour more brightly, even when delustred, than even their mercerised cotton equivalents. This is due to the greater amount of incident light reflected by viscose, even when delustred. The reflected light brightens, or increases the value and chroma of, the dyed or printed viscose. (See also Chapter 8.)

3 The ester-cellulose fibres

Textiles fibres which are composed of ester-cellulose are called **acetate fibres.** There are two types: **acetate** and **triacetate.** Because the acetate fibres have very similar properties, they are considered together here.

Acetate fibres

Fibre classification

The term *acetate* is derived from *acet* and *ate*. The former comes from *acetic acid* (the acid of vinegar), whilst the latter denotes a chemical salt. Acetate means a salt of acetic acid. To make acetate fibres, cellulose is treated to form cellulose acetate; that is, the cellulose salt of acetic acid. In organic chemistry, a salt is known as an ester. As a result acetate fibres are at times referred to as cellulose ester or ester-cellulose fibres. There are two types of acetate fibres, namely:

1 **Acetate**, a man-made, natural polymer based, *secondary* cellulose acetate filament or staple fibre.
2 **Triacetate**, a man-made, natural polymer based, *primary* cellulose acetate filament or staple fibre.

These two fibres are described further in the section called 'The acetate polymers' on page 62. The acetate fibres are medium weight fibres, their fibre density being 1.32 g/cm^3.

Fibre morphology

The macro-structure of acetate fibres

The macro-structure of acetate fibres is very similar to that of viscose so what is said about the macro-structure of viscose fibres (pages 54–55) applies also to the acetate fibres.

The microscopic appearance of the acetate fibres

Under a microscope, the longitudinal sections of the two acetate fibres look very similar. Both acetate and triacetate have one or two heavy striations. These striations result

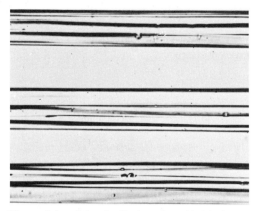

Figure 3.1a A longitudinal section of bright-lustre Dicel, a secondary cellulose acetate fibre, magnified 500 times. Note the heavy striations.

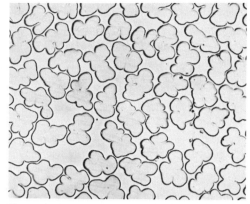

Figure 3.1b A cross-section of bright-lustre Dicel, magnified 500 times. Note the irregularly lobed cross-sections of the fibres which give the heavy striations to the longitudinal appearance.

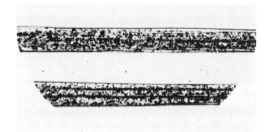

Figure 3.2a A longitudinal section of delustred Dicel, a secondary cellulose acetate fibre, magnified 500 times. Note the heavy striations.

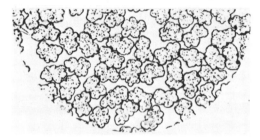

Figure 3.2b A cross-section of delustred Dicel, magnified 500 times. Note the irregularly lobed cross-sections of the fibres which result in the heavy striations of the longitudinal section.

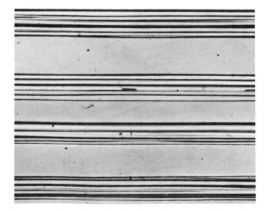

Figure 3.3a A longitudinal section of bright lustre Tricel, a primary cellulose acetate fibre, magnified 500 times. Note the heavy striations.

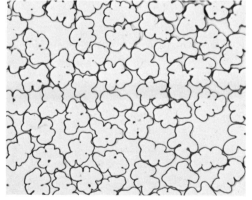

Figure 3.3b A cross-section of bright lustre Tricel, magnified 500 times. Note the irregularly lobed cross sections of the fibres and how similar these are to those of Dicel (Fig. 3.2b)

from the irregular contraction of the extruded filament during the coagulation stage in manufacture. The striations are also responsible for the irregularly lobed cross-section of both acetate and triacetate filaments, as well as the staple fibres. (See Figs 3.1, 3.2 and 3.3.)

The micro-structure of the acetate fibres

Acetate and triacetate filaments, and their staple fibres, are fine, coagulated lengths of ester-cellulose, which display no discernible micro-structure.

The polymer system

The acetate polymers

Both the acetate and triacetate polymers are cellulose polymers, whose $-OH$ groups have been acetylated to form the ester of acetic acid, or acetate (see Figs 3.4 and 3.5). In the manufacture of ester-cellulose fibres, triacetate is produced first; hence, it is also known as **primary cellulose acetate fibre.** It is meant to be fully acetylated; that is in place of the six $-OH$ groups of the cellobiose unit, six acetate groups ($-OCOCH_3$) are formed (see Fig. 3.4).

To obtain the **secondary cellulose acetate fibre**, the primary cellulose acetate is hydrolysed, that is reacted with water, so that, theoretically, only 2.3 to 2.4 acetyl or acetate groups per glucose unit occur. This is normally shown as two acetate groups per glucose unit, or four acetate groups per cellobiose unit (see Fig. 3.5). It should be noted that, with the secondary cellulose acetate polymer, it is the methylol $-OH$ group that is acetylated and one of the other $-OH$ groups (see Fig. 3.5).

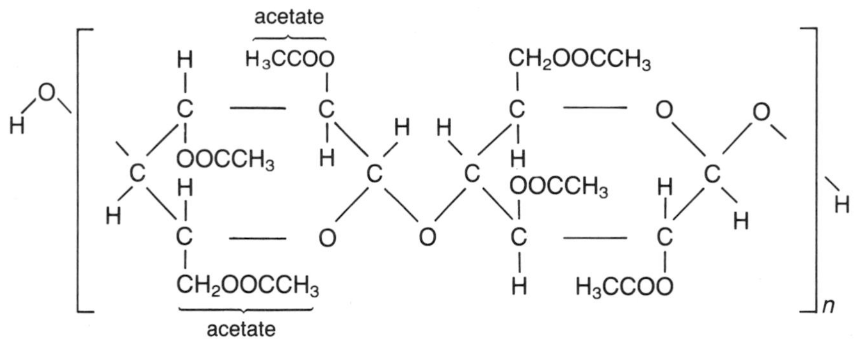

Figure 3.4 The chemical formula of the repeating unit of the triacetate or primary cellulose acetate fibre polymer. The degree of polymerisation, *n*, is about 225.

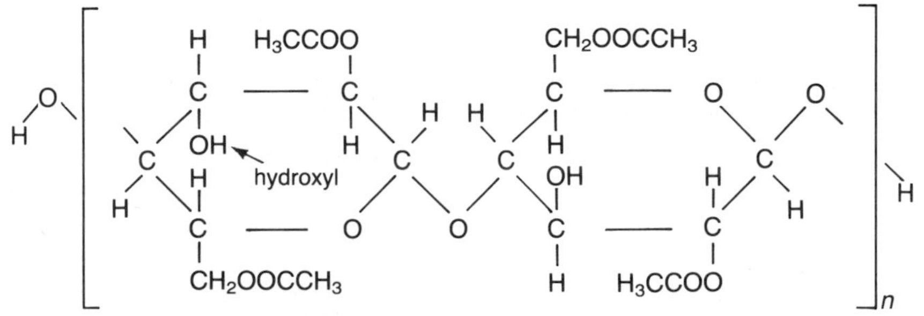

Figure 3.5 The chemical formula of the repeating unit of the acetate or secondary cellulose acetate fibre polymer. The degree of polymerisation, *n*, is about 130.

Both acetate and triacetate polymers are linear, but the acetyl groups form bulky side groups (see pages 25 and 65). The acetate or secondary cellulose acetate polymer is about 160 nm long and about 2.3 nm thick, whilst the triacetate or primary cellulose acetate polymer is about 240 nm long and about 2.6 nm thick. Their degrees of polymerisation range from about 130 for the acetate polymers to about 225 for the triacetate polymers, based upon the cellobiose unit.

The important chemical groupings of the secondary cellulose acetate polymers are the hydroxyl and acetate groups (see Fig. 3.5). The hydroxyl groups tend to indicate the occurrence and presence of hydrogen bonds. However, these hydrogen bonds would be relatively few in number and, hence, not very significant in the acetate fibre polymer system. The acetate groups of the secondary cellulose acetate polymer are essentially non-polar and outnumber the hydroxyl groups. This explains the lack of polarity of secondary cellulose acetate polymers. The definition of triacetate (see also Table 1.1) requires that its polymers have less than 8 per cent of hydroxyl groups. Such a small number of hydroxyl groups cannot form any significant hydrogen bonds. Because of the presence of at least 92 per cent of acetate groups (see also definition in Table 1.1), the triacetate polymer lacks polarity. It is for the above reasons that both acetate and triacetate fibres rely mostly upon van der Waals' forces for their polymer cohesion.

The polymer systems of the acetate fibres

The secondary cellulose acetate polymer system is estimated to be about 40 per cent crystalline and about 60 per cent amorphous, whilst that of triacetate or primary cellulose acetate is considered to be somewhat more crystalline. Both fibres are very amorphous fibres. The polymer systems of both types of acetate fibres are held together mainly by van der Waals' forces. However, some hydrogen bonds contribute towards inter-polymer cohesion in the polymer system of the secondary cellulose acetate fibres.

Since both types of acetate fibres have a polymer 'backbone' of hexagonal units, their polymer systems could be visualised as a disarranged roll of chicken wire, the disarranged portions being in the majority and representing the amorphous regions, whilst the more orderly sections are the crystalline regions of the polymer systems.

Physical properties

Tenacity

Both types of acetate fibres are weak due to the amorphous nature of their polymer systems, which limits the number of inter-polymer forces of attraction which can occur. In addition, the predominant forces of attraction between the polymers are the weak van der Waals' forces.

Acetate and triacetate become weaker when wet. This is because water molecules enter the amorphous regions of the fibres' polymer systems. The ingress of water molecules pushes the fibre polymers somewhat further apart. This may be noticed as a slight swelling of the fibres. As the fibre polymers move further apart, the cohesive effect of the van der Waals' forces is sufficiently reduced to cause a loss in tenacity of the filament or staple fibre.

Elastic-plastic nature

Both acetate and triacetate are plastic. This is because of their amorphous polymer systems and the predominantly weak van der Waals' forces that occur between their polymers. With such weak forces of attraction in these very amorphous polymer systems, polymer slippage occurs readily, even under only slight strains. Hence, acetate and triacetate textile materials readily distort and/or wrinkle.

Both acetate and triacetate fibres become more plastic when wet as sufficient water molecules can enter their amorphous polymer systems to break a significant number of inter-polymer forces of attraction. The rupture of these inter-polymer forces of attraction makes it even easier for polymers to slip past each other, under the slightest strain. Hence, acetate and triacetate textile materials are more likely to distort and/or wrinkle when wet or just damp. Secondary cellulose acetate filaments and staple fibres are the softest handling of all textile fibres in common use, this being due to the very amorphous nature of the polymer system and the occurrence of predominantly van der Waals' forces holding the polymer system together. When pressure, such as handling, is applied to acetate textile material, the inter-polymer forces present little resistance and a resulting soft handling sensation is experienced.

Triacetate or primary cellulose acetate fibres tend to have a stiffer handle, particularly after heat setting. It is considered that, after heat setting, the triacetate polymers move closer together (see also 'Thermal properties' below), providing a more rigid polymer system, which offers greater resistance to any pressure such as handling.

Hygroscopic nature

Despite their very amorphous polymer system, both acetate and triacetate fibres have only a fair moisture absorbency. This is mainly because of the relatively low polarity of the acetate and triacetate polymers.

Secondary cellulose acetate polymers contain about two –OH groups per cellobiose unit (see Fig. 3.4), which makes these polymers slightly more polar, and the filaments and staple fibres of acetate more absorbent than those of triacetate. The latter's polymers are fully acetylated; that is each cellobiose unit contains six ester groups, which impart very little, if any, polarity to the primary cellulose acetate polymer. Hence, triacetate is more hydrophobic than acetate. It becomes even more hydrophobic on heat setting, when the triacetate polymers are thought to move closer together, thereby reducing the size of the inter-polymer spaces. This reduction in the size of the inter-polymer spaces permits considerably fewer water molecules to enter the polymer system of heat set triacetate filaments and staple fibres. In effect, heat setting reduces the moisture absorbency of the triacetate polymer system by about half, making it then even less absorbent than nylon. (See also 'Thermal properties' below.)

Finally, the limited hygroscopic nature of both types of acetate fibres makes them prone to develop static electricity in dry conditions. The limited hygroscopic nature being due, of course, to a lack of polymer polarity which could otherwise attract water molecules and dissipate any static charge which could develop.

Thermal properties

There is no satisfactory explanation as yet for the poor heat resistance and conductivity of acetate and triacetate filaments, and staple fibres.

Both fibres are thermoplastic, which means that acetate and triacetate textile materials may be shaped, set, creased or pleated by the application of heat. When acetate textile materials are heated, the inter-polymer forces of attraction within their polymer systems are broken. This permits the acetate or triacetate polymers to assume the configuration required of them by the set which is being applied to their textile material. On cooling, the inter-polymer forces of attraction reform to hold the polymers in their new positions.

Secondary cellulose acetate cannot be heat set satisfactorily because it has relatively few hydrogen bonds. As its polymer system is mainly held together by the weak and easily broken van der Waals' forces, any heat set of acetate textile material soon becomes ineffective, as the acetate polymers can readily be displaced from their positions within their polymer system, when the system is subject to even the slightest of strains.

On the other hand, primary cellulose acetate will retain a heat set more satisfactorily than its secondary cellulose acetate equivalent, even though the polymer system is only held together by van der Waals' forces. The reason for this is as follows.

Normally, heat setting of a thermoplastic polymer system is thought to occur through a rearrangement of the system's polymers resulting in an increase in tenacity, or strength. However, when triacetate textile materials are heat set, the anticipated increase in strength does not occur. A rearrangement of triacetate polymers, however, does occur, for the triacetate textile material will display a stiffer, more paper-like handle, after heat setting. In addition, heat setting reduces the moisture absorbency of triacetate by about half.

It is suggested that the more satisfactory heat set of triacetate textile materials over their acetate equivalents occurs through the recrystallisation of the primary cellulose acetate polymer system. This means that the triacetate polymers will, on heating, rearrange their internal polymer bond energies and inter-polymer forces of attraction in such a manner that on subsequent cooling, that is setting, they will not be straining against the heat set configuration of their filaments or staple fibres. In addition, the triacetate polymer system is thought to contract, that is reduce in size, its inter-polymer spaces. This reduction in the size of the inter-polymer spaces explains the reduction in moisture absorbency and the resultant stiffer handle of triacetate textile materials after heat setting.

Chemical properties

Effect of acids

As both types of acetate polymers have essentially a cellulose 'backbone', acids hydrolyse them, causing polymer degradation, and resulting in weakening and eventual destruction of their textile materials.

Because the triacetate polymer system is somewhat more crystalline than that of acetate, textile materials of triacetate will be more resistant to acid degradation.

Effect of alkalis

The cellulose 'backbone' makes acetate and triacetate polymers more resistant to alkalis than to acids. However, the acetyl, acetate or ester side groups (see pages 13 and 16) will be hydrolysed, or saponified, on exposure to alkaline conditions. The effect of this alkaline hydrolysis, or saponification, is the conversion of acetate groups to their former –OH groups, as are found in the original cellulose polymer (see Fig. 2.4).

Such alkaline hydrolysis occurs, in the first instance, on the surface of the filaments or staple fibres, resulting in the yellowing of white or the dulling of coloured acetate and triacetate textile materials.

Effect of bleaches

Bleaches in general have the same effect on acetate fibres as they do on cotton fibres (see page 47).

Effect of sunlight and weather

The relative lack of polarity of the acetate and triacetate polymers is one of the factors responsible for the fair to good sunlight and weather resistance of their textile materials. The lack of polarity protects the polymers from destruction because it minimises the attraction of polar degrading agents.

As the acetate groups are acid resistant and are attached to the sides of the acetate and triacetate polymers, they offer protection to the cellulose 'backbone' from acid hydrolysis by the atmosphere, which is usually slightly acidic.

Finally, acetate textile materials have fair to good sunlight resistance because the electron arrangements of the acetate and triacetate polymer 'backbone' can sufficiently resist the degrading effect of the ultraviolet radiation of sunlight.

Colour-fastness

The acetate fibres are not easy fibres to dye or print. The disperse dyes, which are the only dyes which will readily dye or print acetate and triacetate textile materials, had to be specifically developed. The relative lack of polarity of the acetate and triacetate polymers is mainly responsible for most other dyes being unsuitable for the colouration for their textile materials.

Disperse dyes

Because the disperse dyes are relatively non-polar, they are sometimes also known as **non-ionic dyes.** Their lack of polarity makes them compatible with the relatively non-polar polymer systems of acetate and triacetate.

The fair to good light-fastness of disperse dyed and printed acetate and triacetate textile materials is due to the relatively stable electron arrangements of the chromophores of the disperse dye molecules which can withstand the degrading effects of the ultraviolet radiation of sunlight.

The good wash-fastness of disperse dyed and printed acetate and triacetate textile materials cannot be attributed to the van der Waals' forces—the only forces of attraction which can be formed between the non-polar disperse dye molecules and the acetate or triacetate polymers, which themselves lack any significant polarity. Rather, the good wash-fastness has to be attributed to the relatively non-polar, disperse dye molecules. This non-polarity makes them insoluble in water and as a result difficult to wash out of the acetate or triacetate polymer system.

4 The protein fibres

Textiles fibres composed of protein are the **natural protein fibres**: wool, silk, mohair, alpaca, angora, cashmere, etc. Only the commonly used protein fibres, namely wool and silk, will be considered here.

Wool

Textile classification

The word *wool* was *wull* in Old English, *wullo* in Teutonic, and *wlna* in pre-Teutonic days.

Wool is the fibre from the fleece of *domesticated* sheep. It is a natural, protein, multicellular, staple fibre. The fibre density of wool is 1.31 g/cm^3, which tends to make wool a medium weight fibre.

Fibre morphology

The macro-structure of wool

The wool fibre is a crimped, fine to thick, regular fibre. Fine wools may have as many as 10 crimps per centimetre, whilst coarse wools have less than 4 crimps per 10 centimetres. As the diameter of wool fibres increases, the number of crimps per unit length decreases. The number of crimps per unit length may be taken as an indication of wool fibre diameter or wool fibre fineness.

The crimped configuration prevents wool fibres from aligning themselves too closely when being spun into yarn. As a result it is possible to have wool textile materials with air spaces occupying about two-thirds of the volume. The warmth of wool fabrics is due more to the air spaces in the material than to the fibres.

The very good resilience of wool fabrics, partly attributable to the elastic nature of the wool fibre, is mainly due to the crimp. It makes the fibre 'springy' and enables the wool fibre to return to its crimped configuration.

The 'unruliness' of the crimp causes wool fibre ends to project above the wool textile material's surface. These fibre ends cause a prickling sensation, which stimulates the blood circulation of the skin. In warm and temperate climates, the wearer may find this sensation uncomfortable, as it tends to create too much body heat.

The length of wool fibres ranges from about 5 cm for the finest wools to 35 cm for the longest and coarsest wools. For wool textile manufacture, wool fibres of 5 cm to 12 cm in length are preferred. Such fibre lengths permit the most versatile and economical yarn manufacture. Wool fibres vary greatly in their fibre diameter, ranging from about $14\mu m$ for the very finest wools to more than 45 μm for the coarsest wools. Fine, lightweight, pleasant handling fabrics can be manufactured from the finer wools. As a result, a premium is paid for the finer wools particularly if they have a regular or even diameter.

Fibre length to breadth ratio can be critical with wool, since the short, coarse fibres spin into less attractive yarns than do those of fine wools. In general, fibre length to breadth ratio ranges from 2500:1 for the finer, shorter wools to about 7500:1 for the coarser, longer wools.

Wool fibres may vary from off-white to light cream in colour. This variation in colour is due to the disulphide bonds, which seem to be able to act as chromophores. As a result the incident light may be modified to cause the reflected light to have a tinge of yellow, giving the wool fibres their off-white appearance. When the fibre is cream to dark cream in colour, this is due more to polymer degradation on the surface of the fibre. This can readily occur, as the wool polymer is chemically very sensitive to atmospheric oxygen and air pollutants.

The coarser, longer wool fibres have less crimp and are more linear enabling them to reflect incident light more evenly. Such light reflection results in a subdued lustre which is not significant when compared to the lustre of man-made fibres.

Microscopic appearance of wool

The characteristic longitudinal microscopic appearance of wool is the overlapping surface cell structure. These surface cells, known as **epithelial** cells, and commonly called scales, point towards the tip of the fibre. The scales give the wool fibre a serrated surface. The fine lines seen across the fibre are the outlines of the epithelial cells (see Fig. 4.1).

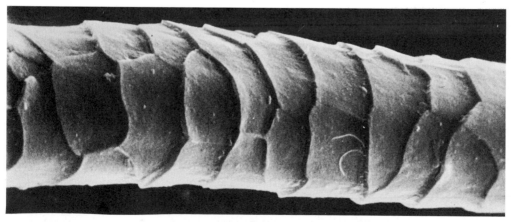

Figure 4.1 A merino wool fibre, magnified more than 2000 times. Note the surface cells, or scales, which overlap towards the tip of the fibre.

Figure 4.2   Very coarse wool fibres showing various stages of medulla formation. Magnified 400 times.

The root end of the wool fibre has an angular appearance as it is this end which was cut during shearing. The tip end, on the other hand, will not show this angular appearance. The tip of the wool fibre may be degraded by the weather. In fact, only lambs' wool fibres will show a distinctly pointed tip, but even this may have been adversely affected by weathering.

The presence of a dark, central line, or canal, along the length of the wool fibre indicates the presence of a **medulla**, which is cortical cell debris. Merino wool fibres seldom, if ever, contain a medulla, since the merino sheep breeders have made the most determined efforts to rid merino fleeces of any medullated fibres. A medullated fibre is usually from a fleece of coarse wool, such as from a cross-bred or English breed of sheep. (See Fig. 4.2.)

The cross-section of the wool fibre is usually oval in shape. The epithelial cells form a distinct perimeter, known as the **cuticle**, around the fibre's cross-section. The cuticle surrounds the **cortex**, which consists of **cortical cells**. Usually, there are about 20 to 50 cortical cells along any one diameter of the cross-section, depending upon the thickness of the wool fibre.

Felting of wool

Felting of wool is the irreversible shrinkage of the length, breadth and/or thickness of the material. This is done by subjecting the wool textile material to agitation in an aqueous solution. (*Note*: Only the natural, protein, staple fibres, that is, hair and wool fibres, can be felted.) This tendency of wool to felt is a disadvantage of woollen articles of clothing that require frequent laundering.

Wool felts because of the serrated surface of its fibres which is formed by the overlapping epithelial cells or scales (see Fig. 4.1). Because of this serrated structure, less friction will result if the fibre moves in a rootward direction than if it moves in a tipward direction. This difference in surface friction between the two directions is known as the **directional friction effect,** abbreviated to **DFE**.

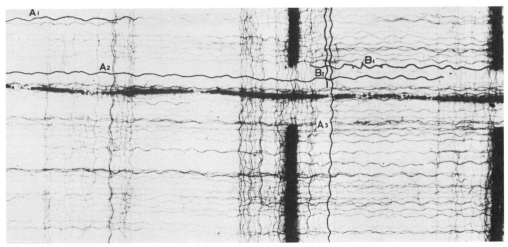

Figure 4.3 This photograph and Figs 4.4 and 4.5 (all magnified 50 times) illustrate the felting of wool. The coarser wool fibres (A_1, A_2, A_3, B_1, B_2 and B_3) were specially dyed and introduced with the others in this woven wool fabric to observe any changes in their configuration during felting. Here, they are shown before any felting has occurred.

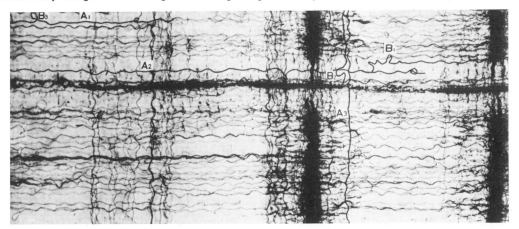

Figure 4.4 The woven wool fabric after laundering. Note how all the fibres have altered their configuration. Fibres B_1 and B_2 display a pronounced new configuration.

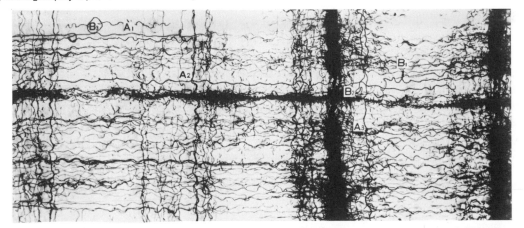

Figure 4.5 The wool fabric after further laundering. Note the overall change in the configuration of all the fibres, but particularly of B_1, B_2 and B_3.

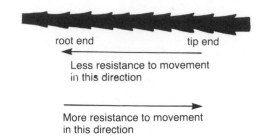

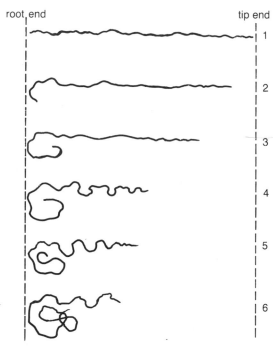

Figure 4.6 A simplified representation of the wool felting shown in Figs 4.3, 4.4 and 4.5. At step 1 the fibre is in its original position. At steps 2 to 6 the fibre curls at the root end, drawing up the tip end. Note that the fibre does not move much outside the distance it originally occupied.

When a wet, untreated wool textile material is agitated, as during laundering, the wool fibres will tend to move in a rootward direction. In actual fact, the root end of the fibre curls upon itself (see Figs 4.3 to 4.6). This movement, caused by agitation and moisture, is due to the DFE of the wool fibre's surface.

Felting of wool is significantly enhanced by heat, acid or alkali. Heat will make the wet fibre more elastic and plastic, easier and more likely to move, and it will make it distort and entangle itself with other fibres. Heat will also cause the fibre to swell more and this effect is enhanced in acid or alkaline conditions. Increased swelling results in more inter-fibre contact and increased inter-fibre friction.

The micro-structure of wool

The wool fibre grows from a follicle in the skin of the sheep and is a highly complex skin tissue. The micro-structure of wool consists of three main components: the **cuticle, cortex** and **fibrils**. (See Fig. 4.7.)

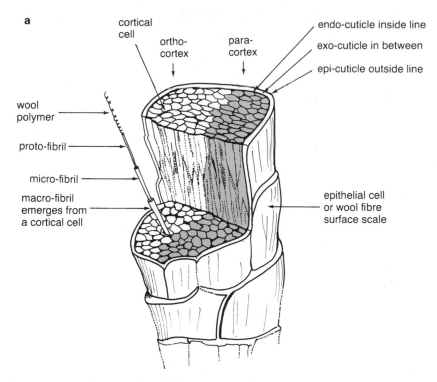

a

cortical cell

ortho-cortex

para-cortex

endo-cuticle inside line

exo-cuticle in between

epi-cuticle outside line

wool polymer

proto-fibril

micro-fibril

macro-fibril emerges from a cortical cell

epithelial cell or wool fibre surface scale

Figure 4.7a A morphological diagram of a wool fibre.

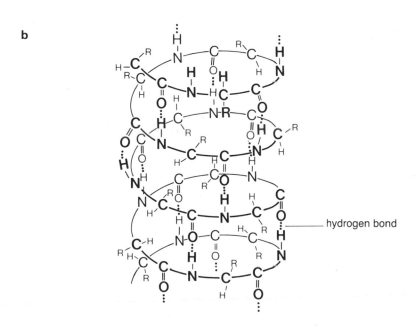

b

hydrogen bond

Figure 4.7b A part of a wool polymer showing its alpha-keratin, spiral or helical configuration. This diagram represents the spiralling wool polymer on the morphological diagram (**a**) labelled 'wool polymer'.
Note: R = a side chain, such as a salt linkage, a disulphide bond, or an amino acid side chain.

73

The **cuticle** is the layer of overlapping epithelial cells surrounding the wool fibre. It consists of the **epicuticle, exocuticle** and **endocuticle**.

The **epicuticle** is the outermost layer or sheath which covers the wool fibre. It is only a few molecules thick and is composed of a water-repellent, wax-like substance. Although the epicuticle is water-repellent, it has countless microscopic pores which enable the wool fibre to absorb moisture, such as perspiration. The epicuticle, being only a few molecules thick, is easily damaged, forms cracks and sloughs off during normal wear. This is evidenced by the greater ease of wetting of worn wool textile materials.

The overlapping epithelial cells form the **exocuticle**. An epithelial cell is about 1 μm thick, about 30 μm long and about 36 μm wide. About 10 μm of the epithelial cell of fine wool fibres can be seen, whereas, with coarse wool fibres, about 20 μm of the epithelial cell can be seen. The remainder of the epithelial cell is covered by the epithelial cell which overlaps it. As stated above, the epithelial cells are largely responsible for the felting shrinkage of untreated wool textile materials.

The **endocuticle** is an intermediate, cementing layer bonding the epithelial cells to the cortex of the wool fibre.

The **cortex,** or core, of the wool fibre forms about 90 per cent of the fibre volume. It consists of countless long, spindle-shaped cells; that is, they are thick at the middle, tapering to pointed tips at each end. These spindle-shaped cells, or cortical cells, are about 100–200 μm in length. At their centre they are about 2–5 μm wide, and about 1–3 μm thick. Fine wool fibres have about 20 such cells, whereas coarse wool fibres have about 50 cortical cells across any diameter of their cross-section.

The cortex of the wool fibre is composed of two distinct sections. These are known as the **ortho-cortex** and the **para-cortex**. If a specially selected dye is applied to the fibre, and the fibre cross-section examined, the ortho- and para-cortex become apparent, the ortho-cortex absorbing more dye than the para-cortex. The reason for this different staining is the different composition of the para-cortex and the ortho-cortex. The chemical composition of the para-cortical cells shows a higher cystine content than the ortho-cortical cells. Cystine is a sulphur — containing amino acid, capable of forming disulphide cross-links. Since there is a greater amount of cystine in the para-cortical cells, a greater number of disulphide cross-links exist in the para-cortex. This increased cross-linking tends towards greater chemical stability resulting in less dye absorption.

The ortho- and para-cortex spiral around one another, along the length of the wool fibre. The para-cortex tends to be on the inside of the spiral. This partly explains the crimped configuration of the wool fibre: the para-cortex is more stable and rigid tends to tighten the spiral, whilst the more elastic and flexible ortho-cortex conforms to the spiral on the outside. A close examination of a greasy wool fibre will show that the crimped fibre has a distinct spiral configuration (see Fig. 4.8).

The cortical cells of the wool fibre consist of a number of **macrofibrils**, each about 100–200 nm in diameter and, as yet, of an indeterminate length. These macrofibrils are held together by a protein matrix.

Each macrofibrils consists of hundreds of **microfibrils** each about 5 nm in diameter and, as yet, of an indeterminate length.

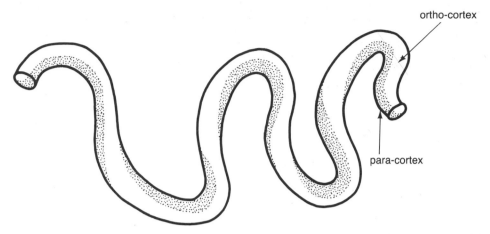

Figure 4.8 A wool fibre showing its spiralling crimp. The para-cortex always tends to be on the inside of the spiral.

Each microfibril consists of eleven **protofibrils**, about 500 nm in length and 2 nm in diameter. The protofibrils spiral about each other.

Finally, each protofibril consists of **three wool polymers**, which also spiral around each other.

It is this fibrillar and spiralling structure, within the cortical cells, which contributes towards the flexibility, elasticity and durability of the wool fibre and wool textile materials.

The polymer system

The wool polymer

The wool polymer is linear, keratin polymer, with some very short side groups (see Fig. 4.7) and it normally has a **helical** configuration. The repeating unit of the wool polymer is the **amino acid** which has the general formula shown in Fig. 4.9.

The steps in the formation of the wool polymer are not known. So the amino acid is considered the repeating unit of wool. As a result, it is not possible to determine the extent or degree of polymerisation for wool.

Amino acids are linked to each other by the **peptide** bond (that is, $-CO-NH-$) to form the wool polymer (see Fig. 4.10). The peptide bond is identical with the amide

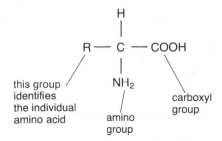

Figure 4.9 The general formula of amino acids

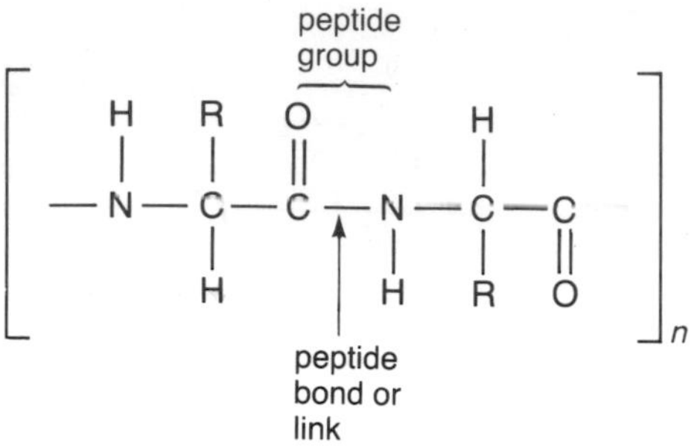

Figure 4.10 The general formula for wool and silk polymers showing the peptide bond or link, which is often also shown as —CO—NH—

bond of the nylon polymer. The wool polymer is composed of twenty amino acids, but only a general formula can be given for the wool polymer (see Fig. 4.7 and Table 1.1). It is known that, in general, the amino acids arginine, cystine and glutamic acid constitute at least one-third of the wool polymer. Table 4.1 lists the amino acids which have been isolated from wool and silk fibres.

A wool polymer is about 140 nm long and about 1 nm thick. In its normal relaxed state, the wool polymer has a **helical** configuration known as **alpha-keratin**. Stretching

Table 4.1 Percentage of amino acids in wool and silk

Name of amino acid	Amino acid content (%)	
	Wool[1]	**Silk**[2]
Alanine	3.31	26.54
Arginine	9.39	1.71
Aspartic acid	6.19	1.29
Cysteic acid[3]	0.03	not present
Cysteine[3]	0.18	not present
Cystine[3]	11.32	not present
Glutamic acid	13.11	0.97
Glycine	4.33	43.99
Histidine	1.18	0.50
Iso-leucine	2.94	0.64
Leucine	7.22	not present
Lysine	3.34	not present
Methionine	0.63	0.58
Phenylalanine	3.49	0.89
Proline	5.90	0.40
Serine	8.97	11.41
Threonine	5.70	0.90
Tryptophan	0.73	0.29
Tyrosine	4.89	5.35
Valine	4.87	2.10
Unidentified residues containing nitrogen	2.28	1.91

1 Data from 'Weathering in Wool', *Wool Science Review*, Vol. 29, April 1966, p. 36.
2 Data from J.W.S. Hearle and R.H. Peters, *Fibre Structure*, The Textile Institute and Butterworths, 1963.
3 The amino acids containing sulphur.

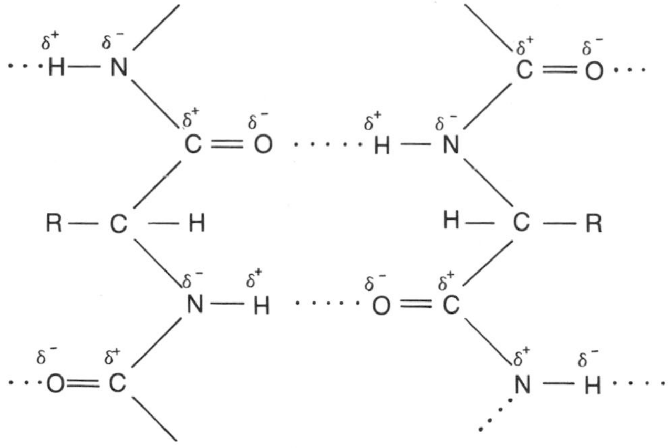

Figure 4.11 The hydrogen bond formation between two wool polymers. The dotted lines indicate the hydrogen bonds. The formula is the same for hydrogen bond formation between two silk polymers.

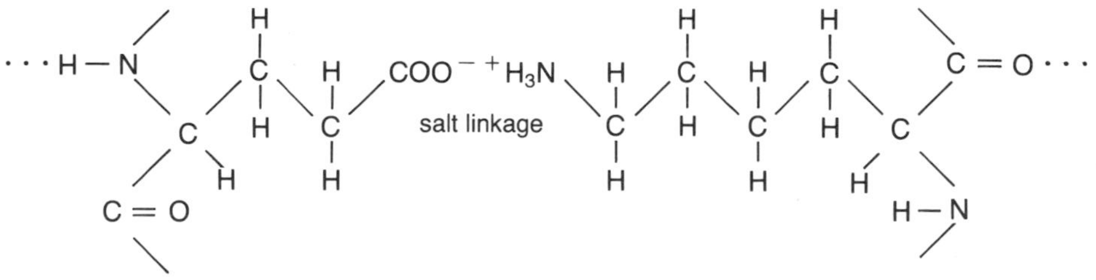

Figure 4.12 A salt linkage between two wool polymers. The formula is the same for a salt linkage between two silk polymers.

the wool fibre will tend to also stretch, straighten or unfold its polymers. The unfolded configuration of the wool polymer is called **beta-keratin**. A beta-keratin wool polymer will always attempt to return to its relaxed alpha-keratin configuration.

The complexity of the wool polymer is illustrated by the different, important chemical groups it contains and the inter-polymer forces of attraction these are able to form. Firstly, there are the polar peptide groups (i.e. $-CO-NH-$). Secondly, the oxygen of the carbonyl groups ($-CO-$) is slightly negatively charged and as a result will form hydrogen bonds with the slightly positively charged hydrogen of the imino groups ($-NH-$) of another peptide group (see Fig. 4.11).

Secondly, some wool polymers have carboxylate groups ($-COO^-$) as side groups, while others have amino groups ($-NH_3^+$) as side groups. Between these two groups, that is the acidic and basic groups, salt linkages or ionic bonds will form (see Fig. 4.12).

Thirdly, cystine, the sulphur-containing amino acid which is present in wool, makes the wool polymer system the only one with cystine linkages, also known as disulphide bonds. Cystine linkages are very strong as they are covalent bonds. They occur within and between wool polymers as shown in Fig. 4.13.

Fourthly, van der Waals' forces also occur in the wool polymer system. However, the existence of the other three types of inter-polymer forces of attraction described above tends to make the van der Waals' forces rather insignificant.

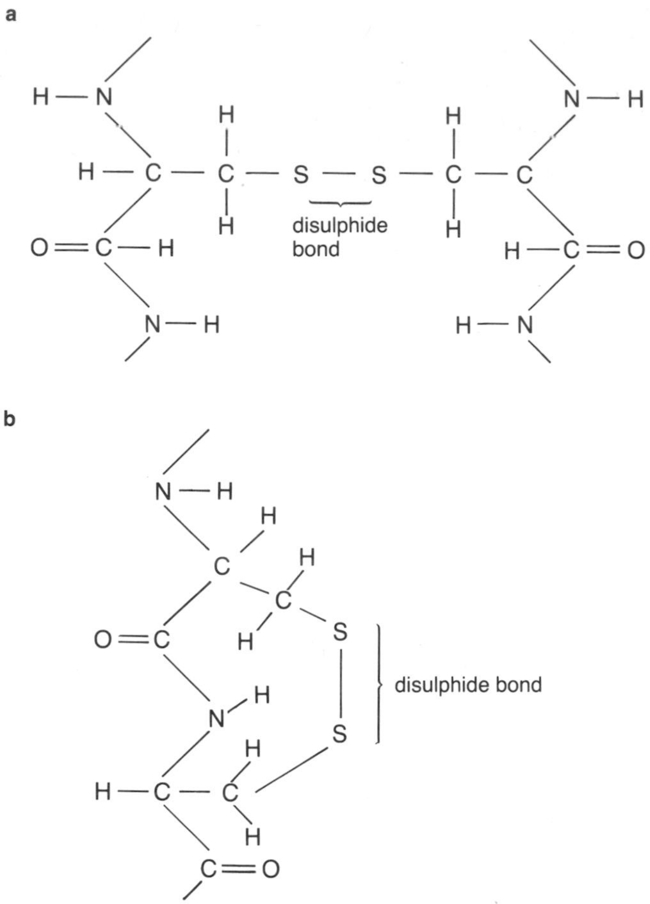

a

b

Figure 4.13 Disulphide bond formation (**a**) between two wool polymers, and (**b**) along one wool polymer.

The polymer system of wool

This should be visualised as helical polymers spiralling about each other; that is, like coils coiling about themselves. In addition, there is a distinct order of spiralling, in which each proto-fibril consists of three alpha-keratin polymers spiralling about each other. Occasionally sections of the proto-fibril exist where the helical polymers lie parallel to each other, rather than spiral about each other. The order of spiralling continues, with eleven proto-fibrils spiralling about each other to form one micro-fibril, whilst hundreds of micro-fibrils spiral about each other to form one macro-fibril.

The proto-fibrils are about 0.4 to 0.8 nm apart. At intervals, proto-fibrils form the covalent disulphide bonds with polymers of adjacent proto-fibrils. Although the actual disulphide bond ($-S-S-$) can span about 0.4 nm, the complete disulphide bond with its appending groups ($-CH_2-S-S-CH_2-$) can span about 0.7 nm. This is a considerable distance in terms of the minute dimensions of the wool polymer system. Where the polymers are somewhat further apart, the reactive ionic bond or salt linkage will form a strong bond between them. At other points, where peptide groups of polymers are closer than 0.5 nm to each other, hydrogen bonds form within and between protofibrils.

Finally, the polymer system of wool is extremely amorphous: it is about 25–30 per cent crystalline and, correspondingly, 75–70 per cent amorphous. The spiralling of the proto-fibrils, micro-fibrils and macro-fibrils does not indicate a well aligned polymer system.

Physical properties

Tenacity

Wool is a comparatively weak fibre. The low tensile strength of wool is due to the relatively few hydrogen bonds that are formed. The lack of strength is compensated by the alpha/beta-keratin configurations which the wool polymers are able to assume.

When wool absorbs moisture, the water molecules gradually force sufficient polymers apart to cause a significant number of hydrogen bonds to break. In addition, the water molecules hydrolyse many salt linkages in the amorphous regions of the wool fibre. Breakage and hydrolysis of these inter-polymer forces of attraction are apparent as swelling of the fibre and result in a loss in tenacity of the wet wool textile material.

Elastic-plastic nature

Wool has very good elastic recovery and excellent resilience. The ability of wool fibres to recover from being stretched or compressed is partly due to its crimped configuration (see 'The macro-structure of wool', page 68) and partly to the alpha-keratin configuration of the wool polymers. When stretched, flexed or compressed, the wool polymers will always tend to return to their alpha-keratin, or coiled, configuration. The ability of the polymers to return to their alpha-keratin configuration is due mainly to inter-polymer di-sulphide bonds, salt linkages and hydrogen bonds. Repeated stretching may permanently deform wool fibres. Should this occur, it means that sufficient inter-polymer forces of attraction have been broken to allow polymers, in their beta-configuration, to slide past each other. Such displacement of polymers would become apparent as a distortion of the wool fibre.

The medium to soft handle of wool fibres may be attributed partly to their crimp (see 'The macro-structure of wool') and partly to the amorphous nature of the polymer system of wool, as well as to the alpha-keratin configuration of its polymers. The amorphous regions provide the spaces into which the wool polymers may be pushed when pressure is brought to bear on the wool fibres. Similarly, the alpha-keratin, or coiled, polymer configuration can give under pressure. This ability to give or yield is responsible for the medium to soft handle of wool fibres.

Hygroscopic nature

The very absorbent nature of wool is due to the polarity of the peptide groups, the salt linkages and the amorphous nature of its polymer system. The peptide groups and salt linkages attract water molecules which readily enter the amorphous polymer system of the wool fibre.

In relatively dry weather wool may develop static electricity. This is because there are not enough water molecules present in its polymer system to dissipate any static electricity which might develop.

Wool textile materials distort more easily in damp or humid conditions, because the polymer systems of their fibres can attract more water molecules. The water molecules tend to hydrolyse sufficient salt linkages and hydrogen bonds to allow some polymer slippage, which will become apparent as distortion of the wool textile material.

Heat of wetting

Wool is renowned for its ability to give off a small steady amount of heat whilst absorbing moisture. This is known as **heat of wetting**. It is considered to be due to the energy given off by the collision between water molecules and the polar groups in the wool polymers. The force of collision between the polar groups of wool and water molecules is severe enough to liberate energy which can be felt by the wearer as a slight warmth. As wool textile materials absorb moisture, they have a much less chilling effect upon the skin in comparison with other textile materials under similar conditions. The wool polymer system will continue to give off heat until it becomes saturated with water molecules. Table 4.2 lists the heats of wetting of the more common textile fibres.

Table 4.2 Heat of wetting of fibres

Fibre	Heat of wetting from dry to saturation (joules per gram)[1]
Acetate	34
Acrylic	7
Cotton	46
Flax	54
Mercerised cotton	73
Nylon	31
Polyester	5
Silk	69
Viscose	106
Wool	113

[1]Converted to joules per gram by reference to *Fibre Structure* by J.W.S. Hearle and R.H. Peters, The Textile Institute and Butterworths, 1963.

The table shows that wool liberates the greatest amount of heat, with viscose a very close second. Heat of wetting is not so apparent with viscose, as it absorbs water molecules into its polymer system much more rapidly than wool. Thus the heat of wetting of viscose is liberated 'in a flash', so to speak, with relatively little benefit to the wearer. The same reasoning would apply to the heat of wetting of mercerised cotton. On the other hand, silk absorbs water molecules more slowly into its polymer system. Thus, compared with the above cellulosic fibres, the heat of wetting of silk is more noticeable to the wearer, but of less significance compared with wool.

Thermal properties

There is no satisfactory explanation as yet for the poor heat conductivity of wool and its low heat resistance. Applying excessive amounts of heat (i.e. too much kinetic energy) will result in disulphide bond rupture and polymer fragmentation. Initially, this polymer fragmentation will only result in surface discolouration of the wool fibre. However, prolonged exposure to heat can result in scorching. The brown to black discolouration of scorched wool is due to the formation of minute particles of carbon, which are black in colour. The carbon is, of course, the ultimate degradation product from wool polymers on exposure to excessive amounts of kinetic energy. Scorching is usually accompanied by a weakening of the fibre.

Wool smoulders rather than burns. This seems to be due to water molecules held by hydrogen bonds to polymer sites on the keratin polymer. Not only that, but water molecules would be held to water molecules by hydrogen bonding between them (see Fig. 1. 10). Therefore, if wool is exposed to a naked flame, much of the heat or kinetic energy is consumed in producing steam.

Setting of wool

A **temporary set** may be induced by drying a wet wool textile material in a chosen configuration. When completely dry, the material will retain the configuration in which it dried, until it is wet again. This occurs because the water molecules entering the polymer system of wool are thought to break the hydrogen bonds and, to some extent, hydrolyse the salt linkages. When the material dries out (i.e. water molecules are removed), the hydrogen bonds and salt linkages reform, but in new positions determined by the configuration in which the wool textile material is being dried.

A **permanent set** in wool textiles may be achieved by prolonged steaming, which hydrolyses any strained disulphide bonds. When the material cools, these hydrolysed disulphide bonds reform as relaxed cross-links, conforming to the configuration in which it was being steamed. The strength of the covalent disulphide bonds tends to maintain the new configuration of the fibres and, hence, the wool textile material. As it will take considerably more steaming to rupture the reformed disulphide bonds, the set is described as permanent, although it is not as permanent as chemical setting.

Chemical setting is achieved by treating wool textile material with such compounds as sodium bisulphite, ammonium thioglycollate, or monoethanolamine sulphite. These compounds are reducing agents, and are used to break the disulphide bonds or cystine linkages by chemical reduction. The material is then manipulated into the desired specific configuration: e.g. laid flat, folded into pleats or a crease line. Steam pressing the wool textile in the new, desired configuration will cause the disulphide bonds to reoxidise (i.e. reform). The oxidation of the disulphide bonds occurs, of course, in new positions appropriate to the new, desired configuration of the textile. Because they are cross-links, the disulphide bonds are very strong. They will therefore ensure that the wool fibres hold their new configuration and impart a permanent set to the material.

Chemical properties

Effect of acids

Wool is more resistant to acids than to alkalis. Acids hydrolyse the peptide groups but leave the disulphide bonds, which cross-link the wool polymers, intact. Although the polymer system of wool is weakened in acidic solutions, the fibre does not dissolve. However, under such conditions the fibre is very vulnerable to further degradation, because the hydrogen bonds and salt linkages are also hydrolysed to an extent. It is essential, therefore, that wool be neutralised after any acid treatment.

Effect of alkalis

Wool dissolves readily in alkaline solutions. Alkalis hydrolyse the disulphide bonds, hydrogen bonds and salt linkages of wool and cause the wool polymers to separate from each other, which is seen as dissolution of the wool fibre. Prolonged exposure to alkalis causes hydrolysis of the peptide bonds of wool polymers leading to polymer fragmentation and complete destruction of the wool fibre.

Effect of bleaches

There is little theoretical information on the effects of applying bleaches to the wool fibre. An effective method of bleaching wool is to use a reducing bleach followed by an oxidising bleach. The effectiveness of this type of wool bleaching is explained as follows. Treating the wool textile material with a reducing bleach, such as acidified sodium sulphite, sodium bisulphite or sodium dithionite, converts the discolouration on the fibre surface to colourless compounds. If an oxidising bleach, such as hydrogen peroxide, is then applied, the now colourless compounds are converted to water-soluble products. These can then be rinsed off the wool fibre. No method is known for bleaching wool permanently. Exposure of bleached wool to atmospheric oxygen, moisture and pollutants in the atmosphere tends to cause the wool to revert to its off-white colour and eventually to a yellow colour.

Effect of sunlight and weather

Exposure to sunlight and weather tends to yellow white or dull coloured wool textile materials. The cause for this is attributed largely to the ultraviolet radiation of sunlight. The ultraviolet rays cause the peptide and disulphide bonds to sever. Fracture of these bonds results in polymer degradation products on the surface of the wool fibre. These degradation products cause the wool fibre surface not only to absorb more light, but to scatter the incident light to a greater extent. The result is the yellowing or dulling mentioned above.

Prolonged exposure to sunlight and weathering severely weakens wool fibres by excessive severing of peptide and disulphide bonds.

Colour-fastness

Wool, like cotton, is considered a relatively easy fibre to dye. It is coloured most readily by the following classes of dyes: acid dyes, chrome or mordant dyes, premetallised dyes and reactive dyes. The ease with which the polymer system of wool will take in dye molecules is due to the polarity of its polymers and its amorphous nature. The polarity will readily attract any polar dye molecules and draw them into the polymer system.

However, as with all textile fibres, the dye molecules can only enter the amorphous regions of the polymer system of wool. This is because the inter-polymer spaces in the crystalline regions of the polymer system are too small and prevent the relatively large and bulky dye molecules from entering.

Acid dyes

Acid dyes are so called as they are normally applied from an acidic dye liquor. The good sunlight resistance of acid dyed and printed wool textile materials is due to the electron stability of the acid dye's chromophores. This electron stability enables the acid dye molecule to resist the photochemical degradation which the ultraviolet rays of sunlight might cause.

In general, acid dyed and printed wool textile materials have only a fair wash-fastness. This is because many acid dyes are essentially direct dyes, whose molecules attach themselves to the wool polymers with van der Waals' forces. As these forces are extremely weak, and very easily broken by water molecules, the acid dye molecules are readily rinsed out of the wool polymer system by laundering.

Mordant or chrome dyes, and premetallised dyes

Premetallised dyes have largely replaced the mordant or chrome dyes. The general fastness properties of these two classes of dye are similar. These classes of dyes are normally considered when it is desirable to have coloured wool textile materials with satisfactory wash-fastness.

The very good wash-fastness of premetallised dyed and printed wool textile materials is attributed to the chemical stability imparted to the premetallised and mordant dye molecule by the metal atom, usually chromium. The chromium atom is able to make the electron arrangement of the whole dye molecule more stable and hence, more resistant to chemical degrading agents, such as alkaline laundry liquors. In addition, the relatively large size of these dye molecules causes them to become trapped and entangled in the polymer system of the wool fibre.

The good light-fastness of premetallised or mordant dyed and printed wool textile materials is due to the relatively large size of the dye molecules which, because of the chromium atom they usually contain, have a sufficiently stable electron arrangement to resist the photochemical degradation caused by the ultraviolet rays of sunlight.

Reactive dyes

The molecules of these dyes react with the wool polymer to form a covalent bond. Reactive dyed and printed wool textile materials have very good light-fastness. This is due to the electron stability of the reactive dye molecules, which is able to resist the photochemical degradation caused by the ultraviolet rays of sunlight. The very good wash-fastness of reactive dyed and printed wool textile materials is due mainly to the covalent bond formed between the reactive dye molecules and the wool fibre polymers.

Silk

Fibre classification

In Old English, silk was *sioloc*. The name is thought to have originated from the Greek *seres*, meaning the people from Eastern Asia, namely the Chinese.

Silk is a natural, protein filament. Its filament density is 1.34 g/cm^3, which makes it a medium weight fibre. However, very light weight silk textile materials may be manufactured from silk filaments.

Fibre morphology

The macro-structure of silk

The raw silk strand consists of two silk filaments encased by a protein called **sericin**. The thickness of the raw silk strand and its uneven and irregular surface are due to the coating of sericin, which gives raw silk a coarse handle.

The ability of a silk cocoon to withstand prolonged exposure to weather shows that sericin is very weather resistant. However, sericin is readily soluble in mild alkaline solution, and when it is removed the two shiny silk filaments composing the raw silk strand are revealed. (See Figs 4.14 and 4.15.)

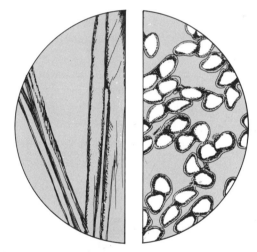

Figure 4.14 Longitudinal and cross-sections of raw silk, magnified 400 times. Note the lack of longitudinal features, but the pairs of triangular cross-sections, at the right.

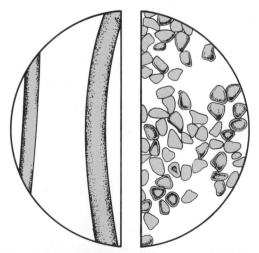

Figure 4.15 Longitudinal and cross-sections of degummed silk, magnified 400 times. Note the characteristic triangular cross-section but featureless longitudinal section.

Silk is a very fine, regular, translucent filament. It may be up to 600 m long, but averages about 300 m in length. Depending upon the health, diet and state under which the silk larvae extruded the silk filaments, their diameter may vary from 12 μm to 30 μm. This gives a fibre length to breadth ratio well in excess of 2000:1.

The beauty and softness of silk's lustre is due to the triangular cross-section of the silk filament. As the silk filament is usually slightly twisted about itself, the angle of light reflection changes continuously. As a result, the intensity of the reflected light is broken, resulting in a soft, subdued lustre.

The microscopic appearance of silk

The irregular, random, longitudinal striations seen on the raw silk strand and the silk filament are not sufficiently distinctive to identify both forms under the microscopic.

The triangular cross-section of the silk filament (see Fig. 4.15), can be used to identify silk. This characteristic microscopic appearance is due to the slit-like opening of the silk secreting glands, one each being located on either side within the mouth of the silk moth larvae.

The micro-structure of silk

The silk filament is a fine, coagulated stream of fibroin solution, and has no identifiable micro-structure. In this regard it resembles the man-made fibres. Fibroin is the chemical name for the protein which constitutes silk.

The polymer system

The silk polymer

The silk polymer is a linear, fibroin polymer. It differs from the wool polymers as follows:

1 Silk is composed of sixteen different amino acids compared with the twenty amino acids of the wool polymer (see Table 4.1). Three of these sixteen amino acids, namely alanine, glycine and serine, make up about four-fifths of the silk polymers' composition.
2 The silk polymers are not composed of any amino acids containing sulphur. Hence, the polymer system of silk does not contain any disulphide bonds.
3 The silk polymer occurs only in the beta-configuration (see 'The wool polymer', page 75.)

It is thought that the silk polymer is about as long as (140 nm), or only slightly longer than the wool polymer, and about 0.9 nm thick.

Silk may be considered to have the same composition as that of wool except that the silk polymer system contains no disulphide bonds.

Like wool the repeating unit of silk is the amino acid. The way in which the silk polymer is formed is not known. The important chemical groupings of the silk polymer are the peptide groups (see Fig. 4.10) which give rise to hydrogen bonds, and the carboxyl and amine groups (see Fig. 4.12) which give rise to the salt linkages.

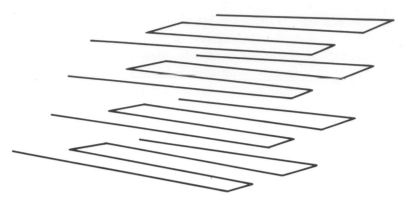

Figure 4.16 How the folded or beta-configuration, linear fibroin polymers are thought to be arranged to provide the very crystalline polymer system of silk.

The polymer system of silk

This is considered as being composed of layers of folded, linear polymers, as shown in Fig. 4.16. Such a polymer system explains why silk is estimated to be about 65–70 per cent crystalline and, correspondingly, about 35–30 per cent amorphous. The major forces of attraction between silk polymers are thought to be hydrogen bonds. These are only effective across a distance of less than 0.5 nm. Fibroin polymers must, therefore, lie closer together than this.

Physical properties

Tenacity

The silk filament is strong. This strength is due to its linear, beta-configuration polymers and very crystalline polymer system (see Fig. 4.16). These two factors permit many more hydrogen bonds to be formed in a much more regular manner.

When wet, silk loses strength. This is due to water molecules hydrolysing a significant number of hydrogen bonds and in the process weakening the silk polymer.

Elastic-plastic nature

Silk is considered to be more plastic than elastic because its very crystalline polymer system does not permit the amount of polymer movement which could occur in a more amorphous system. Hence, if the silk textile material is stretched excessively, the silk polymers, which are already in a stretched state (they have a beta-configuration) will slide past each other. The process of stretching ruptures a significant number of hydrogen bonds. When stretching ceases, the polymers do not return to their original position, but remain in their new positions. This disorganises the polymer system of silk, which is seen as a distortion and wrinkling or creasing of the silk textile material.

The handle of the silk is described as medium, as its very crystalline polymer system imparts a certain amount of stiffness to the filaments. This is often misinterpreted, in that the handle is regarded as soft, because of the smooth, even and regular surface of silk filaments.

Hygroscopic nature

Because silk has a very crystalline polymer system, it is less absorbent than wool. The greater crystallinity of silk's polymer system allows fewer water molecules to enter than does the more amorphous polymer system of wool.

The other hydroscopic properties of silk are rather similar to those of wool, so refer to the section on the hygroscopic nature of wool on page 79.

Thermal properties

Silk is more sensitive to heat than wool. This is considered to be partly due to the lack of any covalent cross links in the polymer system of silk, compared with the disulphide bonds which occur in the polymer system of wool. The existing peptide bonds, salt linkages and hydrogen bonds of the silk polymer system tend to break down once the temperature exceeds 100°C.

With regard to discolouration due to heat, scorching and burning, reference should be made to wool, under the above heading, as the two fibres are rather similar in these properties.

Chemical properties

Effect of acids

Silk is degraded more readily by acids than is wool. This is because, unlike the wool polymer system with its disulphide bonds, there are no covalent cross-links between silk polymers. Thus perspiration, which is acidic, will cause immediate breakdown of the polymer system of silk. This is usually noticed as a distinct weakening of the silk textile material.

Effect of alkalis

Alkaline solutions cause the silk filament to swell. This is due to partial separation of the silk polymers by the molecules of alkali. Salt linkages, hydrogen bonds and van der Waals' forces hold the polymer system of silk together. Since these inter-polymer forces of attraction are all hydrolysed by the alkali, dissolution of the silk filament occurs readily in an alkaline solution. It is interesting to note that initially this dissolution means only a separation of the silk polymers from each other. However, prolonged exposure would result in peptide bond hydrolysis, resulting in polymer degradation and complete destruction of the silk polymer.

The yellowing of white or the dulling of coloured silk textile materials on laundering is due to filament surface rearrangement of polymers, as well as some polymer degradation. These two factors affect light reflection and result in yellowing or dulling.

Effect of bleaches

What has been stated for wool also applies to silk.

Effect of sunlight and weather

The resistance of silk to the environment is not as good as that of wool. This lower resistance is due mainly to the lack of covalent cross-links in the polymer system of silk.

For any further explanations for silk with regard to the effects of sunlight and weather, refer to the section on wool, page 82.

Colour-fastness

The explanations and descriptions of the dyeing, printing and resultant colour-fastness of coloured wool textile materials (on pages 82–83) apply also to silk. However, the lustre of silk will cause its dyed and printed silk textile materials to appear much brighter in colour than any equivalent dyed or printed wool textile material. (See page 201.)

5 The synthetic fibres

Textile fibres composed of synthesised polymers not found in nature are the man-made, synthetic polymer fibres: **acrylic, chlorofibres, elastomeric, modacrylic, nylon, polyester, polyethylene, polypropylene, polyvinyl alcohol**, etc.

Of the many synthetic fibres, only the commonly used ones, namely acrylic, modacrylic, elastomeric, nylon and polyester, will be considered here.

Acrylic

Fibre classification

The term acrylic is derived from the Latin word *acryl*, which means bitter, irritating or pungent, and is descriptive of the compound, acrylic acid. Acrylonitrile is chemically related to acrylic acid and the term acrylic is short for polyacrylonitrile.

The acrylic fibres are man-made, synthetic polymer based, polyacrylonitrile filaments or staple fibres. They are divided into two types:

1 Polyacrylonitrile fibres generally referred to as the **acrylic fibres.**
2 Modified polyacrylonitrile fibres generally referred to as the **modacrylic fibres.**

By definition, it is necessary for the acrylic fibres to be composed of at least 85 per cent by weight of acrylonitrile units (see Fig. 5.2). On the other hand, the modacrylic fibres must be composed of at least 35 per cent but not more than 85 per cent by weight of acrylonitrile units. The remaining percentage of their respective polymer systems is a polymer (or polymers), which makes the dyeing and printing of these fibres easier. This will be covered more fully later in this chapter under the heading 'Colour-fastness'.

The density of both types of acrylic fibres averages 1.16 g/cm^3. The low density means that these fibres are relatively light weight enabling the production of bulky knitwear of lighter weight than comparable wool equivalents.

Fibre morphology

The macro-structure of acrylics

The acrylic fibres appear as regular, translucent, slightly wavy filaments or staple fibres.

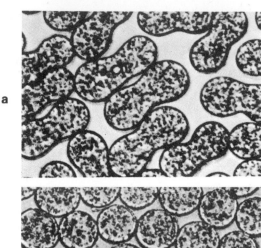

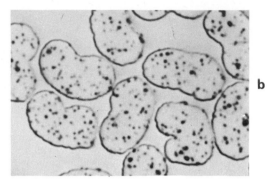

Figure 5.1 The three types of cross-section which acrylic and modacrylic fibres may have, magnified 500 times.
a dog-bone or dumb-bell shaped;
b kidney shaped;
c circular, with or without a serrated edge.

Acrylic fibres are slightly wavy, unlike the rod-like nylon and polyester fibres. The slight waviness of the acrylic fibres provides a slight bulkiness to their yarns. Texturising will enhance the bulk of acrylic yarns. The reasons for texturising, and also crimping, acrylic staple fibres are similar to those given for viscose rayon in Chapter 2. Nearly all acrylic fibre production is in the form of staple fibre which is staple spun and texturised to enhance tactile appeal, enabling acrylic articles to compete more successfully with wool equivalents.

In general, acrylics are produced as delustred fibres and are used to produce such items as knitwear, curtains, pile fabrics, upholstery fabrics, imitation furs, etc. which are usually available with a dull lustre.

The diameter of acrylic fibres ranges from about 15 μm to 25 μm, depending on end-use requirements. The fibre length to breadth ratio is usually in excess of 2000:1. This ensures that even the shortest staple fibre will satisfactorily spin into yarn.

Microscopic appearance

The longitudinal appearance of the acrylic fibres is regular in width, sometimes showing several fine but more usually only one heavy striation.

The shape of the cross-section (see Fig. 5.1) depends upon the particular acrylonitrile polymer or copolymer, the type of coagulation solution in the spinning bath and the rate of coagulation.

The microscopic appearance cannot be used to identify the acrylic fibre.

Micro-structure of the acrylic fibres

Acrylic filaments or staple fibres do not have an identifiable micro-structure.

The polymer system

The acrylic polymer

The main component of the acrylic polymer is the acrylonitrile monomer. Polyacrylonitrile or the acrylic polymer is illustrated in Fig. 5.2. It is a linear polymer, with a degree of polymerisation of about 2000. This makes it about 500 nm long, with a thickness ranging from 0.3 nm at the methylene groups to about 0.53 nm at the nitrile groups (see Fig. 5.2). The acrylic polymer is one of the longest man-made fibre polymers extruded to form a textile filament. Because the acrylic polymer system depends for its cohesion on weak van der Waals' forces, the length of its polymer is essential for the formation of a maximum number of these weak forces of attraction.

The acrylic polymer is a copolymer composed of two or more monomers. By definition, acrylic fibres must contain up to 15 per cent of a monomer other than acrylonitrile, whereas modacrylics must contain at least 35 per cent but not more than 65 per cent of a monomer other than acrylonitrile. This other monomer, also referred to as the comonomer, may be one, or a combination, of the following: acrylamide, methacrylate, vinyl acetate, vinyl chloride, vinylidene chloride, etc. Less frequently mentioned are such comonomers as acrylic acid or sodium vinylbenzene sulphonate (see also Fig. 5.4). These two comonomers each have an anionic group which will attract the cationic coloured radical of a basic dye molecule; basic dyes being used predominantly to colour acrylic and modacrylic textile materials. The earlier comonomers listed do not have anionic radicals and they cannot, therefore, attract the cation of basic dyes. Thus whenever an acrylic or modacrylic fibre can satisfactorily be coloured with basic dyes, then its polymers must contain anionic groups such as those of acrylic acid and/or sodium vinylbenzene sulphonate.

The polymer composition of the modacrylic fibre Zefran, seemingly a graft copolymer of acrylonitrile and vinylpyrrolidene, is given on page 7. The latter monomer must confer upon Zefran the ability to be satisfactorily coloured with azoic, direct, metal complex, sulphur, and vat dyes but not basic dyes. Regular Acrilan type modacrylic fibre is a copolymer obtained by polymerising acrylonitrile, apparently with vinylpyridene. Under acidic conditions the pyridene radical becomes sufficiently cationic to attract the anionic coloured radical of acid dyes. This permits it to be dyed with acid dyes, as well as chrome, direct, metal comples, and reactive dyes, but not basic dyes. (See also Fig. 5.3a.) Creslan, another modacrylic, is apparently polymerised from acry-

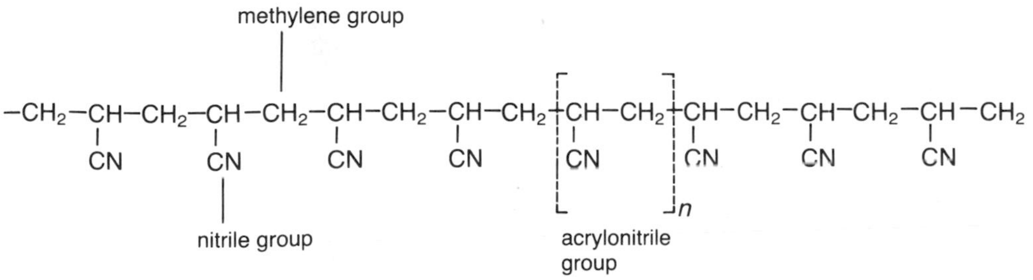

Figure 5.2 Part of an acrylic polymer. Note that the section illustrated does not contain any copolymer. The degree of polymerisation, *n*, is about 2000.

a

(i)

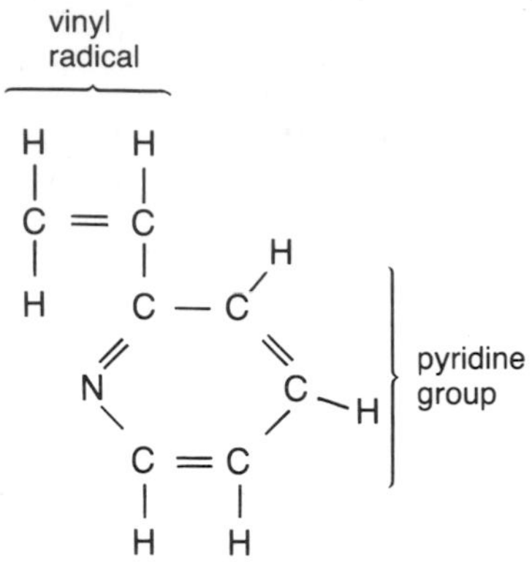

pyridine group

vinyl radical

(ii)

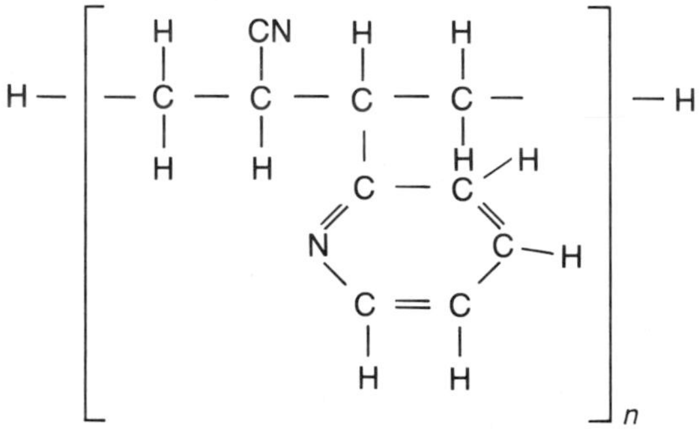

Copolymer from acrylonitrile and vinylpyridene; under acid conditions, such as in the dye bath of an acid dye, the nitrogen atom of the pyridene group will become positively charged or cationic.

(iii)

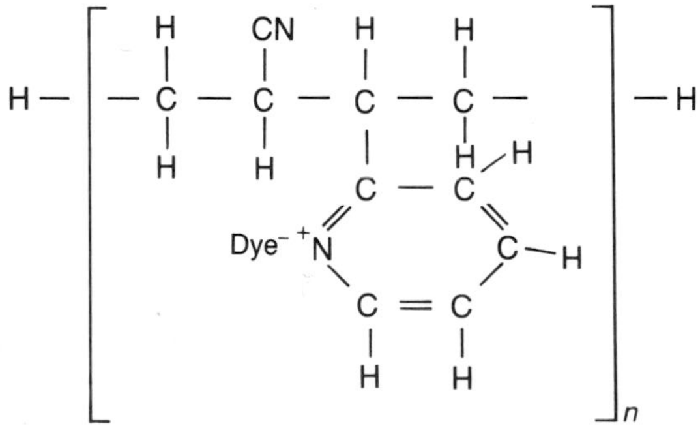

In acidic conditions, such as during acid dyeing, the nitrogen atom of the pyridine group becomes positively charged or cationic and thus capable of attracting the anionic or negatively charged coloured group of the acid dye molecule, i.e. Dye⁻.

b

(i)

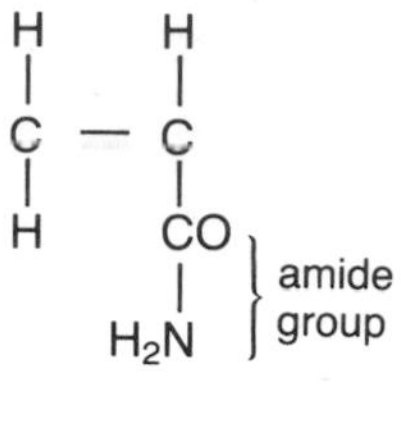

amide group

acrylamide

(ii)

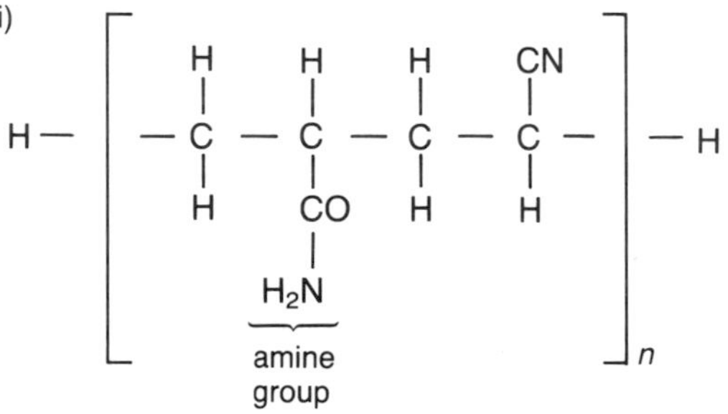

amine group

Copolymer from acrylonitrile and acrylamide; under acid conditions the amine group of the amide group will become positively charged or cationic.

(iii)

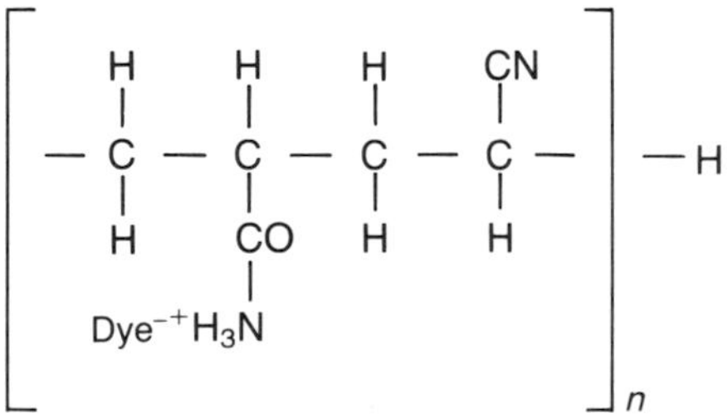

In acidic conditions, such as during acid dyeing, the amine group becomes positively charged or cationic and thus capable of attracting the anionic or negatively charged coloured group of the acid dye molecule, i.e. Dye⁻.

Figure 5.3 Two examples of polymerising an acrylic or modacrylic copolymer so as to have cationic or negatively charged groups in the copolymer capable of attracting the anionic or negatively charged coloured group of acid dye molecules

(i)

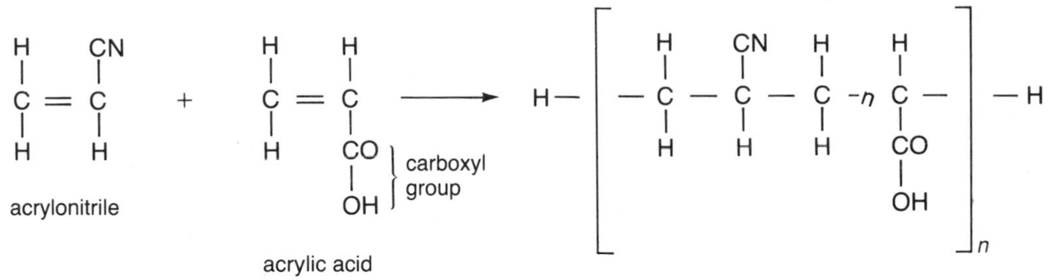

acrylonitrile

acrylic acid

Copolymer from acrylonitrile and acrylic acid; the carboxyl group will ionise or dissociate in the dye bath to form the anionic carboxyl group.

(ii)

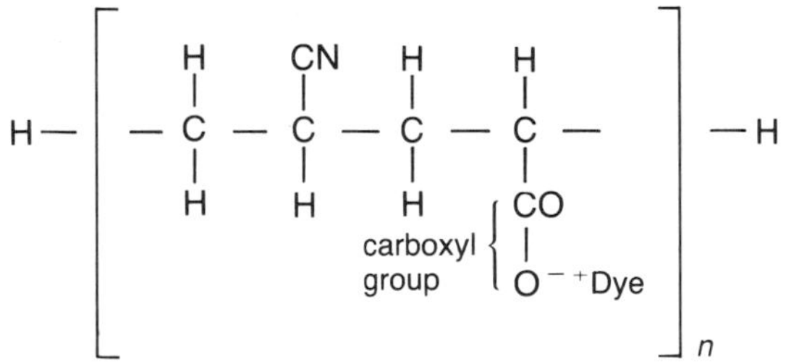

The carboxyl group is anionic or negatively charged in the dye bath and will, therefore, attract the cationic or positively charged coloured group of the basic dye molecule, i.e. $^{+}$Dye.

(i)

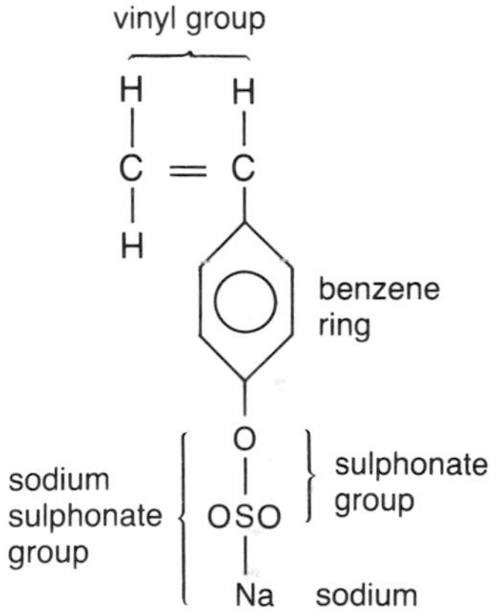

sodium vinylbenzene sulphonate

(ii)

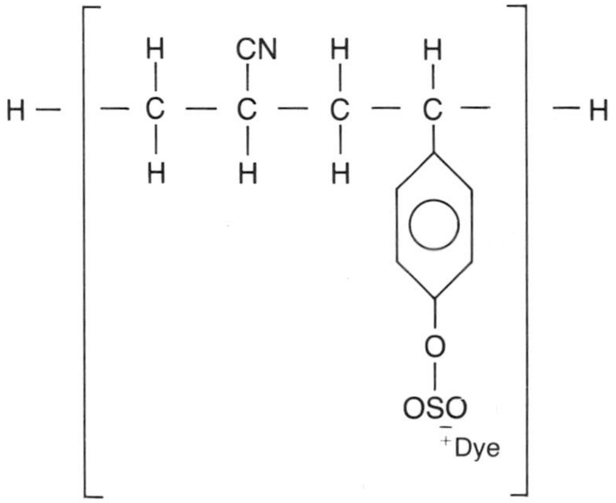

Copolymer from acrylonitrile and sodium vinylbenzene sulphonate; the sodium sulphonate group will ionise or dissociate in the dye bath to form the anionic sulphonate group which will attract the cationic coloured group of the basic dye molecule, i.e. $^{+}$Dye.

Figure 5.4 Two examples of polymerising an acrylic or modacrylic copolymer so as to have anionic or strongly negatively charged groups capable of attracting the cationic or positively charged coloured group of basic dye molecules

lonitrile and acrylamide (see Fig. 5.3b). The acrylamide would, as part of the copolymer, make the Creslan substantive to the same dyes as Acrilan, but not basic dyes. The reason for this is that under acidic conditions the amine radical of the acrylamide becomes slightly positively charged, enabling it to attract the anionic or negatively charged coloured radical of the dyes mentioned.

It becomes apparent, therefore, that the textile dyer needs to be aware of the polymer composition of acrylic and modacrylic fibres in order to be able to select the most suitable dye.

The polymer system

There is not as yet a generally accepted description of the acrylic polymer system. It has been considered that the nitrogen atoms of the nitrile side groups on the acrylic polymers have a slightly negative polarity. This would enable them to form hydrogen bonds with hydrogen atoms of the methylene groups on adjacent polymers (see Fig. 5.3). However, as the acrylic polymer is essentially non-polar, it has been more or less accepted that van der Waals' forces hold the acrylic polymer system together. This seems to be borne out by the fact that the acrylic polymer is one of the longest synthetic fibre polymers made. If such a long, non-polar polymer can give a useful polymer system, then the predominant existence of van der Waals' forces between polymers appears to be confirmed. Furthermore, for the van der Waals' forces to be effective, excellent alignment or orientation of polymers is necessary. This indicates a crystalline polymer system, which has been estimated to be about 70–80 per cent crystalline and, correspondingly, 30–20 per cent amorphous. This tends to make the acrylic polymer system very crystalline.

This does not explain the ability of acrylic fibres to contract in length when subjected to hot, wet conditions, such as immersion in boiling water. This lack of length stability is much more pronounced in acrylic and modacrylic fibres than in any other synthetic fibres. The longitudinal instability of acrylic fibres is explained as follows. During fibre manufacture the acrylic polymer system becomes highly ordered in a lateral direction, i.e. across the width of the fibre. There seems insufficient evidence to indicate that the polymer system assumes any particular order in a longitudinal direction, i.e. along the length of the fibre. The difference between lateral and longitudinal orderliness of the acrylic polymer system permits 'overstretching' of the fibre during manufacture, placing the polymers and the polymer system under considerable stress. In other words, the polymers are forced to assume unnatural configurations. The intrapolymer bonding forces of the polymers are strained in these unnatural polymer configurations and will, if given the opportunity, return the polymers to their natural or relaxed configurations. This will occur in the presence of wet heat, e.g. during dyeing in boiling water. Under such conditions, the inter-polymer forces of attraction, which would be mainly van der Waals' forces holding the polymer in the unnatural configurations, are broken. This permits the intrapolymer bonding forces of the polymers to return them to their natural configuration. All this would be apparent as a contraction in length of the acrylic fibre and/or an increase in bulk of the acrylic textile material. It should be noted that, in this explanation, the description 'very crystalline' is not used. Instead, the oriented acrylic polymer system is described as being highly ordered. This is based upon the consideration that the acrylic polymers apparently do not form sufficiently distinct crystal-like arrangements when oriented.

In summary, subject to further evidence becoming available, the acrylic polymer system may be regarded as very crystalline and held together by van der Waals' forces.

Physical properties

Tenacity

The fair to strong tenacity of the acrylic fibres is attributed to the very crystalline nature of their polymer systems, as well as to their very long polymers. These two characteristics enable van der Waals' forces to develop between polymers; although these forces are weak, they act in this case very efficiently and effectively.

The loss in tenacity that occurs when acrylic fibres become wet indicates that the fibres are slightly amorphous, enabling water molecules to enter and reduce the van der Waals' forces between polymers.

Elastic-plastic nature

Acrylics have a soft handle. This means that, although the polymer system is very crystalline, acrylic polymers must be able to give or slide over each other when the acrylic filament or staple fibre is bent or crushed. The displacement of polymers in the acrylic polymer system is evidenced by the wrinkling and distortion of the textile materials in response to bending, stretching and/or crushing. The lack of dimensional stability of acrylic textile materials tends to reinforce the opinion that the main forces of attraction within their polymer systems are van der Waals' forces. Further evidence is supplied by the ease and relatively low temperature at which wrinkles in acrylic materials can be ironed out.

Hygroscopic nature

Acrylic fibres are hydrophobic because the polymer system is highly crystalline. Very few water molecules are absorbed because of the very slightly amorphous nature of the polymer system, the slight polarity of the nitrile groups in the acrylic polymer, and the somewhat stronger polarity of the anionic groups introduced by copolymerisation.

The hydrophobic nature of acrylic textile materials results in the ready development of static electricity. This is an undesirable effect and occurs because the acrylic polymers are unable to attract sufficient water to dissipate the static build-up.

Thermal properties

Acrylics are the most heat sensitive of the synthetic fibres commonly used for apparel purposes. The weak van der Waals' forces which hold the acrylic polymer system together contribute to the heat sensitivity of the fibres. Body heat, in conjunction with the stresses and strains of wearing, can provide sufficient heat energy to reduce the cohesive effectiveness of the van der Waals' forces in the acrylic polymer system. This is apparent as wrinkling and/or distortion of the acrylic textile material.

When near a naked flame, acrylic fibres tend to ignite immediately, rather than melt and then burn as do nylon and polyester fibres. Acrylic fibres are the most flammable synthetic fibres in common use.

The ease with which acrylics ignite does not apply to certain modacrylic fibres which have been copolymerised with chlorine-containing monomers. These modacrylic fibres will not burn, but will melt, char and disintegrate. The reason for this is that the carbon-chlorine bond in these polymers (see Table 1.2) is endothermic (absorbs heat energy) when dissociated by heat, for example by exposure to a flame. The bonds in the polymers, such as carbon–hydrogen and carbon–oxygen bonds (see Fig. 5.), are exothermic (give off heat) when dissociated by heat. Under normal circumstances the evolution of heat by these exothermic bonds would further the propagation of the flame. However, in chlorine-containing polymers, as found in certain modacrylics, there are insufficient of the carbon–hydrogen and carbon–oxygen bonds to produce heat energy in excess of that absorbed by the numerous carbon–chlorine bonds. Hence, chlorine-containing modacrylics such as Teklan will not readily ignite when in contact with a naked flame. In addition, they do not support combustion because the dissociation of the carbon–chlorine bonds reduces the flame sufficiently to cause its extinction.

Chlorine-containing modacrylics, however, are more heat sensitive than other modacrylics or acrylics. Chlorine-containing modacrylics have weaker van der Waals' forces between their polymers and will soften and distort at lower temperatures than conventional acrylic fibres.

Chemical properties

Effect of acids

The acrylic fibres are resistant to acids because their polymers do not contain any chemical groups which will attract or react with acid radicals.

Effect of alkalis

The very crystalline nature of the acrylic polymer system prevents the ready entry of alkaline substances. However, surface alkaline hydrolysis or surface saponification will occur. This means that any nitrile groups and/or anionic or basic groups on the surface of the fibre will react with the sodium or cation of the alkali. It must be remembered that the anionic or basic groups were introduced during copolymerisation, while sodium is a major constituent of such common alkalis as soap, laundry detergent powders or liquids, washing soda, etc. This fibre surface saponification is gradual; it will eventually lead to surface discolouration, yellowing and/or dulling of the acrylic textile material.

Effect of bleaches

Acrylic fibres are not usually bleached in practice. As a result, little is known about the effect of bleaches on acrylic polymers.

Effect of sunlight and weather

Acrylic fibres are the most sunlight- and weather-resistant fibres in common use. Their resistance to the atmosphere, which is slightly acidic, is attributed in part to the acid resistance of the acrylic polymers.

Acrylic textiles, when exposed to sunlight, will initially suffer a small loss in tenacity. After this initial loss there is a 'levelling off' in any further reduction in tenacity From then onwards acrylics have excellent sunlight and weather resistance. The 'levelling off' in tenacity loss is considered to be due to a slight internal polymer rearrangement. Exposure to sunlight provides the necessary heat energy to cause particular portions of some polymers to assume ring structures, which have a much more stable electron arrangement. This enables the polymers to withstand much more effectively the influence of ultraviolet radiation and other degrading agents.

Colour-fastness

The acrylic and modacrylic fibres are most commonly dyed and printed with basic dyes and disperse dyes.

Basic dyes

When these dyes were originally developed for acrylic fibres, they were referred to as modified basic dyes. Since the original basic dyes, which were in the past used on cellulosic fibres, are no longer used, this new range of modified basic dyes is now commonly referred to as basic dyes.

Basic dyes are also known as cationic dyes, since the coloured portion of the basic dye is the cation or positively charged radical of the dye molecule. This cationic (basic) radical is attracted to the anionic (acidic) radicals on the acrylic and modacrylic copolymers. (See 'The acrylic polymer', page 00, for some further details about basic dye molecule attraction to the acrylic copolymer.)

Basic dyes are also known as cationic dyes, since the coloured portion of the basic dye molecule is the cation or positive portion of the dye molecule. This cationic, or basic radical, is attracted to the anionic groups in the acrylic polymer.

The very good light-fastness of basic dyed or printed acrylic textile materials is attributed to the hydrophobic and very crystalline polymer system of their fibres. The crystalline and hydrophobic nature of the fibre minimises the entry of water molecules and the effect of the ultraviolet component of sunlight, both of which have a destructive effect on dye molecules.

Basic dyes or printed textile materials have very good wash-fastness. This is directly attributed to the polar or ionic bond which holds the basic dye cation to the acrylic copolymer. The hydrophobic nature of the acrylic fibre minimises the entry of water molecules which would have a hydrolysing effect on the bond holding the dye within the polymer system of the acrylic fibre.

Disperse dyes

Acrylic fibres which are hydrophobic are readily dyed with the non-ionic disperse dyes. The fair to good light-fastness of disperse dyed or printed acrylic textile materials may be attributed to the non-ionic nature of the disperse dye molecules. This non-ionic character tends to indicate a relatively stable electron arrangement of its chromophores, requiring somewhat prolonged exposure to be adversely affected by the ultraviolet component of sunlight.

Disperse dyed or printed acrylic textile materials have *good* wash-fastness, because the dye molecules are non-ionic and insoluble in water and the acrylic polymer system is both very crystalline and hydrophobic.

The acrylic polymer as well as being crystalline is hydrophobic, with the result that few water molecules enter the polymer system of the acrylic fibre. Even the few water molecules that do enter the fibre polymer have little effect on the aqueously insoluble disperse dyes.

Elastomeric

Fibre classification

The word elastomeric was coined from *elastic* and *polymer*, to imply an elastic fibre. Chemically the elastomerics are polyurethane-based fibres, whose polymers are characterised by **urethane** groups: $-NH-COO-$ (see Figs 5.6 and 5.7). Polyurethane is synthesised from urea: H_2NCONH_2. Elastomerics are man-made, synthetic polymer based, segmented polyurethane filaments. They are seldom manufactured as staple fibres.

Elastomerics consist of polymers which are at least 85 per cent segmented polyurethanes. The meaning of segmented polyurethanes is explained under the heading 'The elastomeric polymer' on page 99.

Spandex is the generic term used in the USA for elastomeric fibres. This term was coined by reversing syllables in the word *expand*. The intention was to convey the elastic properties of elastomerics.

Elastomerics have a fibre density of 1.0 g/cm^3, making them the lightest apparel fibre in common use. Their lightness in weight and excellent elastic property have revolutionised the construction of women's foundation garments, or lingerie. Such garments are now very light in weight, very much simpler in construction, and much more convenient to wear than the heavy cumbersome equivalents of yesteryear.

Fibre morphology

The macro-structure of elastomerics

Elastomerics are mainly available as fine, regular, off-white strands. Such strands of elastomeric are 'quasi-monofilaments', or multifilament yarns of coalesced filaments (see Figs 5.5 and 5.6).

Elastomerics are also available in the form of elastic-type tape, produced by coalescing numerous multifilament yarns. Elastomerics are usually produced with a dull lustre similar in appearance to white rubber yarn or elastic tape.

Microscopic appearance of elastomerics

The longitudinal appearance has distinct striations and specks. The striations are due to the coalesced filaments, where as the specks are the minute particles of titanium dioxide used in the delustring of the elastomeric.

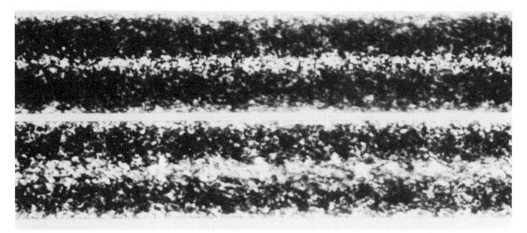

Figure 5.5 A longitudinal section of coalesced elastomeric filaments which form a quasi-monofilament or strand, magnified 600 times.

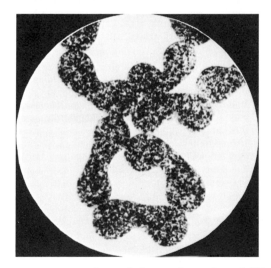

Figure 5.6 A cross-section of coalesced elastomeric filaments showing how the quasi-monofilament is formed (see Fig. 5.5). Note the air spaces between the coalesced, dumbbell shaped cross-sections of the filaments.

The cross-section of the coalesced multifilament yarn has the dumb-bell or dog-bone shape of the individual filaments. The cross-section also reveals the considerable number of air spaces which exist within the elastomeric multifilament yarn due to the coalesced filaments. Elastomerics cannot be identified by their microscopic appearance. (See Fig. 5.5.)

Micro-structure of elastomerics

The elastomerics do not have a discernible micro-structure.

The polymer system

The elastomeric polymer

To date this is the most complex textile fibre polymer that has been synthesised. Two types of elastomeric polymers are synthesised. Each is extruded into filaments with excellent elastic properties but differing in their resistance to alkalis.

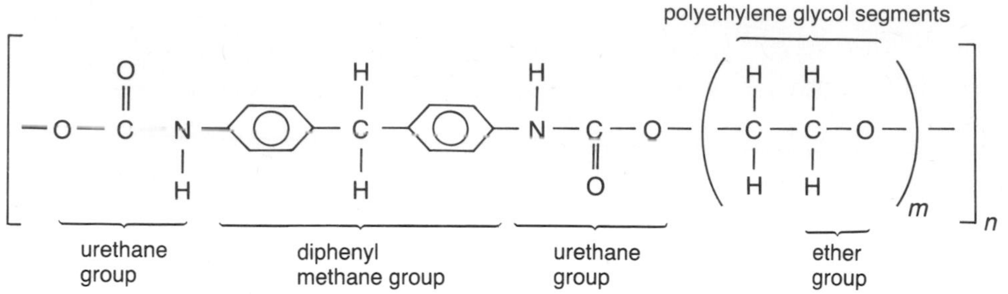

Figure 5.7 The polyether type repeating unit of an elastomeric polymer. The value of *m* depends on the actual polyether type of elastomeric polymer being polymerised. The degree of polymerisation (*n*) is not known.

1   *The polyether type* (for example Lycra) This is depicted in Fig. 5.6. It illustrates the complexity of this type of polymer. The repeating unit is about 7.1 nm long and about 0.7 nm thick. The length of the actual polymer is difficult to determine because of a certain amount of cross-linking between polymers. These cross-links contribute significantly to the excellent elastic property of the elastomeric filament. The presence of the ether groups (see Fig. 5.6) greatly contributes to making this type of elastomeric polymer resistant to alkalis.

2   *The polyester type* (for example, Vyrene) The repeating unit of this type of elastomeric (see Fig. 5.7) is about 37.2 nm long and about 0.5 nm thick. It is even more complex than the polyether elastomeric polymer and is so long that were its formula to be reproduced in the typeface used here, it would extend over about four pages of this book. It is for this reason that its detailed formula is not reproduced. The most relevant parts of this type of elastomeric polymer are the ester groups. These, as explained in the section on 'Polyesters' (page 84), hydrolyse in alkaline solutions, such as laundry liquors.

Each type of elastomeric polymer is linear and consists of rigid and flexible segments.

The rigid segments

These are also called hard segments. They consist of a diphenyl methyl group with a urethane group at each end (see Figs 5.7 and 5.8). The aromatic or benzene structure of the diphenyl methyl groups with their urethane groups impart a certain degree of

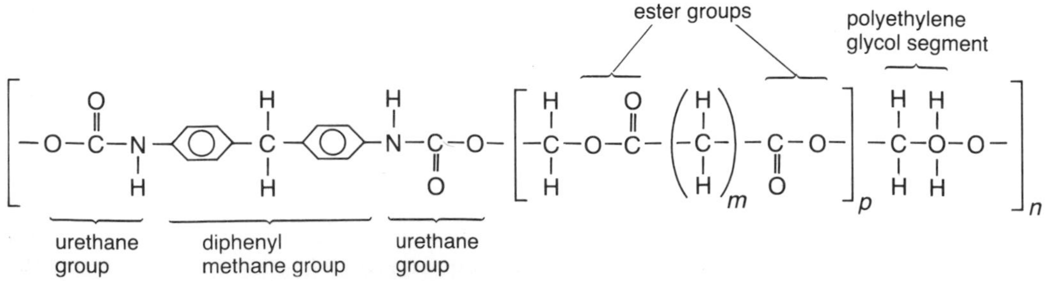

Figure 5.8 Polyester type repeating unit of elastomeric polymer. The values of *m* and *p* depend on the actual polyester type of elastomeric polymer being polymerised. The degree of polymerisation (*n*) is not known.

rigidity to the elastomeric polymer. The polarity of the urethane groups causes hydrogen bond formation with adjacent urethane groups. The rigid polymer segments are chemically more inert and thereby contribute to the stability of the elastomeric polymer.

The flexible segments

These are also called soft segments. They may consist of long polyethylene glycol segments, as shown in Figs 5.7 and 5.8, and/or long polypropylene adipate segments. These long segments polymerise in a linear as well as a multidirectional fashion (see Fig. 5.9). The flexible segments are responsible for the amorphous nature of the elastomerics when their polymer system is in a relaxed state (see Fig. 5.9).

The urethane groups are polar and should be able to attract water molecules. However, as these groups are usually well aligned, water molecules are not attracted in significant numbers.

The polymer system

The elastomeric polymer system is held together by a significant number of cross-links, which are formed in the final stages of the quite involved polymerisation of the elastomeric polymers. Such polymerisation is often only completed at the moment when the elastomeric filament has been extruded. When the filament is at rest (i.e. not stretched or extended), its polymer system is predominantly amorphous. This is largely due to the flexible segments which are folded upon themselves and generally present a random arrangement. The rigid segments tend to be more aligned. This causes the polar groups of the urethane groups in these segments to form hydrogen bonds, enhancing the rigidity of these sections of the elastomeric polymer system. The alignment of the rigid segments, with their polar groups, is considered sufficient to exclude the entry and attraction of a significant number of water molecules; hence the hydrophobic nature of the elastomerics.

When the elastomeric filament is stretched, its polymers unfold their flexible segments. At the same time, the rigid segments tend to align themselves so that the polymer system becomes quite crystalline (see Fig. 5.9b). Stretching the filament beyond its extensible limit will result in polymer rupture, and cause the breakdown of the excellent elastic recovery property of the elastomeric polymer system.

Physical properties

Tenacity

Elastomeric filaments are weak. Their excellent elastic recovery properties may give the impression that elastomerics are stronger than they actually are. Because of the hydrophobic nature of the fibres, the tenacity is unaffected whether wet or dry.

Elastic-plastic nature

This is the most important property of the elastomeric filaments. It is also the property which makes them technologically and commercially so important.

The excellent recovery property of the elastomerics is due to a relatively small

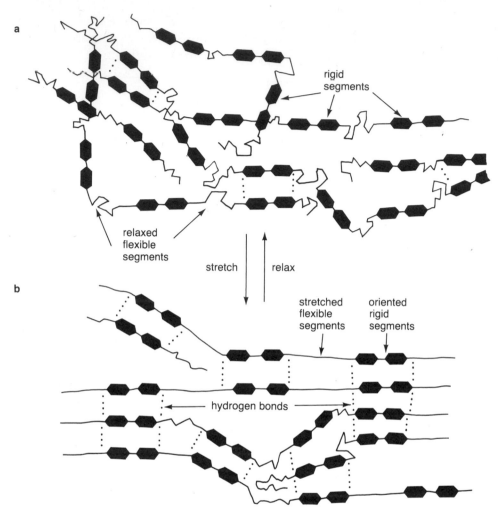

a

rigid
segments

relaxed
flexible
segments

stretch | relax

b

stretched
flexible
segments

oriented
rigid
segments

hydrogen bonds

Figure 5.9a The unstretched or amorphous state of the polymer system of an elastomeric
     b The stretched or more crystalline state of the polymer system of an elastomeric

amount of cross-linking between the polymers in their polymer system. The presence of the flexible segments which form the amorphous regions of the elastomeric polymer system enables the filaments to be stretched, as illustrated in Fig. 5.9. When the filaments are released, the multi-directional bonding of the flexible segments and the cross-links pull the polymers back into their original configuration. Elasticity is relatively permanent because, on extension of the elastomeric filament, few if any intra-polymer bonds are broken. Intra-polymer and inter-polymer bonds are only strained, and the polymers will readily return to their resting configuration whenever the load causing the extension is released.

The elastic properties of the elastomeric polymer system are unaffected by moisture because of its hydrophobic nature. The rubbery, wax-like handle of elastomeric textile materials is due to the alkane or saturated hydrocarbon constituents of the long, flexible segments: polyethylene glycol and/or polypropylene adipate.

Hygroscopic nature

Elastomerics are hydrophobic, despite the fact that the urethane groups which form part of the rigid segments of the elastomeric polymer are polar. Of course, some water molecules are attracted by the polarity of the urethane groups. However, the number attracted is insufficient to make the elastomeric polymer system hydrophilic, because the rigid segments are always sufficiently aligned to prevent entry of water molecules in significant numbers. The amorphous regions formed by the non-polar flexible segments do not attract water molecules.

Because of their hydrophobic nature, elastomeric textiles readily develop static electricity. A build-up of static electricity may lead to severe soiling, and explains the need to launder, or at least rinse, elastomeric garments after each wearing.

Thermal properties

Elastomerics, like all other synthetic textile fibres, are thermoplastic. The application of heat to elastomeric polymers may cause the development of sufficient kinetic energy to rupture the covalent cross-links of the polymer system. This may result in the elastic properties of elastomerics being adversely affected. Excessive application of hear may result in a complete loss of the excellent elastic property of elastomerics.

Chemical properties

Effect of acids

Elastomeric textile materials in general are resistant to acids. Acid radicals have little effect on the polymer system. This is further assisted by the hydrophobic nature of the fibre minimising the entry into the polymer system of acid radicals.

Effect of alkalis

The elastomerics, whose polymers contain **ester** groups, are sensitive to alkalis such as laundry liquors. The detrimental effect of such alkalis upon the elastomerics with ester-containing polymers is first seen as a yellowing of the white or a dulling of the coloured elastomeric textile material. This occurs as a result of alkaline hydrolysis of the ester groups which is explained in more detail in the section on 'Polyesters' (page 13). Elastomerics of the polyether type are alkali resistant.

Effect of bleaches

Hydrogen peroxide is the only bleach that can be used safely on elastomeric textile materials. No satisfactory explanation is available to date for the effect of bleaches on elastomerics.

Effect of sunlight and weather

The relative inertness of the elastomeric polymers, as evidenced by their hydrophobic nature and resistance to acids, is probably the main reason for their good resistance to the degrading effects of the sun's ultraviolet radiation. It is probable that the stability of the electron arrangement in the aromatic or di-isocyanate segments of the elastomeric polymers also contributes towards their sunlight and weather resistance. As a result, it requires prolonged exposure to the usually slightly acidic atmosphere to have a significant and detrimental effect on the elastomeric polymer.

Colour-fastness

Elastomeric textile materials tend to be difficult to dye owing to the hydrophobic and very crystalline nature of their polymer system. Disperse dyes, acid dyes and metal complex dyes are used for elastomeric materials. The fastness to washing and light is only fair. No satisfactory explanation can be offered for this.

Nylon

Fibre classification

The term *nylon* was derived from '*no-run*', the name originally considered by its inventors to emphasise the durability of ladies' hosiery manufactured from it.

The most important polyamide fibre in terms of amount produced is **nylon 6,6**; that is, polyhexamethylene adipamide. The notation **6,6** denotes that there are two monomers, each containing six carbon atoms, which are required to form the polymer of this type of nylon. **Nylon 6** is the second most important polyamide fibre. It is extruded from polycaprolactam. The notation **6** denotes that only one monomer containing six carbon atoms is required to polymerise this type of nylon.

The following descriptions and explanations of the properties of nylon will be based upon nylon 6,6 as the two nylon fibres have similar properties unless otherwise stated.

Nylon is a man-made synthetic polymer, polyamide filament or staple fibre. Textile materials composed of nylon tend to be light in weight because the density of nylon filaments or staple fibres is 1.14 g/cm^3.

Fibre morphology

The macro-structure of nylon

Nylon is a regular, translucent, fine filament or staple fibre. Staple fibres of nylon are usually crimped for reasons similar to those given for viscose in Chapter 2. Nylon filaments are textured for reasons similar to those given for crimping the staple fibres.

The length of nylon filaments is only limited by the yarn package onto which it is wound. The length of the staple fibre tends to be comparable to that of either cotton or wool, depending upon the end-use requirements of the nylon fibre.

The diameter of nylon filaments or staple fibres ranges from about 14 μm to 24 μm depending on end-use requirements. The fibre length to breadth ratio usually exceeds 2000:1. This ensures that even the shorter nylon staple fibres can be satisfactorily spun into yarn.

The descriptions and explanations given for viscose of fibre colour, lustre and translucency are also applicable to the nylon fibres.

Microscopic appearance of nylon

The nylon filament or staple fibres display no characteristic microscopic appearance. Their longitudinal structure is very regular and essentially featureless because of their almost circular cross-section. The nylon filament or staple fibre may, in fact, be likened to a glass rod (see Figs 5.10a and b).

A combination of factors is responsible for the rod-like, featureless microscopic appearance of nylon. These are the viscosity of the spinning solution, the nature of the polyamide material and the rate of coagulation in cold air of the extruded stream of polymers. These factors cause the coagulated filament to retain the round cross-section of the spinneret orifice.

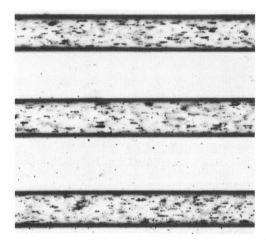

Figure 5.10a The featureless longitudinal section of nylon, magnified 500 times. Note the specks of delustring agent.

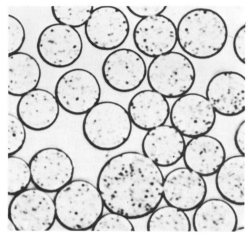

Figure 5.10b The circular, featureless cross-section of nylon, magnified 500 times. Note the specks of delustring agent.

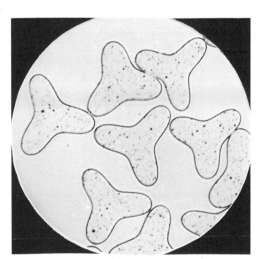

Figure 5.11a A cross-section of tri-lobal or profiled nylon, magnified 1000 times. Tri-lobal nylon is a man-made, readily available fibre whose cross-section has been purposely modified. See also Figure 1.5.

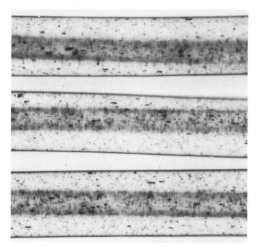

Figure 5.11b A longitudinal section of tri-lobal nylon, magnified 600 times. The broad shadow line is due to the indentation between the lobes.

A speckled appearance under the microscope in any nylon filament or staple fibre indicates the presence of the delustring agent titanium dioxide, which is usually used for delustring man-made fibres. Nylon which has a modified, for example a tri-lobal, cross-section, may have longitudinal striations (see Figs 5.10a and 5.10b).

The objective of developing nylon fibres with a modified cross-section is to provide a fibre surface which will have less intimate contact with the skin during wear. The more random the skin contact the fibre can achieve, the more comfortable will it feel. Most man-made fibres to date have the disadvantage of having a regular and smooth surface.

The micro-structure of nylon

Nylon filaments or staple fibres do not have an identifiable micro-structure.

The polymer system

The nylon polymer

Nylon is a linear, polyamide polymer. The nylon 6,6 polymer has a linear but zig-zag arrangement of carbon atoms. The carbon atom can form four single covalent bonds which are arranged about the atom as the vertices of a triangular pyramid, i.e. a tetrahedron. This tetrahedral arrangement of bonds causes the carbon atoms to form a zig-zag but linear polymer. This polymer configuration is partly responsible for the very good elastic properties of nylon.

Table 5.1 summarises the most relevant physical data for the two most common types of nylon polymers.

The most important chemical group in the nylon polymer is the polar amide group, $-CO-NH-$. This owes its polarity to the slightly negative charge on the oxygen atom, that is carbonyl oxygen, and the slightly positive charge on its hydrogen atom, that is

Table 5.1 Physical data for nylon polymers

Characteristic	Nylon 6,6	Nylon 6
Monomer details	Hexamethylene diamine, $H_2N (CH_2)_6NH_2$ and adipic acid, $HOOC(CH_2)_4COOH$	Cyclic caprolactam, [ring structure: CH_2 connected to CH_2, CH_2; CH_2, NH; CH_2-CO]
Repeating unit	Hexamethylene diaminoadipate, $[-HN(CH_2)_6NHOC (CH_2)_4CO-]_n$	Linear caprolactam, $[-HN (CH_2)_5CO-]_n$
Estimated degree of polymerisation	$n = 50$ to 80	$n = 200$
Estimated polymer length	90 to 140 nm	90 nm
Estimated polymer thickness	0.3 nm	0.3 nm

imino hydrogen. The other important groups are the amino groups, that is $-NH_2$, found at the ends of the nylon polymers.

These chemical groups, or radicals, are the ones which will form the hydrogen bonds in the nylon polymer system. The terminal groups on a nylon polymer provide the sites for dye molecules.

The polymer system

The polymer system of nylon is estimated to be about 65–85 per cent crystalline and, correspondingly, about 35–15 per cent amorphous. This gives nylon a very crystalline, very well aligned or oriented polymer system, with the inter-polymer distances on average about 0.3 nm. This very short inter-polymer distance enables the nylon polymer to form an optimum number of strong, uniform hydrogen bonds (see Figs. 5.12 and 5.13). Remember, hydrogen bonds can be formed across a maximum inter-polymer distance of 0.5 nm.

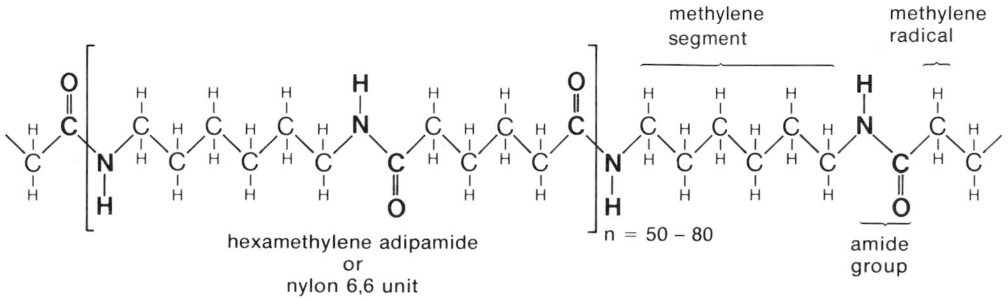

Figure 5.12 The nylon 6,6 polymer. The chemical formula has been given in a zigzag fashion in order to represent the three-dimensional nature of the nylon 6,6 or any other polymer. The degree of polymerisation, *n*, is about 50–80.

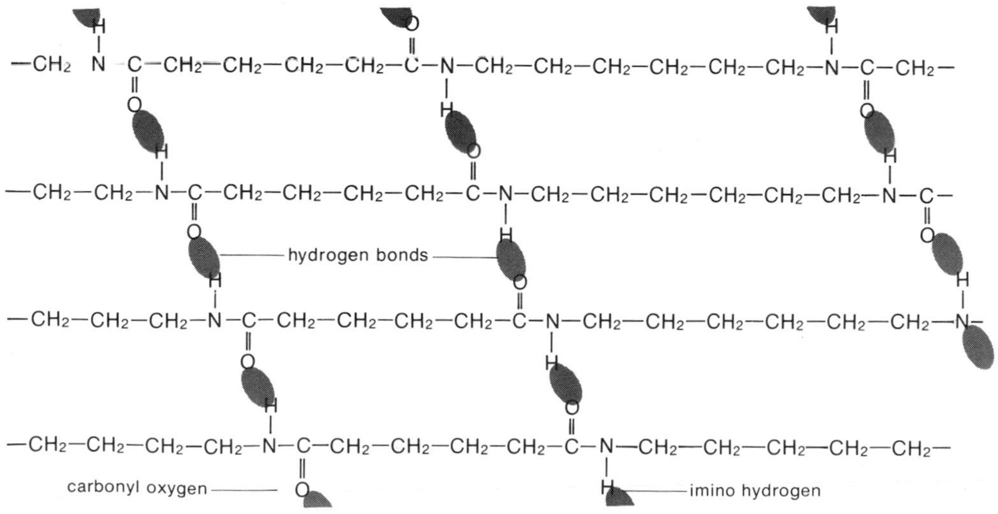

Figure 5.13 Part of a crystalline portion of the polymer system of a nylon 6,6 fibre. To simplify the diagram, no attempt has been made to portray the three-dimensional nature of the fibre. The shaded areas represent hydrogen bonds.

Physical properties

Tenacity

The good to very good tenacity of nylon is due to its very crystalline polymer system and the excellent potential of the nylon polymers to form hydrogen bonds (see Fig. 5.12).

Nylon 6,6 illustrates very well how relatively short polymers are aligned to form a very crystalline polymer system containing hydrogen bonds of the strongest kind; that is, those between hydrogen and oxygen atoms (see Fig. 5.12). The result is a strong, elastic and durable fibre.

The loss of tenacity by nylon when wet is due to water molecules hydrolysing a significant number of hydrogen bonds in the amorphous regions of the polymer system.

Elastic-plastic nature

The very good elastic property of nylon filaments or staple fibres is due to the very regular grid of strong hydrogen bonds in the nylon polymer system. As these hydrogen bonds operate over very short distances, they are able to exert their optimum strength, preventing polymer slippage and causing the polymers to return to their original position in the polymer system, once the strain has been removed from the nylon textile material. This means that nylon textile materials return readily to their original configuration, shedding any wrinkles or creases. There is a limit to which this can occur. Severe straining of the nylon polymer will cause hydrogen bond breakage, resulting in polymer slippage. This may result in distortion, wrinkling or creasing of the nylon textile material.

It has been estimated that about 22 per cent of the elasticity of nylon filaments or staple fibres is due to the straightening of the zig-zag configuration of the nylon when a load is applied. The zig-zag configuration is only possible because of the very strong bonds namely, the hydrogen bonds, in the nylon 6,6 polymer system.

Weight for weight, nylon 6,6 is the toughest textile fibre in common use. The toughness of nylon is due to its elasticity and is related to the grid of very strong hydrogen bonds. It is the strength of these hydrogen bonds plus the inherent strength of the nylon polymer itself which contribute to the toughness and durability of nylon textile materials.

The loss in elasticity and the resultant increase in extensibility of nylon filaments or staple fibres when nylon is wet is due to water molecules hydrolysing a significant number of hydrogen bonds in the amorphous regions of the polymer system.

The medium to hard handle of nylon filaments or staple fibres is due to nylon's very crystalline polymer system and the grid of strong hydrogen bonds. These two form a rather rigid polymer system which does not permit the nylon filament or staple fibre to give or yield readily.

Hygroscopic nature

Nylon filaments or staple fibres are not absorbent even though there is a relatively strong attraction for water molecules by the polar amide groups. Nylon's very crystalline polymer system allows few water molecules to be absorbed. The nylon fibre registered under the trade mark Qiana is claimed to be more absorbent than all other nylon types. The basis of this claim is that its nylon polymers contain hydroxyl groups; that is, –OH. These more polar groups attract more water molecules. In addition the Qiana polymer is somewhat more amorphous enabling a few more water molecules to enter the polymer system.

Nylon textile materials readily develop static electricity, as they are unable to absorb sufficient water molecules to dissipate any build-up of it. Nylon sold as 'anti-static' nylon has had compounds containing hydroxyl groups added to its spinning solutions. The addition of such compounds will attract an increased number of water molecules because of the polarity of the hydroxyl groups and will thus minimise the build-up of static electricity.

Thermal properties

There is no satisfactory explanation as yet for the poor heat conductivity of nylon and its low heat resistance. Heat causes the nylon polymers to become excited and this results in a breakdown of inter-polymer bonding. The fact that nylon becomes limp

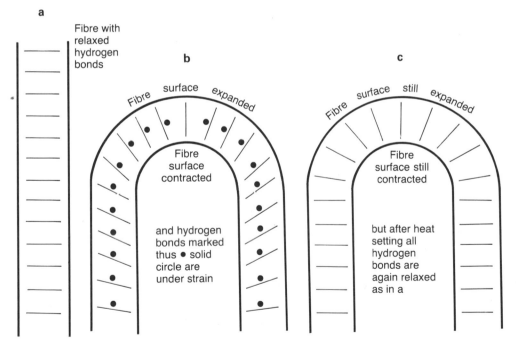

Figure 5.14 The three steps involved in heat setting a fibre whose polymer system is mainly held together with hydrogen bonds; for example nylon.
a The hydrogen bonds (shown as fine lines) are formed in relaxed positions, across short distances, thus holding the fibre in a relaxed configuration.
b The fibre is now bent. As it curves about the bend, its surface on the outside of the curvature expands, whilst the surface on the inside of the curve contracts. This strains the hydrogen bonds (marked with a dot) because they have to reach across greater distances.
c Applying heat or kinetic energy causes the strained hydrogen bonds to rupture. On cooling, the hydrogen bonds reform but across the shortest distances possible. This will cause the fibre to retain the bend configuration. The fibre is now said to be heat set.

when warmed illustrates this. The handle is restored as soon as the nylon is cooled because most of the broken hydrogen bonds are reformed.

The application of excessive heat to the polymer system of nylon causes the polymers to become so excited that most of the nylon textile material melts. The application of even more heat will result in burning.

If heat is applied under controlled conditions so as to break a few of the inter-polymer hydrogen bonds, the nylon material can be heat set. During heat setting of nylon, or any other thermoplastic textile material, the objective is to break those hydrogen bonds which are under strain to enable the material to assume the desired configuration. (See Fig. 5.14 and also 'Thermoplasticity', page 116.)

Chemical properties

Effect of acids

Nylon is less resistant to acids than it is to alkalis. The amide groups in the nylon polymers are readily hydrolysed under acidic conditions. Acid hydrolysis fragments nylon polymers with the result that the effectiveness of the inter-polymer hydrogen bonding is lost, and the nylon filament or staple fibre is weakened. Exposure to slightly acidic conditions, such as perspiration or a polluted atmosphere, will cause some polymer hydrolysis on the surface of the filaments or staple fibres. This changes their light reflection properties somewhat, with the result that white nylon textile materials will assume a yellow hue, whilst coloured nylon may appear duller.

It should be pointed out that the yellowing of white nylon may also be due to the absorption of molecules of body oils and fats by the nylon polymer system. The presence of the molecules on the surfaces of the polymer alters the reflection of light and results in a yellowing of white nylon textiles or a dulling of coloured materials.

Effect of alkalis

Prolonged and frequent exposure to alkalis will cause significant alkali hydrolysis of nylon polymers. This is noticed as a weakening of the nylon textile material. The effect of alkalis on the nylon polymer is the same as for acid hydrolysis; namely, yellowing of the white fibre or dulling of coloured nylon textiles.

Effect of bleaches

Nylon textile materials are inherently white and do not require bleaching. On the few occasions when bleaching is necessary, the only bleaches that can be used under slightly alkaline conditions are oxidising bleaches. These bleaches have the least detrimental effect upon the nylon polymer system. The most common oxidising bleaches used on nylon are peracetic acid, hydrogen peroxide and sodium chlorite. The bleaching effect of these chemicals is not fully understood. It is considered that the oxygen from these bleaches reacts with the degraded surface polymers which cause the discolouration of the nylon to form water soluble products which are washed off the textile material by the bleach liquor.

The bleaching is not permanent. In fact, nylon that has been bleached may discolour more readily than nylon which has not.

Effect of sunlight and weather

Nylon has only a fair resistance to sunlight and weather. This is attributed to the ultraviolet rays of sunlight causing the imino groups of the amide groups to react with the oxygen in the air. This produces groups that are more reactive and more water soluble. The groups that are produced react further causing polymer fragmentation and the breaking of inter-polymer hydrogen bonds resulting in the severe weakening of the nylon textile material.

In polluted atmosphere (which is acidic) these processes are accelerated.

Colour-fastness

The following classes of dye are most frequently used to dye or print nylon textile materials: acid, disperse and premetallised dyes.

Acid dyes

Acid dye molecules are sodium salts and will dissociate in an aqueous dye liquor to form the acid dye anion. The dye anion is negatively charged and is attracted to the cationic, or positively charged, groups in the nylon polymer. The cationic sites are the terminal amino groups which have acquired a hydrogen cation from the acid in the dye liquor.

The wash-fastness of acid dyed or printed nylon textile materials is fair to good and depends on the specific acid dye. The strength of the bond between the dye molecules and the nylon polymer varies with different dyes. If the bond is relatively weak, alkaline detergents can cause colour to be removed from nylon textile materials.

The good light-fastness of acid dyed and printed nylon textile materials is due in part to the acid resistance of the acid dye anion which will resist the slightly acidic conditions of the atmosphere. More importantly, the electron arrangement within the acid dye chromophores is reasonably resistant to the degrading effects of the sun's ultraviolet radiation. Under humid conditions the light-fastness of acid dyed or printed textile materials may be detrimentally affected as the acid dye anion will react more readily with oxygen from the atmosphere causing degradation of the dye anion, and result in fading.

Premetallised dyes

The molecules of premetallised dyes contain a metal atom which is usually chromium. The presence of the metal atom provides the premetallised dye molecule with enough stability to resist the degrading effects of the sun's ultraviolet radiation. The stable electron arrangement of the dye molecule is considered to be the main reason for the good light-fastness of premetallised dyed or printed nylon textile materials. As with acid dyes   breakdown of nylon polymers in sunlight contributes towards the fading of premetallised dyed or printed textile materials. Premetallised dye molecules dissociate to produce a dye anion in an aqueous dye liquor, which is attracted to the cationic groups in the nylon polymers. The premetallised dye anion is larger than the acid dye anion and has a greater substantivity to nylon textile materials compared with the acid dyes. This results in premetallised dyed and printed nylon textile materials having very good wash-fastness.

Disperse dyes

The molecules of disperse dyes are non-polar and hydrophobic. Disperse dye molecules are more substantive to the hydrophobic polymer system of nylon than they are to the aqueous dye liquor. Disperse dyes have a fair to good light-fastness on dyed and printed nylon textile materials. This may be attributed to the aromatic, or ring, structures within the disperse dye molecules. These aromatic structures provide the disperse dye molecules with a reasonably stable electron arrangement which resists the degrading effects of the sun's ultraviolet radiation.

The good wash-fastness of disperse coloured nylon materials is mainly due to the insolubility in water of disperse dyes making it difficult for their molecules to be washed out of the polymer system of the nylon filament or staple fibre.

Polyesters

Fibre classification

The word **ester** is the name given to salts formed from the reaction between an alcohol and an acid. Esters are organic salts and **polyester** means many organic salts. Polyester is a man-made, synthetic polymer, polyester filament or staple fibre. The most common polyester apparel filament or staple fibre is usually composed of polyethylene terephthalate polymers.

Polyesters are a medium weight fibre with a density of 1.39 g/cm^3. Compared with nylon, polyesters are rather heavy fibres. For this reason polyester textile materials are manufactured as lightweight or 'thin' fabrics, since thick polyester fabrics are too heavy.

Fibre morphology

The macro-structure of polyester

Polyester filaments or staple fibres are fine, regular and translucent. Both filament and staple fibres are usually crimped or textured for the same reasons as those outlined for viscose in Chapter 2.

The length of the polyester filaments is limited by the size of the yarn package onto which it is wound. The length of the staple fibre is comparable to cotton or wool and depends on the machinery used for spinning the staple yarn.

The fibre diameter of polyester filaments or staple fibres ranges from 12 μm to 25 μm depending on end-use requirements. The fibre length to breadth ratio usually exceeds 2000:1 and ensures that even the shorter polyester staple fibres can be satisfactorily spun into yarn.

The sections on viscose in Chapter 2, dealing with fibre colour, lustre and translucency, apply also to polyester.

Microscopic appearance of polyester

Polyester filaments or staple fibres have no identifiable microscopic appearance. The longitudinal appearance of the fibre is very regular and featureless because of the near circular cross-section. In fact, the magnified appearance of polyester can be likened to that of a glass rod. (See Figs 5.15(a) and 5.16(b).)

The reasons for polyester's microscopic appearance are the same as those given for nylon. The speckled appearance under the microscope of polyester filaments or staple fibres is due to the minute white particles of titanium dioxide used for delustring the polyester.

The micro-structure of polyester

Polyester filaments or staple fibres do not display a discernible micro-structure.

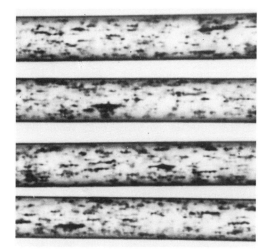

Figure 5.15a The longitudinal section of delustred polyester filaments, magnified 600 times. Note the even diameter, lack of other features, and specks of delustring agent. Most polyester fibres have a featureless microscopic appearance.

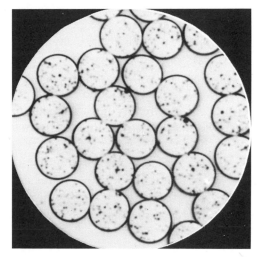

Figure 5.15b Cross-section of polyester filaments, magnified 1000 times. Note the circular shape which is characteristic of the cross-section of most polyester fibres. Note the specks of delustring agent.

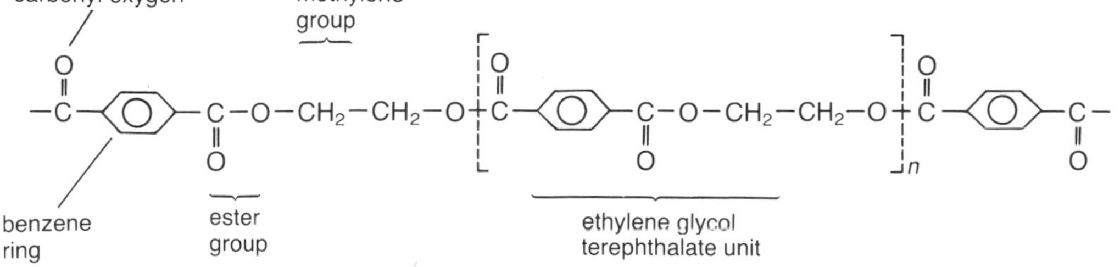

Figure 5.16 A section of a polyester polymer. It is thought that the carbonyl oxygen of the ester group gives rise to very weak hydrogen bonds with the relatively non-polar hydrogen atoms in the methylene groups of adjacent polymers. The degree of polymerisation, n, is about 115–140.

113

The polymer system

The polyester polymer

The polyester polymer is linear and is usually based on polyethylene terephthalate, as shown in Fig. 5.15. The degree of polymerisation ranges from about 115 to 140, resulting in a polymer length of about 120 nm to 150 nm, with a thickness of about 0.6 nm.

The important chemical groups in the polyester polymer are the methylene groups, $-CH_2-$, the slightly polar carbonyl groups, $-CO-$, and the ester groups, $-OCO-$. As the polarity of the polyester polymer is only slight, it is considered to be held together mainly by van der Waals' forces and to a lesser extent some very weak hydrogen bonds.

The polymer system

The polymer system is estimated to be about 65–85 per cent crystalline and, correspondingly, about 35–15 per cent amorphous and may be described as *very crystalline*. This is supported by the hydrophobic nature, poor dyeability, but good overall chemical resistance of polyester filaments or staple fibres.

Very weak hydrogen bonds are thought to exist between polyester polymers. These very weak hydrogen bonds are thought to occur at the weakly polar carbonyl oxygen atoms. These weakly polar carbonyl oxygen atoms are considered to cause any adjacent methylene hydrogen atoms to develop just sufficient polarity to form very weak hydrogen bonds. (See Fig. 5.17.)

The significant and predominant forces of attraction in the polymer system of polyester filaments or staple fibres are van der Waals' forces. For van der Waals' forces to be effective, excellent polymer orientation is required and this occurs in the extremely crystalline polyester polymer system.

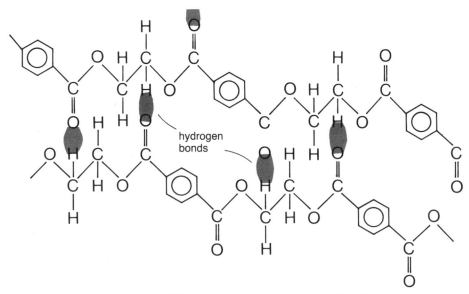

Figure 5.17 Part of a crystalline portion of the polymer system of a polyester fibre. The shading represents the very weak hydrogen bonds which are thought to occur between carbonyl oxygens and methylene groups.

For the very weak hydrogen bonds to exist in addition to the van der Waals' forces, the inter-polymer distance must average less than 0.3 nm in the polymer systems of polyester filaments and staple fibres.

Physical properties

Tenacity

Polyester filaments and staple fibres are strong to very strong because of their extremely crystalline polymer system. This allows the formation of the very effective van der Waals' forces as well as the very weak hydrogen bonds, resulting in the very good tenacity one associates with polyester polymers. The tenacity of polyester filaments or staple fibres remains unaltered when wet. This occurs because of the completely hydrophobic and extremely crystalline polyester polymer system which resists the entry of water molecules to any significant extent.

Elastic-plastic nature

The stiffness and hard handle of polyester filaments or staple fibres and their textile materials are due to their extremely crystalline polymer system, which prevents the polyester polymers from yielding readily when the filament of staple fibre is bent or flexed.

This also explains the wrinkle-resistance of polyester textile materials. The extreme crystallinity of the polymer system prevents the polyester filament of staple fibre from bending readily with the result that it will not wrinkle or crease easily.

Polyester filaments or staple fibres are about as plastic as they are elastic — as can be seen from their distortion on repeated stretching and straining. This is entirely due to the van der Waals' forces which hold the polyester polymer system together. Van der Waals' forces cannot withstand much stretching or straining and will very soon allow polymer slippage. The hydrogen bonds, which are thought to exist also in the polyester polymer system, are very weak, readily broken and unable to prevent polymer slippage.

The distinctly waxy handle of polyester textile materials, compared with their nylon equivalents, is due to the lack of significant polar groups in the polyester polymer. This enables the methylene groups and benzene rings (see Fig. 5.16) to cause the waxy nature of the polyester polymers and their polymer systems.

Hygroscopic nature

Polyester filaments and staple fibres are hydrophobic. The lack of polarity and the extremely crystalline structure of polyester polymers resists the entry of water molecules into the polymer system. The insignificant amount of moisture which may be present in polyester textile materials exists as a molecular film of water on the surface of filaments of staple fibres.

The hydrophobic nature of the polyester polymer system attracts fats, greases, oils and any other greasy soils. In other words the polyester polymer system is **oleophilic**. The oleophilic nature of the polyester polymer system presents considerable laundering problems.

The water insolubility of greasy soils and the hydrophobic nature of polyester makes it almost impossible to remove greasy soils from dirty polyester textile materials. The problem is made more difficult because the hydrophobic polyesters readily develop static electricity; this attracts airborne dust and grease particles, leading to rapid soiling. It is only through the use of an organic solvent, as is used in dry cleaning, that greasy soils can be effectively removed from polyester textile materials. The problem does not exist to the same extent with nylon, which is slightly more hydrophilic and does not attract greasy soils as readily.

Thermal properties

There is no satisfactory explanation as yet for the poor heat conductivity of polyester and its low heat resistance. The section on the thermal properties of nylon dealing with handle, fibre melting and burning (page 109) may also be applied to polyesters.

Thermoplasticity

Polyester textile materials can be permanently heat set. Textile fibres classed as thermoplastic are acetate, triacetate, acrylic, nylon and polyester. Polyesters retain a heat set permanently, whereas acetate fibres do not hold a set as satisfactorily.

This is an appropriate time to provide a more detailed explanation of heat setting of textile fibres.

The difference in the handle of a plastic garden hose on a hot sunny afternoon to that on a chilly morning is probably familiar to most of us. On a hot sunny afternoon the plastic hose is limp and easily extended. On a chilly morning the hose is hard, stiff and somewhat harder to control. This is because temperature influences the handling properties of a plastic garden hose. The handling properties of thermoplastic fibres are similarly affected by changes in temperature.

'Thermoplastic' means capable of being shaped or moulded when heated. Thermoplastic fibres heated under strictly controlled temperatures soften and can then be made to conform to a flat, creased or pleated configuration. When cooled, thermoplastic fibres will retain the desired configuration; that is, remain flat, pleated or creased.

The extent to which a thermoplastic fibre will retain its heat set will depend entirely on its second order transition temperature. This may be explained as follows.

The change in physical state, from solid to liquid for instance, is regarded as a **first order transition**, the temperature needed to achieve the changed state being the **first order transition temperature**. Another example of a first order transition temperature is the temperature at which a liquid is converted to a gas, as in the case of boiling water changing into steam. The reverse process, that is, changing from a gas to a liquid and from a liquid to a solid, also occurs at first order transition temperatures.

Returning to the plastic garden hose for a moment, on a chilly morning it is hard, stiff and unmanageable. As the sun begins to shine on it, the hose warms and becomes softer, more limp and more manageable. In fact when it is very hot it may become so soft and limp that it may be quite distorted if pulled and strained too severely. The hard stiff state of the garden hose is referred to as its 'glassy' state. When the sun has warmed it and it has become softer and more pliable, the hose is said to have entered the 'rubbery' state. The temperature at which the change from 'glassy' to 'rubbery' state or at which a **glass-to-rubber transition** occurs is the **second order transition temperature**. The higher the glass-to-rubber temperature of a substance, the less is its tendency to be affected by temperature; that is to say, the higher the second order transition temperature, the more likely are thermoplastic fibres to retain their heat set.

The best heat set is obtained with polyester fibres and the least effect is obtained with acetate. This implies that the second order transition temperature for polyester is the highest of the five commonly used thermoplastic fibres whereas acetate has the lowest. The second order transition temperatures for textile fibres cannot be readily determined. In addition there are some difficulties in interpreting second order transition temperatures with reference to other fibre properties. It is easier, therefore, to *rank* the thermoplastic fibres in terms of their second order transition temperature; that is, polyester, nylon, acrylic, triacetate, acetate. Polyester has the highest second order transition temperature and acetate has the lowest. At the same time the order represents the highest to the lowest ability to retain a heat set.

Chemical properties

Effect of acids

The ester groups of the polyester polymers are resistant to acid hydrolysis, as are the other chemical groups of the fibre polymer. This resistance is further enhanced by the extreme crystallinity of the polyester polymer system which prevents the entry of any acid and water molecules into the filament of staple fibre.

Effect of alkalis

Alkaline conditions as encountered during laundering may hydrolyse the polyester polymers at their ester groups. The extreme crystallinity of the polyester polymer restricts the hydrolysis (or saponification) to the surface of the polyester filament or staple fibre.

As the hydrolysis of polyesters is restricted to the surface, polyester textile materials retain their whiteness during laundering. The surface polymers of polyester filaments or staple fibres are hydrolysed as shown in Fig. 5.18.

With time, regular laundering and continued hydrolysis, the polyester textile material will become finer and silkier. Each laundering causes the loss of a surface film of polyester polymers.

Effect of bleaches

Normally polyester textile materials do not need to be bleached. As explained above, white polyester tends to retain its whiteness during normal domestic laundering. If bleaching is required this is effected using sodium chlorite.

Sunlight and weather resistance

The acid resistance of polyesters helps protect polyester textile materials from the slightly acidic conditions that occur in polluted atmospheres. The benzene rings of the polyester polymer provide stability to the whole polymer, enabling the polymers to withstand the detrimental effects of the sun's ultraviolet radiation.

Figure 5.18 A cross-section of a polyester fibre showing dyeing under atmospheric pressure. Under atmospheric pressure, dye molecules do not penetrate the fibre completely, leaving an undyed fibre core. Also the concentration of the dye in the fibre is not as great, resulting in a pastel shade only. Alkaline surface hydrolysis which occurs with laundering will cause fibres dyed in this way to fade.

This explains the very good sunlight and weather resistance of polyester textile materials, which is second only to acrylics.

Colour-fastness

It is very difficult for dye molecules to penetrate the extremely crystalline polymer system of polyester fibres. Only the relatively small molecules of disperse dyes are used to dye or print polyester fibres.

Disperse dyes

The hydrophobic nature of the disperse dye molecules makes them substantive to the hydrophobic polyester polymer system. Only pastel-coloured polyester textile materials are obtained under conventional dyeing techniques, even with the dye liquor at the boil. The limited dye uptake which occurs using conventional techniques is illustrated in Fig. 5.18, which shows the cross-section of such dyed polyester filaments or staple fibres. To obtain deeper shades, pressure dyeing is necessary. Under conditions of about 130°C to 140°C and pressures of 1 kg/cm^2 to 1½ kg/cm^2, medium and even deep shades can be obtained on polyesters.

Pressure dyeing tends to be the most commonly used method of disperse dyeing of polyester textile materials. Pressure dyeing 'opens' up the polyester polymer, enabling the dye to penetrate. When the polyester material is removed from the pressure dyeing vessel, the polymer system 'closes' again, 'trapping' the disperse dye molecule inside.

The fair to good wash-fastness of disperse dyed and printed polyester textile materials is due to the hydrophobic or water insoluble dye molecules and the extremely crystalline polymer system.

The fair to good light-fastness of disperse dyed and printed polyester textile materials is due to the electron stability of the aromatic structure of the dye molecules. This stability enables the dye molecules to withstand the detrimental effects of the ultraviolet radiation of sunlight.

6 Dyeing and printing

The molecules of the organic compounds called dyes are responsible for the colour of dyed and printed textile fibre materials.

In white light, the colour of a textile material depends upon which incident light waves are absorbed and which are reflected from the dye molecules within the polymer system of its fibres (see Table 6.1).

The dye molecule

Why dye molecules are coloured

Dye molecules are coloured because they are selectively able to absorb and reflect incident light. Light is a form of energy; it is also the visible portion of the electromagnetic spectrum as shown in Fig. 8.1.

Organic molecules become coloured, and thus useful dye molecules, if they contain at least one of each of the radicals called **chromophores** and **auxochromes** (see Tables 6.2 and 6.3, and Fig. 6.1).

In general, the chromophores give the dye molecule its particular colour, while the auxochromes intensify the hue of the dye molecule's colour, makes the dye mole-

Table 6.1 Colours observed when certain wavelengths from sunlight are absorbed

Predominant wavelength absorbed	Colour observed
ultraviolet	none
violet	yellow-green
blue	yellow
green-blue	orange
blue-green	red
green	purple
yellow-green	violet
yellow	blue
orange	green-blue
red	blue-green
infrared	none

Table 6.2 Chromophores, the radicals or chemical groups without which dye molecules would have no colour.

Name of chromophore	Basic formula of chromophore	How the chromophore exists in the dye molecule
Azo group	$-N = N-$	Azo-benzene radical
Quinonoid group	(see structure)	Anthraquinone radical
Tri-aryl methane group	$=C\big\langle$	(see structure)
Nitro group	$-N\!\!\begin{smallmatrix}\nearrow O\\ \searrow O\end{smallmatrix}$	$-NO_2$
Nitroso group	$-N = O$	$-NO$

Table 6.3 Auxochromes, the radicals or chemical groups which intensify the hues of the chromophores in dye molecules.

Name of auxochrome	Basic formula of auxochrome	How the auxochrome exists in the dye molecule
Acidic auxochromes Carboxyl group Sulphonic group	$-COOH$ $-SO_3H$ or $-\overset{\overset{O}{\|\|}}{\underset{\underset{O}{\|\|}}{S}}-OH$	Sodium carboxylate radical, $-COONa$ Sodium sulphonate radical, $-\overset{\overset{O}{\|\|}}{\underset{\underset{O}{\|\|}}{S}}-ONA$ or $-SO_3^-\,Na^+$
Basic auxochromes Amino group	$-NH_2$	$N\big\langle\begin{smallmatrix}H\\H\end{smallmatrix}$
Substituted amino group; for example,		
methyl amino or	$-N\big\langle\begin{smallmatrix}H\\CH_3\end{smallmatrix}$ or	$-N\big\langle\begin{smallmatrix}H\\CH_3\end{smallmatrix}$ or
dimethyl amino	$-N\big\langle\begin{smallmatrix}CH_3\\CH_3\end{smallmatrix}$	$-N\big\langle\begin{smallmatrix}CH_3\\CH_3\end{smallmatrix}$
Hydroxyl group	$-OH$	$-OH$

cule more water soluble, and improves the colour-fastness properties of the dyed or printed fibre. A more specific explanation of chromophores and auxochromes is given below.

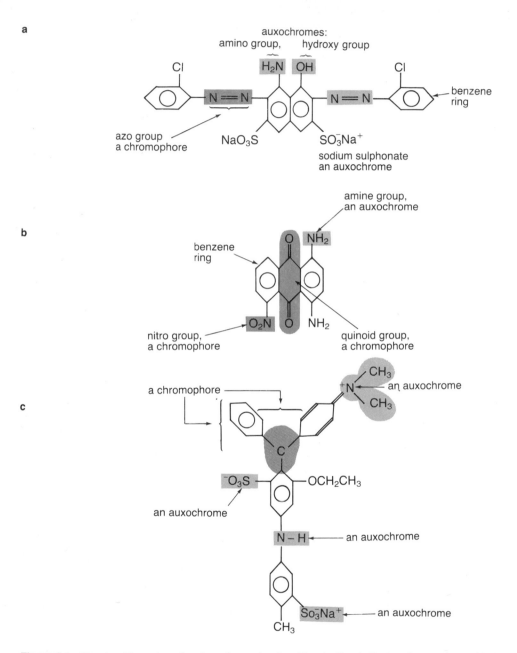

Figure 6.1 Structural formulae of various dye molecules. The shading indicates chromophores (dark) and auxochromes (light).
a C.I. Acid Blue 86, 44075 — an acid dye
b C.I. Disperse Violet 8, 62030 — a disperse dye
c C.I. Acid Violet 15, 43525 — an acid dye.
Note: The five-digit number for each dye is its Colour Index number.

Chromophores

The name is derived from the Greek *chroma* = colour and *phore* from *pherein* = to bear.

Chromophores are unsaturated organic radicals as shown in Table 6.2 and Fig. 6.1 Their specific state of unsaturation enables them to absorb and reflect incident electromagnetic radiation within the very narrow band of visible light, as shown in Fig. 8.1. More specifically: it is the loosely held electrons in the unsaturated bonds of the chromophores which cause in the absorption of certain incident light waves. Table 6.1 gives an indication of the colours observed, i.e. reflected, when certain wavelengths of the incident light are absorbed.

A molecule possessing no chromophores would be colourless.

Auxochromes

The name is derived from the Greek *auxein* = to increase, and *chroma* = colour.

Auxochromes are organic radicals as shown in Table 6.3 and Fig. 6.1. Auxochromes fulfil the following important functions.

1   Their presence influences the orbits of the loosely held electrons of the unsaturated bonds of the chromophores. This causes these electrons to absorb and reflect incident light energy of specific wavelengths only. This also intensifies and deepens the hue of the dye molecule's colour.

A dye molecule without auxochromes would lack intensity of colour. This is because the incident light waves would not be absorbed and reflected as selectively as occurs in the presence of auxochromes.

2   Auxochromes tend to be polar. This increases the overall polarity of the dye molecule and makes it more readily soluble in water. This allows easier preparation of dye liquors, assists in more even dye uptake by the fibre, and results in more level dyeing.

3   The polarity of auxochromes enables the formation of forces of attraction between the dye molecule and the fibre polymer(s). This improves the colour fastness properties of the dyed or printed fibre.

As a result of the physical interaction between chromophores and auxochromes, textile dyes have some of the highest colour intensities of all colourants in common use. Under ideal conditions, the normal healthy eye will perceive colour from as low a concentration as about 10 000 dye molecules, which is less than the diameter of a pin point.

The configuration of the dye molecule

The configuration or shape of the dye molecule determines how:
1   readily the dye molecule can penetrate the fibre surface;
2   deeply the dye molecule will enter into the polymer system of the fibre;
3   securely the dye molecule will be able to attach itself and/or become trapped in the polymer system of the fibre.

Textile materials are coloured when dye molecules enter the amorphous regions of the fibres' polymer systems. Usually, it is not possible for dye molecules to enter the crystalline regions of textile fibres, because the inter-polymer spaces in the crystalline regions of the fibres' polymer systems are too small for the relatively large dye molecules.

In crystalline regions, where hydrogen bonding may predominate, the inter-polymer distances would be no more than about 0.5 nm. This is the maximum distance across which a hydrogen bond can be effective. On the other hand, where van der Waals' forces predominate, the inter-polymer spaces are even smaller; less than about 0.2 nm. The spaces are usually less than those stated, as van der Waals' forces are only really effective over much shorter distances.

Table 6.4 compares the dimensions of dye molecules, for the various dye classes. Estimates of the distances between polymers in the amorphous regions of various fibres are given in Table 6.5. The information provided by these two tables suggests that it

Table 6.4 Size of dye molecules.

Class of dye	General description of size of dye molecules	Estimated average dimensions:			Relative size diagrammatically
		Length (nm)	Breadth (nm)	Thickness (nm)	
Acid and basic	Average	1.20	0.80	0.40	
Azoic	Small	1.00	0.60	0.40	
Direct	distinctly linear	2.00 up to 3.60	0.70	0.40	
Disperse	Very small	0.80	0.40	0.40	
Mordant and premetallised	1 : 1 complex is average 2 : 1 complex is large and bulky	1.20	0.80	0.40	
Reactive	Average and linear	1.40 up to 2.70	0.70	0.40	
Sulphur	Distinctly linear	2.70	0.60	0.40	
Vat	Large to very large	1.50 up to 1.70	0.90 up to 1.40	0.40	

Table 6.5 Estimated inter-polymer distances in the amorphous regions of the fibre's polymer system.

Fibre	Dry fibre (nm)	Wet fibre (nm)
Cotton and viscose	0.5	2 to 3 and up to 10
Wool	0.6	Up to 4
Acetate and synthetics	Less than 1	No more than 1

may be quite difficult for dye molecules to enter the fibre. Once the dye molecule is somewhere near the fibre, a general force of attraction will draw it towards and onto the fibre surface. It is not known how the dye molecule enters the fibre's polymer system. The linear, coplanar dye molecule configuration is the one which is thought to have the greatest chance of entering the polymer systems of the fibres.

Dye molecules can be described as having the shape of slips of paper; that is, having length and breadth, but relatively little depth or thickness. The linear, coplanar configuration of dye molecules means that there are no bulky side groups. This coplanar configuration assists the dye molecules to enter the fibre's polymer system and enables the linear, coplanar dye molecule to align itself within the fibre polymer. This alignment assists forces of attraction to occur between dye and fibre. The intensity of these forces of attraction will determine the degree of fastness of a particular dye.

The general theory of dyeing

Dyeing is the process of colouring textile materials by immersing them in an aqueous solution of dye, called dye liquor. Normally the dye liquor consists of dye, water and an auxiliary. To improve the effectiveness of dyeing, heat is usually applied to the dye liquor. The theory of aqueous dyeing, as explained below, is modified when an organic solvent is substituted for water.

The general theory of dyeing explains the interaction between dye, fibre, water and dye auxiliary. More specifically, it explains:

1 **forces of repulsion** which are developed between the dye molecule and water; and
2 **forces of attraction** which are developed between the dye molecules and fibres.

These forces are responsible for the dye molecules leaving the aqueous dye liquor and entering and attaching themselves to the polymers of the fibres.

The dye molecule

Dye molecules are organic molecules which can be classified as:

1 **anionic** — in which the colour is caused by the anionic part of the dye molecule;
2 **cationic** — in which the colour is caused by the cationic part of the dye molecule;
3 **disperse** — in which the colour is caused by the whole molecule.

The first two dye molecule types are applied from an aqueous solution. The third is applied from an aqueous dispersion.

The fibre

Textile fibres are organic compounds and develop a slight negative surface charge or potential when immersed in an aqueous solution. Since the dye molecule and textile fibre both become slightly negatively charged in aqueous solution, there is a tendency for the dye and the fibre to repel each other. Sufficient energy has to be built up in the dye liquor to overcome this repulsive force and allow the dye and textile fibre to be attracted to one another, so that the dye molecules can enter the polymer system of the fibre.

The role of water

In addition to dissolving the dye, water acts as the medium through which the dye molecules are transferred into the fibre.

The polar groups in the dye molecules attract water molecules, and cause the dye to dissolve in water. This attraction between water and dye is on the whole undesirable, as the dye molecules resist leaving the water and entering the fibre. In some instances, however, it is desirable to reduce the rate at which dye leaves the water and enters the fibre so as to ensure a uniform colouration of the fibre.

In general, heat is necessary to encourage the dye to leave the water and enter the fibre, as well as to ensure adequate penetration of the polymer system of the fibre. Heating the dye liquor causes water to dissociate somewhat more than at prevailing room temperatures and to become slightly more ionic. In this state, water tends to repel the organic dye molecule to a greater extent, ensuring readier uptake of the dye molecules by the fibre's polymer system.

Water, assisted by heat, also swells fibres that are hydrophilic, making the polymer system more accessible to the relatively large dye molecules.

The role of electrolytes

The addition of an electrolyte to the dye liquor of anionic dye increases the uptake of the dye by the fibre. The electrolytes used in dyeing dissociate completely in the aqueous dye liquor. This increases the forces of repulsion between the dye molecules and water so the dye is attracted by the fibre.

The addition of electrolytes to the dye makes the dye liquor more ionic and thus increases the forces of repulsion between the electrolyte and the dye molecules. This attracts the dye to the fibre and increases the chances of the dye molecules entering the fibre. For the dye to enter the fibre, the surface charge of the fibre, which is negative, will have to be neutralised since both anionic dyes and textile fibres have the same charge. This is effected by the addition of cheap electrolytes such as sodium chloride or sodium sulphate. Both these electrolytes are extremely soluble and dissociate completely in an aqueous medium. The presence of these electrolytes makes the dye liquor more ionic which, together with the application of heat to the dye liquor, increases the energy of the molecules in the dye liquor and the forces of repulsion.

The use of electrolytes such as sodium chloride or sodium sulphate means that one of the dissociation products is sodium ions (Na^+). Sodium ions are cationic, or positively charged, and in the dye liquor are attracted to the negatively charged textile fibres. Once on the surface of the fibre, the sodium cations neutralise the anionic surface charge of the fibres, by forming a layer of Na^+ about 10 nm thick on the surface of the fibres. The neutralised fibre can now attract the organic dye molecules which have a greater affinity for the fibre than the aqueous solution. The migration of the dye from the dye liquor to the fibres is accelerated by the application of heat to the dye liquor.

Why the dye liquor is heated

Heat is a form of energy. It is applied to increase the energy of the molecules of all constituents in the dye liquor and thus to increase the rate of the dyeing process. The application of heat not only results in an increased rate of dyeing but assists the dye molecules to penetrate the fibre polymer system. The application of heat to the dye liquor swells the fibre polymer making it easier for the dye molecules to penetrate the fibre surface and enter deeper into its amorphous regions. When the dye liquor has cooled and the fibres dried, the polymer system will close up again, that is, return to its former dimensions, trapping and entangling the dye molecules which entered it. In such circumstances, van der Waals' forces may develop to assist the polymer system retain the dye molecules within the fibre polymer.

High temperature dyeing

Dyeing at temperatures from 100° to 130°C, under pressure to about 170 kPa (about 1¾ kg/cm^2) is termed high temperature dyeing. Hydrophobic fibres, such as polyester fibres, are dyed in this way because under normal atmospheric conditions, their extremely crystalline polymer system will not allow good dye uptake.

When dyeing at high temperatures, dye molecule penetration of the fibre polymer system is increased significantly. At temperatures above 100°C and therefore under pressure the heat generates a very large amount of energy in the constituents of the dye liquor. This swells the fibre, enabling the dye molecules to penetrate the fibre polymer system more readily.

Dye auxiliaries

These chemical compounds include **carriers** or **swelling agents, levelling agents, antifoaming agents, dispersing agents, detergents** and **wetting agents.** The way in which these auxiliaries affect the dyeing process and their chemical constitution is fairly complex and beyond the scope of this book. However, the following provides some explanation for the way in which carriers and levelling agents are used in the dye liquor.

Carriers or swelling agents

Carriers are added to the dye liquor to improve the dye exhaustion for highly crystalline fibres such as polyesters. Because of their very crystalline nature, only pale colours can be achieved by aqueous dyeing without carriers. The addition of carriers to the dye liquor assists the dye to penetrate the extremely crystalline polyester fibre. There is no universally accepted explanation for the way in which carriers improve the dyeability of polyester fibres. The most widely accepted explanation is that carriers help to swell the fibre and make it easier for the dye molecules to enter the polymer system. As a general rule carriers are only used to dye polyester fibres with disperse dyes.

Levelling agents

The addition of levelling agents to the dye liquor helps produce a more uniform colour in textile fibres. Levelling agents which tend to slow down the dye uptake of the fibres, are also termed **retarding agents** or **retarders**. The use of retarders is essential in situations in which dyes tend to 'rush on to fibre' and result in an unevenly coloured textile material.

Levelling agents are surface active agents, and are chemically related to soaps, synthetic detergents and wetting agents. They may be anionic, cationic or non-ionic organic compounds.

Anionic levelling agents

The molecules of these compounds consist of a large negatively charged, or anionic, organic radical, with a cationic radical which is usually a sodium cation that assists the levelling agent's water solubility. When anionic agents are added to the dye liquor, their anions will be attracted to any positive site in the fibre. The anionic levelling agent tends to repel the similarly charged anionic dye molecule. As the dye bath is heated, the anionic dye molecules develop sufficient energy to overcome the repulsive forces between the retarder and the dye, both of which are anionic. The retarder slows the dye uptake of the fibre and results in a more uniformly dyed textile material.

Cationic levelling agents

The molecules of these compounds consist of a large positively charged, or cationic, organic radical, with an anionic radical which is usually a chloride ion and sometimes a bromide ion.

When cationic levelling agents are added to the dye liquor, their cations are attracted to the anionic dye molecules. This neutralises the electric charge on the dye molecules and minimises their substantivity for the fibres. The energy provided from heating the dye bath will cause the cationic radicals of the levelling agents to gradually dissociate from the anionic dye molecules. This gradual dissociation of the cationic agents from the dye molecules slowly releases the dye and this ensures a more uniform absorption of the dye by the polymer system of the fibre.

Scouring after dyeing

Dyeing always leaves some dye molecules on the surface of the fibres of the dyed textile materials. It is essential that these dye molecules be removed when dyeing is completed. If these dyes are not removed they may result in two problems:

1 poor rub-fastness which may result in the dye rubbing off onto adjacent materials;
2 poor wash-fastness which may result in other fabrics being coloured by this excess dye during laundering.

The general theory of printing

The printing of textile materials is the application of colour according to a predetermined design.

The printing paste which is applied to textile material consists of dye, water, thickener and hydrocarbon solvent or oil. After the printing paste is applied, the textile material is usually steamed. This is to enable the dye molecules to migrate from the surface of the fibres and to enter the fibre polymer system. Steaming swells the fibres and ensures better penetration of the dye and improved colour fastness properties of the textile material.

The general theory of printing explains the interaction, on steaming, between the dye, fibre, water, thickener and hydrocarbon solvent. More specifically, it explains how within the printing paste:

1 **forces of repulsion** are developed between the dye molecules and the constituents of the printing paste; and

2 **forces of attraction** are developed between the dye molecules and the fibres of the textile material to be printed.

The dye molecule

This has already been covered under 'The general theory of dyeing' on page 125.

The role of the water

A relatively small amount of water is used; enough to dissolve the dye into a paste. Water is used as it is a convenient and readily available medium to mix, or disperse, the dye molecules in the thickener.

The role of the thickener

The purpose of the thickener is to produce a medium for the dye paste and the resultant product is called the **printing paste**. The printing paste is an emulsion of **thickener** and **hydrocarbon**, such as white spirit or very light hydrocarbon oil, plus a **surface active agent**. This surface active agent enables the emulsification of the thickener with the hydrocarbon to form a printing paste of uniform consistency. The uniform consistency of the printing paste is referred to as its **viscosity** (the ease with which the paste will flow). The viscosity of the printing paste is very important as it influences the clarity and appearance of the printed pattern. The clarity of the printed pattern depends very much on the particular thickener used. The physical–chemical properties of the thickener must be such that immediately after printing, it will form a film of sufficient plasticity and elasticity not to flake or crack when dry. The thickener is present to prevent capillary action from causing the dye to run. The success of printing textile materials depends very much on the type and quality of the thickener.

Thickeners can be any of the following:

1 **natural gums**, such as gum arabic, acacia gums or gums prepared from starches and other polysaccharides;

2 the **man-made, natural polymer-based gums**, for example, water soluble cellulose ethers, such as carboxymethyl cellulose, methyl and ethyl cellulose, and sodium alginate; or

3 occasionally, **made-made, synthetic compounds** such as polyvinyl alcohol.

When selecting a thickener, one must ensure that it does not compete with the fibre for the dye. For instance, if a cellulosic textile material is to be printed, the paste must not be mixed with a cellulosic based thickener. Selection of such a thickener may cause difficulties as the dye may be more substantive to the thickener than to the fibre.

The role of steam

After printing, it is usual to steam the textile material. This is done to achieve colour-fastness.

Steaming ensures the adequate penetration of the fibre by dye molecules. This is possible because steaming:

1 generates sufficient energy in the dye molecules for them to enter the fibre polymer system; and
2 swells the fibre so that the dye molecules can enter the fibre polymer system.

Dry heating

Thermoplastic fibres tend to be hydrophobic and do not swell sufficiently in water or when subjected to steaming. Dry heating, however, will soften the fibres; that is, it will cause the polymers in the amorphous regions of the polymer system to more far enough apart to allow the entry of the dye molecules. This method of fixing, or setting, the printed patterns is particularly suitable when the colourant is a pigment. Pigments have little substantivity for the polymer system of the fibre with the result that pigment particles are trapped in the polymer system of the fibre.

Washing off

This has to be done to remove the thickener and other printing paste constituents which have not entered the polymer system of the fibre. There will always be some dye molecules left on the surface of the fibres and these must be removed in the washing off process.

Fading

Fading is seen as a colour loss by the dyed or printed textile material. It is the result of some change in the structure of the dye molecule due to absorption of light, reaction with air pollutants, laundering, dry cleaning and/or other agency. The actual mechanism which causes fading is complex and not yet fully understood.

Fastness to sunlight

There is no universally accepted explanation for the fading of dyed or printed colours in sunlight. It is suggested that fading may be due to some kind of breakdown in the light energy absorption capacity of the electrons of the chromophores or a breakdown in the structure of the dye molecule. When sunlight energy is absorbed, the loosely held electrons of the chromophores are raised to a higher energy level; that is, they become more active. It is known that the ultraviolet component of sunlight will in time initiate chemical reactions. Such chemical reactions will be accelerated under moist conditions. Fading in sunlight is due partly to ultraviolet radiation which initiates chemical degradation of the dye molecule through the loosely held electrons of the chromophores. Fading of dyed or printed textile materials does not occur so readily in artificial light, mainly incandescent and fluorescent light, as these light sources do not emit significant quantities of ultraviolet radiation.

Wash-fastness

The loss of colour during laundering is referred to as a lack of wash-fastness or 'bleeding'. Colour loss will occur during laundering if dyes have been used which are held loosely by the fibre; that is, dyes that have not penetrated the fibre sufficiently or dyes which are held only by weak forces such as hydrogen bonds or van der Waals' forces.

If bleaches are used at some stage in laundering, then fading may also be the result of chemical degradation of the dye.

Dry-cleaning-fastness

The loss of colour during dry-cleaning is referred to as a lack of dry-cleaning-fastness. Colour loss will occur during dry-cleaning if dyes have been used which are held loosely by the fibre and which are soluble in a dry-cleaning solvent. Loss of colour during dry-cleaning varies according to the particular dye and dry-cleaning solvent used.

In general, loss of colour during dry-cleaning is rare.

Fastness to perspiration

Perspiration is a complex combination of body oils, fats and saline solution. Perspiration may result in a loss of colour for reasons similar to that given for poor wash-fastness and poor dry-cleaning-fastness.

It is possible for the constituents of perspiration to react chemically with the dye and cause the chemical degradation of the dye molecule, but this is somewhat rare.

Fastness to compounds and bleaches containing chlorine

In recent years the increasing number of swimming pools has meant that, in addition to chlorine bleach being used in laundering, chlorine-containing compounds are used for killing bacteria in swimming pools. This means that swimwear and towels have to withstand the oxidation effect of chlorine-containing compounds.

The chlorine for domestic bleaches is sodium hypochlorite whereas the chlorine used in pools is usually calcium hypochlorite of dichloroisocyanuric acid. The chemical degradation of dyes sensitive to both these reagents is due to their oxidising effect.

Fastness to sea water

The main constituent of sea water is sodium chloride (NaCl), also known as common salt. When textile materials are wet with sea water, direct, intense sunlight will cause the sodium chloride to hydrolyse. Therefore, fading from sea water is also due to sunlight and should be referred to as *fading due to sea water and sunlight*. This hydrolytic reaction produces hydrochloric acid which degrades the dye molecules.

Dye molecules which provide good colour-fastness to sea water are those which can resist prolonged exposure to dilute hydrochloric acid, ultraviolet radiation and heat.

Fading due to other causes

Fading can also be caused by inorganic acids, alkalis, fruit juices, etc. Such fading is usually a chemical degradation of the dye molecules which results from a reaction with these compounds.

Fading due to dry ironing and steam pressing is the result of degradation of the dye molecules. In the case of dry ironing, the degradation of the dye molecules is due to the heat sensitivity of some dye molecules. Fading due to steam pressing would be due to the inability of some dye molecules to withstand the hydrolytic effects of steaming.

Classification of dyes

Dyes may be classified in two ways:

1 according to the chemical constitution of the dye molecule, or;
2 according to the method of application of the dye.
    In this text, they are classified according to the their method of application.

Acid dyes

Acid dyes are so called because they are usually applied under acidic conditions. The fibres most readily coloured with acid dyes are man-made, synthetic, nylon fibres and the natural protein fibres (mohair, silk, wool, etc.).

Dyeing with acid dyes

The following abbreviations are used when dyeing with acid dyes is described.

$DSO_3^-Na^+$	the generalised formula for the acid dye molecule
D	the colour radical or component of the acid dye molecule
DSO_3^-	the dye anion
Na^+	the sodium ion
H^+	the hydrogen ion
nylon	the nylon polymer
wool	the wool polymer

The application of acid dyes to protein fibres results in an ionic or salt link between the dye molecule and the fibre polymer. The point of the fibre polymer at which the dye is attached is termed the dye site. In wool the dye sites are the many amino groups of the fibre. Under dyeing conditions, the amino group becomes positively charged and attracts the negatively charged dye anion. This can be represented as follows:

$wool-NH_2$	+	H^+	$wool-NH_3^+$
wool polymer with amino group		hydrogen or acid ion	wool polymer with positively charged amino group

then

$wool-NH_3^+$	+	DSO_3^-	$wool-NH_3^{+-}SO_3D$
wool polymer with positively charged amino group		dye anion	ionic link formed between positively charged amino group on wool polymer and dye anion

There are a large number of amino groups in the wool fibre. As a guide, there are approximately twenty times as many amino groups on wool as on nylon and five times as many amino groups on wool as on silk. Dark shades can readily be obtained on wool because of the highly amorphous nature of the fibre, which results in relatively easy penetration of the fibre polymer by the dye molecule, and because of the presence of numerous amino groups.

The application of acid dyes to nylon also results in ionic bonds or salt links between the dye molecules and the polymer. The point at which the ionic link is formed is the terminal amino group of nylon. The greater crystalline fibre structure of nylon compared with wool as well as the relatively lower number of amino groups means that dark shades on nylon cannot be obtained with acid dyes.

The dyeing of nylon with acid dyes can be represented as follows:

$nylon-NH_2$	+	$H^+ \longrightarrow$	$nylon-NH_3^+$
nylon polymer with terminal amino group		hydrogen or acid ion	nylon polymer with positively charged terminal amino group

then

$nylon-NH_3^+$	+	$DSO_3^- \longrightarrow$	$nylon-NH_3^+ SO_3D$
nylon polymer with positively charged terminal amino group		dye anion	ionic link formed between positively charged terminal amino group on nylon polymer and dye anion

In addition to ionic bonds, when protein and polyamide fibres and dyed with acid dyes, hydrogen bonds as well as van der Waals' forces will be formed between the acid dye molecules and the fibre polymer system. However, the ionic bonds between the acid dye molecules and the fibre polymer play a more dominant role in the dye being retained by the fibre polymer than the hydrogen bonds and van der Waals' forces.

Some of the acid dyes have a relatively high substantivity to protein fibres. Therefore, if the fibres are dyed non-uniformly, it is difficult if not impossible to produce a uniform dyeing once the uneven result has occurred. To overcome this, a retarder needs to be added to the dye liquor. The addition of an electrolyte, such as sodium sulphate, will retard the rate of dyeing of protein fibres with acid dyes. The retarding effect of sodium sulphate can be explained as follows.

Because the sulphate radical is negatively charged and smaller than the dye anion it can move more rapidly in the dye liquor. The dye sites of the fibre polymer are rapidly occupied by the sulphate radical and in effect compete with the acid dye anion for the dye sites. The dye molecule has the greater affinity for the dye site but the sulphate radicals retard the rate at which the dye molecule occupies the dye sites. This produces a uniform dyeing. The application of heat assists the dyeing process by increasing the kinetic energy of the dye molecules which are slowly overcoming the retarding effect of the sulphate radicals. Thus, the dye anion will gradually replace the sulphate radical that has been attached to the dye site.

Printing with acid dyes

Once the acid dye printing paste has been applied to the textile material, steaming of the printed pattern is necessary. The steam provides the water molecules and heat energy to enable the dye molecules of the printing paste to transfer from the fibre surface into the polymer system.

The process of printing is different to dyeing in that it requires a lower liquor ratio and a thickener to ensure that the acid dye will not run when applied to the textile material. However, once the acid dye is attached to the fibre (i.e. after steaming), the bonds holding the acid dye molecule in the fibre polymer system are the same as those developed during dyeing.

Molecular configuration and characteristics

The chemical constitution, and thus the molecular structure, of acid dyes varies. Generally, acid dyes are the sodium salts of sulphonic acids. However, many direct dyes also are the sodium salts of sulphonic acids. Dyes are classified as acid if they can be applied satisfactorily to protein fibres.

Acid dyes may be divided into three distinct types, based on their levelling characteristics (see below). An example of each type of acid dye is shown in Fig. 6.2.

Properties of acid dyes

Light-fastness

Dyed and printed acid colours have good light-fastness. The light-fastness rating of acid dyes is about 4–5. (Refer to the Glossary entry **light-fastness** for an explanation of light-fastness ratings.)

The electron arrangement in the chromophores of the acid dye molecules is such that acid dyes can resist the degrading effects of the sun's ultraviolet radiation for a considerable time.

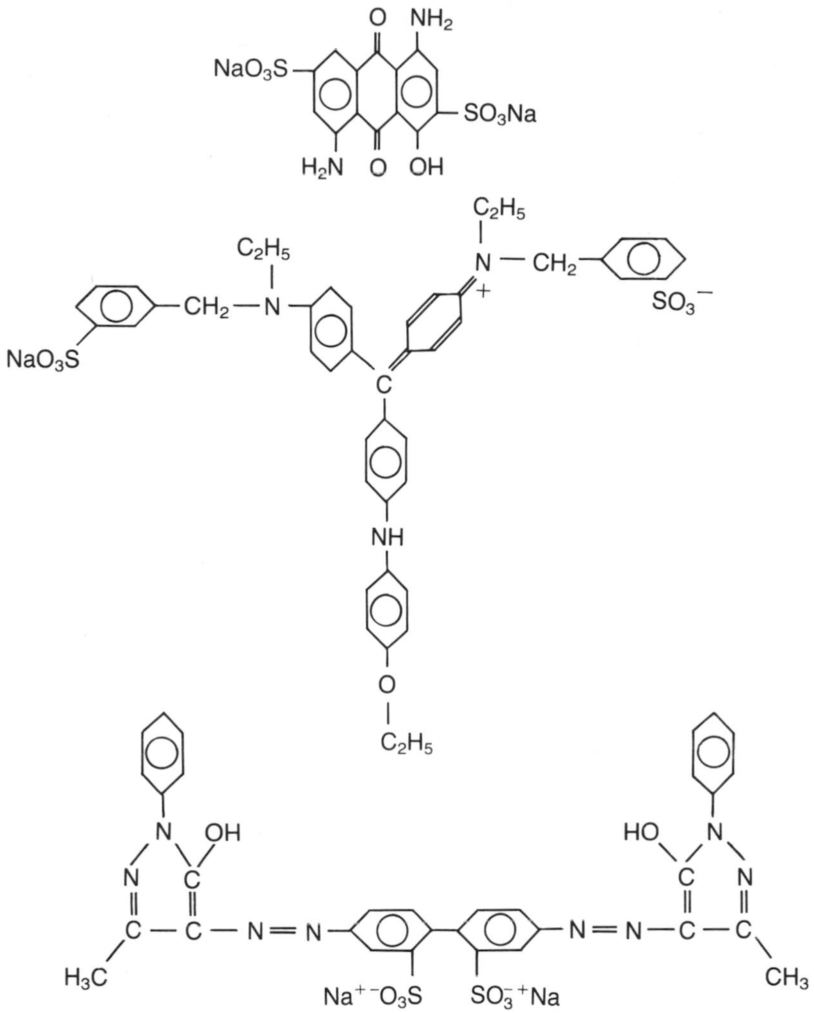

Figure 6.2 Structural formulae of acid dyes with different levelling characteristics
a C.I. Acid Blue 45, 63010 — an acid dye with good levelling characteristics, a light-fastness rating of 6 to 7, and a wash-fastness of 2
b C.I. Acid Blue 83, 42660 — an acid dye with average levelling characteristics, a light-fastness rating of 5 to 6, and a wash-fastness rating of 3 to 4
c C.I. Acid Yellow 42, 22910 — an acid dye with poor levelling characteristics, a light-fastness rating of 4 to 5, and a wash-fastness rating of 4 to 5

Wash-fastness

The wash-fastness rating is about 2–3 for acid dyes with good levelling characteristics, 3–4 for those with average levelling characteristics, and 4–5 for those with poor levelling characteristics. (See the Glossary entry **wash-fastness** for an explanation of wash-fastness ratings.)

Two factors may influence the wash-fastness of acid dyed or printed textile materials. Firstly, the acid dye molecule attaches itself by ionic and hydrogen bonds to nylon and wool fibre polymers. These bonds may be hydrolysed in water. Acid dye molecules which are held loosely or which have not penetrated the polymer sufficiently may be removed from the polymer system of wool and nylon during laundering.

Secondly, acid dyes are acidic in nature and so are resistant to acids. Being acidic they will combine with alkalis such as the detergents used for washing. The result is that excess or loosely attached dye molecules combine with the alkaline detergent and are removed from the textile material.

Levelling characteristics

Acid dyes are divided into three groups according to their levelling characteristics.

Acid dyes with good levelling characteristics (see Fig. 6.2a).

The relatively poor substantivity of this type of acid dye is responsible for their good levelling characteristics. As the dye molecules have less attraction for the fibre they will migrate only slowly into the polymer systems of the wool or nylon fibres. However, to obtain sufficient substantivity, and ensure adequate exhaustion, sulphuric acid is added to the dye liquor to obtain a pH of about 3.5–4.5. Their lack of substantivity is evidenced by their poor wash-fastness. However, their light-fastness is very good to excellent.

Acid dyes with average levelling characteristics (see Fig. 6.2b).

Acetic acid is used to acidify the dye liquor to a pH of 5 to 6. At this pH adequate exhaustion of the dye occurs; that is, optimum absorption of dye molecules by the fibre is obtained. Lowering the pH would probably lead to uneven dyeing. The wash-fastness of these acid dyes is fair, whilst their light-fastness is good to very good.

Acid dyes with poor levelling characteristics (see Fig. 6.2c).

These dyes are also known as **fast acid dyes, acid milling dyes** or **neutral dyeing acid dyes**. They have the best substantivity of all the acid dyes, but have relatively poor levelling characteristics. Unless care is taken during dyeing, their relatively good substantivity for the fibre may result in too rapid an uptake and consequently unlevel dyeing.

The excellent substantivity of these dyes may be attributed to the two, sometimes more, sodium sulphonate groups ($NaSO_3^-$) in their dye molecules. The greater polarity of the acid milling dyes is due to the extra sulphonate groups and gives higher substantivity thus requiring a pH range of 6 to 7 in order to obtain slower exhaustion and more level dyeing.

The wash-fastness of these dyes is good to very good, whilst their light-fastness is fair to good. The better wash-fastness, compared with the other two types of acid dyes, is due to the greater number of sodium sulphonate groups.

Dye uptake

Heating of the acid dye liquor is essential to ensure satisfactory dye uptake. Below about 40°C, there is practically no transfer of dye molecules from the dye liquor to the fibre polymer system. However, the rate of dyeing increases steadily as the temperature rises. Increasing the temperature of the dye liquor provides the energy required by the dye molecules to leave the dye liquor and enter the polymer system of the fibre.

Azoic dyes

Azoic dyes are so called because their molecules contain an azo group (see Table 6.2). Azoic dyes are also called **naphthol dyes, ice colours** or **developed colours.**

The fibres most readily coloured with azoic dyes are the man-made and natural cellulose fibres, e.g. viscose, cotton, etc.

Dyeing with azoic dyes

Colouring textile materials with azoic dyes involves the reaction within the fibre polymer system of the two components which constitute the azoic dye. These two components are the **naphthol** or **coupling component**, and the **base** or **diazo component**. Dyeing or printing with azoic dyes is a two stage process (See Fig. 6.3).

The first stage of dyeing with azoic dyes is called naphtholation and involves dissolving the naphthol in water using sodium hydroxide. The fibre is impregnated with this solution of naphthol. To assist penetration, a temperature of 80–85°C is used for viscose rayon, but with cotton room temperature is adequate. The impregnated material is passed through rollers which squeeze any excess solution from the material.

The second stage in azoic dyeing, called diazotisation, involves the preparation of a diazo component by converting this component to the soluble diazonium salt using sodium nitrite and hydrochloric acid. The dye liquor is now ready for the next stage of azoic dyeing. To this dye liquor, ice may be added, as diazonium salts are stable only at relatively low temperatures.

Once the fabric has been treated with the naphthol it is passed through the liquor containing the diazonium salt to effect the reaction between the naphthol and diazonium salt. This reaction is referred to as **coupling**. It is at this stage that the azo group (—N = N—) is formed. *Note*: dye manufacturers supply the diazo component as a stable diazonium salt. When this is used, coupling becomes the second stage in azoic dyeing.

It should be noted that the naphthol component is mostly in the fibre polymer system. It is necessary that most of the diazonium salt also enters the polymer system to effect the reaction between the naphthol component and the diazonium salt. However, invariably, some reaction occurs on the surface of the fibre with the result that some of the azoic dye is formed on the surface of the fibre. The removal of this surface dye is essential since azoic dyes are insoluble and, unless removed, the textile material will have poor rub-fastness properties. This removal is effected by a thorough final rinse of the dyed material. Care must be taken at each stage of dyeing that most dye formation occurs within the polymer system of the fibre.

Printing with azoic dyes

The application of azoic dye by printing is similar to that of dyeing except that the fabric is impregnated with the coupling component according to the printed design. This is followed by the application of the diazonium salt to produce the insoluble azoic dye.

As in dyeing, care must be taken that the insoluble dye is formed within the polymer system of the fibre to minimise the possibility of poor rub-fastness.

Molecular configuration and characteristics

The equations in Fig. 6.3 show the formation of the azoic dye molecules within the polymer system of the fibre. Azoic dyes are essentially non-polar and as such as re-

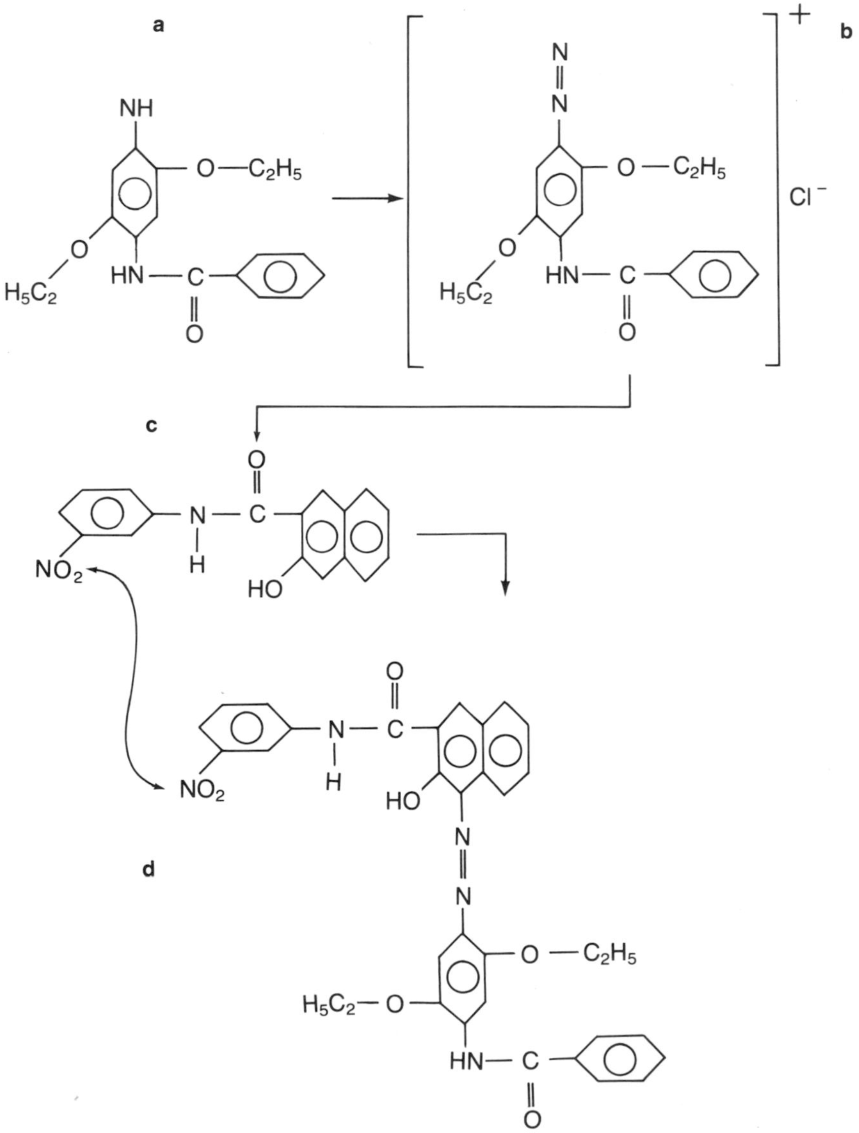

Figure 6.3   The formation of an azoic dye
a   The base component, in this case C.I. Azoic Diazo Compound 20, which is converted to its diazonium salt to form the azo group —N=N—
b   The diazonium salt of the base component. Note the azo group (—N=N—) which enables it to react with naphthol or coupling component to form the azo dye molecule.
c   The naphthol component or coupling component, in this case C.I. Azoic Coupling Compound 17.
d   The azo molecule formed from the reaction between the base component and the coupling component. In this case, the dye molecule formed will have a blue colour.

latively insoluble in water. Although most dye groups have molecules in which the azo group is present, the azoic dyes are distinct in that the dye molecule is formed within the fibre during the dyeing/printing process.

Properties of azoic dyes

Light-fastness

Dyed and printed azoic colours have very good to excellent light-fastness which may be attributed to the very stable electron arrangement in azoic dyes, particularly in their chromophores. It requires very prolonged exposure to sunlight for azoic dyes to be adversely affected. The light-fastness rating of azoic dyes is about 6–7.

Wash-fastness

The very good wash-fastness of textile materials that have been dyed or printed with azoic dyes is due to the fact that azoic dyes are insoluble. This means that they are unaffected during laundering. The wash-fastness rating of azoic dyes is about 4–5.

Bright colours

Azoic dyes are characterised by their very bright red and orange colours. This means that the particular azoic dye molecules responsible for these bright, pure colours must be able to absorb *all* those wavelengths *not responsible* for the bright orange and red colours.

Rub-fastness

At times textile materials dyed with azoic dyes suffer from poor rub-fastness. This occurs because of the formation of the insoluble azoic dye on the surface of the fibre which is not removed during the final stage of dyeing/printing, a thorough rinsing of the textile material. This rinsing stage is referred to as soaping-off and involves a thorough treatment of the dyed/printed textile with a detergent.

If all stages of azoic dyeing are carefully controlled and followed by a thorough soaping-off, poor rub-fastness is unlikely to occur.

Blinding

At times azoic dyes may cause a matt or delustred effect. This effect, called blinding, is more common on viscose rayon than on cotton.

It is thought that blinding occurs when the dye forms aggregates of dye molecules which are not uniformly distributed throughout the fibre polymer. The more likely occurrence of this effect on viscose rayon than on cotton is probably due to the more amorphous or open structure of viscose rayon which makes it easier for aggregates of dye to form.

Basic dyes

These are also called **cationic dyes**, because in solution the basic dye molecule ionises, causing its coloured component to become a cation or positively charged radical.

When they were first synthesised, the basic dyes were used on wool and silk, but they had very poor colour-fastness properties. They were therefore displaced for these fibres by acid dyes.

When acrylic fibres began to become established a new form of basic dye was evolved which came to be known as the **modified basic dyes**. These are now essentially the only basic dyes used in textile dyeing and printing. They are generally referred to merely as basic dyes. They tend to be distinguishable from the other classes of textile dyes by their brilliance of colour.

The fibres most readily coloured with basic dyes are mainly the synthetic acrylic and modacrylic fibres.

Dyeing with basic dyes

Basic dyes are applied to acrylic fibres from a slightly acidic dye liquor. Basic dyes have good substantivity for acrylic fibres and exhaust well within narrow limits of temperature. Because of their poor levelling properties, care must be exercised when applying basic dyes to acrylic fibres to avoid unlevel dyeing. This is achieved through the use of a retarder and carefully regulating the temperature during dyeing.

The colouring component of basic dyes is the cation. The dye cation is absorbed on the fibre surface which is negatively charged. The negative potential of the fibre is thus neutralised. Increasing the temperature of the dye liquor provides the dye with sufficient energy to enter the fibre polymer system. It is thought that there is an intermediate stage in which the dye is dissolved in the fibre to form polar bonds. As the number of acid groups in the fibre is limited, one can determine quantitatively the extent to which the basic dyes can combine with acrylic fibres.

The dyeing process can be represented as follows:

Ac	=	acrylic fibre polymer
SO_3^-	=	negatively charged sulphonate group
$AcSO_3^-$	=	acrylic fibre polymer containing negatively charged sulphonate group which is the acidic group and also the dye site
D^+	=	dye cation

$$AcSO_3^- \;+\; D^+ \;\rightarrow\; AcSO_3^{-+}D$$

$AcSO_3^-$	D^+	$AcSO_3^{-+}D$
acrylic fibre	dye	dye attached to dye
polymer with	cation	site on acrylic fibre polymer
dye site		

As stated earlier, to prevent uneven dyeing of acrylic fibres with basic dyes a cationic retarder is added to the dye liquor. The cationic retarder competes with the cationic dye molecules for the dye sites on the acrylic fibre polymers. This prevents the dye molecules from rushing onto the fibre. The presence of the cationic retarders on the dye sites means that the basic dye, which has greater substantivity for the acrylic fibre compared with the retarder, will only be able to replace the cationic retarder slowly, ensuring a more level dyeing.

Printing with basic dye

When basic dyes are applied to acrylic fibres by printing, steaming is required to achieve adequate penetration of the polymer system of the fibres. The steam provides the energy required for the dye molecules to enter the acrylic fibres and attach themselves to the negatively charged dye sites within the polymer system of acrylic fibres.

Molecular configuration and characteristics

Basic dyes are unique in that the coloured component of the dye is a *cation*, not a dye anion as is the case with most other dyes. The anion of basic dyes is usually a chloride anion. The chloride ion helps to make the basic dye water soluble. Once in the dye liquor, the dye dissociates into the dye cation and the chloride anion (see Fig. 6.4).

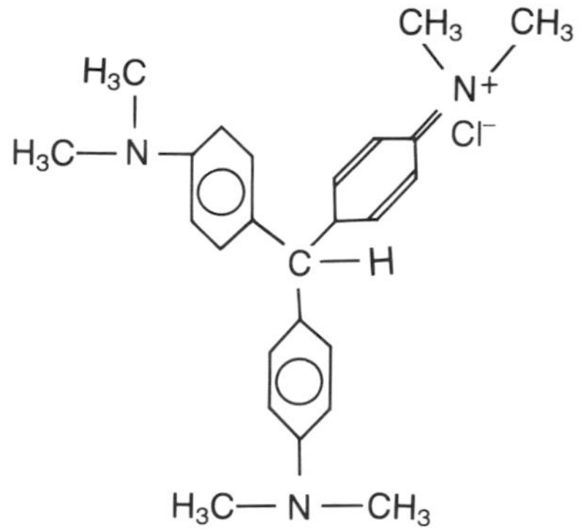

Figure 6.4   The structural formula for C.I. Basic Violet 3, 42555 — a basic dye

Properties of basic dyes

Light-fastness

Dyed and printed acrylic textiles using basic dyes have excellent light-fastness. The light-fastness rating of basic dyes is about 6–7. This excellent light-fastness is attributed partly to the hydrophobic nature of acrylic fibres, which minimises their absorption of water, and their excellent resistance to sunlight. These two factors tend to minimise the destructive effect of the ultraviolet rays of sunlight on the dye molecule.

Wash-fastness

Acrylic textiles dyed with basic dyes have very good wash-fastness. This may be attributed in part to the good substantivity of basic dyes for acrylic fibres and the hydrophobic nature of acrylic fibres minimising the absorption of water into the polymer system of acrylic fibres. The wash-fastness rating of basic dyes is about 4–5.

Bright colours

Basic dyes are characterised by their brilliance and intense hues. The bright colours achieved from basic dyes do not usually occur with other dye classes. No satisfactory explanation can be offered for this.

Direct dyes

Direct dyes are also called **substantive colours** because of their excellent substantivity for cellulosic textile materials

The fibres most readily coloured with direct dyes are the man-made and natural cellulose fibres; that is, cotton and viscose fibres.

Dyeing with direct dyes

Direct dyes are applied to cellulosic fibres from an aqueous liquor to which is added an electrolyte, which is usually sodium chloride. The addition of the electrolyte to the dye liquor is essential to obtain adequate exhaustion of the dye molecules by the fibre polymer system.

When sodium chloride is added to the dye liquor it dissociates completely into sodium ions (Na^+) and chloride ions (Cl^-). The cellulosic fibre in the dye liquor has a negative surface charge attracting to it the sodium cation. This neutralises the negative surface charge of the fibre, also referred to as the **zeta potential** enabling the dye anion of the direct dye to enter the fibre more readily. The presence of the chloride ions in the dye liquor also assists the dye anion to leave the dye liquor and enter the fibre polymer system. This is the result of repulsive forces between the dye anion and the chloride anion.

The application of heat to the dye liquor increases the energy of the components of the dye liquor, swells the fibre and accelerates the rate at which dyeing occurs.

Printing with direct dyes

The application of direct dyes by printing is in principle the same as dyeing. However, a thickener is added to restrict the dye and thus ensure the colour does not run. Dye fixation is achieved through the application of steam heating which assists the dye molecule to leave the printing paste and penetrate into the polymer system of the fibres. The dye leaves the printing paste for reasons similar to those given in the earlier section on dyeing with direct dyes; that is, conditions are created by the presence of an electrolyte and the application of steam to ensure that the dye is attracted to the fibre and has enough energy for the dye to leave the printing paste and enter the polymer system of the cellulosic fibre.

Molecular configuration and characteristics

Figure 6.5 illustrates the characteristic linear configuration of direct dye molecules. The auxochromes in the dye molecule are responsible for the good aqueous solubility of direct dyes. Many direct dyes are sodium salts of sulphonic acids. In this respect direct dyes are similar to acid dyes. In fact, some dyes which are applied as direct dyes

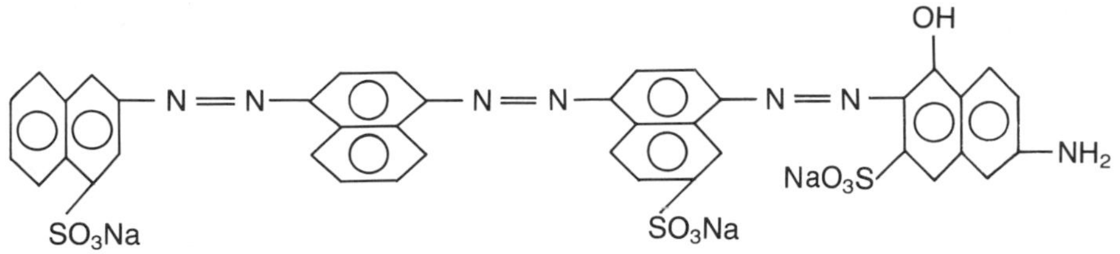

Figure 6.5   The structural formula for C.I. Direct Blue 71, 34140 — a direct dye

and acid dyes may have the same formula. An examination of their molecular formula will not categorise the dye into one class or the other.

Properties of direct dyes

Light-fastness

Dyed and printed direct colours have a moderate light-fastness, the light-fastness rating being about 3. This means that the direct dye anions seem to lack a stable electron arrangement, particularly in the chromophores. A relatively short exposure to direct sunlight is enough to initiate degradation of the dye molecule. The resultant breakdown of the direct dye anion is seen as fading of the dyed or printed cellulosic textile material.

Wash-fastness

The wash-fastness rating of direct dyes is about 2–3. The comparatively poor wash-fastness of cellulosic textile materials dyed with direct dyes can be explained as follows.

The relatively large number of auxochromes in the direct dye anion which contributes to the aqueous solubility of these dyes contributes to the poor wash-fastness of this class of dye.

Direct dyes, or more specifically the direct dye anion, are attached to the cellulose polymers by hydrogen bonds and van der Waals' forces both of which are weak. Under aqueous conditions such as occur in laundering these weak bonds may be hydrolysed by the water molecules resulting in the removal of these dyes from the polymer system. The loss of dyes is seen as fading of the cellulosic textile material.

Improving wash-fastness

Direct dyes are relatively easy to apply to cellulosic textiles. However, although easy to apply, they are also relatively easy to remove and this gives rise to the saying 'easy on easy off'. The advantage of direct dyes is their ease of application, comparatively low cost and wide range of available colours. It is for these reasons that direct dyes are still used on cellulosic textile materials.

The importance of direct dyes has resulted in the development of means to improve their wash-fastness. These after-treatments, as they are called, all aim to increase the size of the direct dye molecule once it is located within the polymer system of the fibre. The larger dye molecule increases the forces of attraction between the dye molecule and the polymer. The increased molecular size makes it more difficult for the dye to be removed (washed out) from the polymer system.

Some of the methods used for improving wash-fastness of direct cellulosics are as follows:

Diazotisation

Certain direct dyes have a structure similar to the base of azoic dyes. This enables these dyes to be treated with naphthols as is the case with azoic dyes. This increases the size of the dye molecule within the polymer system of the cellulosic fibre and improves the dyes' wash-fastness from poor to good. Diazotisation does, however, cause an alteration in the hue of the direct dye and this factor has to be considered when this method is used to improve the wash-fastness of direct dyes.

Copper after-treatment

When certain dyes are treated with copper sulphate a chemical reaction results in which copper forms a metal complex with the dye molecule. The metal complex is slightly larger in size than the original dye molecule and results in a slight improvement in wash-fastness.

Cationic agents

A cellulosic textile that has been dyed with direct dye may be after-treated with special cationic agents. In aqueous solution the direct dye molecules situated in the fibre's polymer system ionise slightly, and their colour component becomes an anion, i.e. negatively charged. As soon as the cationic agent is added to the aqueous solution it will also ionise, and the main, important component of the cationic agent becomes a cation, i.e. positively charged. The cation of the cationic agent is attracted to the anion of the direct dye, the result being a complex molecule which is also much bigger than the original direct dye molecule. It will now be more difficult to wash out this bigger, complex molecule and the direct dyed textile will therefore have a somewhat better wash-fastness. On the other hand, cationic after-treatment of textile material which has been coloured with direct dyes results in a reduced light-fastness for which no explanation can as yet be given.

Formaldehyde after-treatment

Certain direct dyes will react with formaldehyde (HCHO) when heated to about 70–80° under slightly acid conditions. Dye molecules appear to be joined together by methylene cross-links, giving very large dye molecule complexes which are much more difficult to wash out of the fibre.

Note: although after-treatments improve the wash-fastness of direct dyes to some extent, the improvement achieved still leaves much to be desired.

Disperse dyes

These dyes derive their name from their insoluble aqueous properties and the need to apply them from an aqueous dispersion.

The fibres most readily coloured by disperse dyes are the man-made ester-cellulose and synthetic fibres, especially the acetate fibres and polyester, and less often acrylic and nylon.

Dyeing with disperse dyes

Disperse dyes are added to water with a surface active agent to form an aqueous dispersion. The insolubility of the disperse dyes enables them to leave the dye liquor as they are more substantive to the organic fibre than to the relatively inorganic aqueous dye liquor. The application of heat to the dye liquor increases the energy of the dye molecules and accelerates the dyeing of the textile fibre.

Heating the dye liquor swells the fibre to some extent and assists the dye to penetrate the fibre polymer system resulting in the dye being located in the amorphous regions of the fibre. Once within the fibre polymer system, the dye molecules are held by hydrogen bonds and van der Waals' forces.

Polyester fibres are extremely crystalline and hydrophobic, and it is difficult to obtain medium or dark shades even by dyeing at the boil. In order to obtain medium to dark shades, polyester fibres are dyed using carriers or by using high temperature dyeing techniques.

Dyeing with carriers

The extremely crystalline nature of polyester fibres presented problems in obtaining dark shades by conventional dyeing methods, even with the temperature of the dye liquor at the boil. Then it was found that certain organic compounds assisted the disperse dyes to enter the polyester fibre polymer enabling dark shades to be produced. There is no universally accepted explanation for the way in which carriers assist in dyeing polyester fibres using disperse dyes. The most common explanation is that carriers swell the polyester fibre polymer and in so doing allow the disperse dye molecules to enter the polyester fibre more readily.

High temperature dyeing

This dyeing technique is carried out at temperatures above the boil (in the range 100–130°C) and under pressures ranging from 0 to 170 kPa. This method of dyeing is also called pressure dyeing; it is generally used for the highly crystalline synthetic fibres or for fibre blends containing these fibres. The technique causes the fibres to swell even more than at 100°C, so that dye molecules enter and penetrate deeper into the fibre's polymer system. High temperature dyeing is particularly useful for dyeing polyester fibres. It eliminates the need for carriers which add extra cost and, in most cases, have a rather unpleasant odour which has to be removed by thorough scouring and rinsing of the material.

Printing with disperse dyes

Disperse dyes can be applied by normal printing methods. Dye fixation in the fibre polymer system is achieved by wet or dry steaming the material. In both cases the heat applied increases the energy of the dye molecules, ensuring their adequate penetration of the fibre polymer system.

Transfer printing

Disperse dyes are able to sublime at temperatures from 170° to 250°C. The specific temperature at which sublimation occurs varies according to the particular disperse dye. This property of disperse dyes has enabled the process of transfer printing to be developed. This process involves printing disperse dyes according to a predetermined design on suitable paper. The printed paper and the textile material are then passed between heated rollers at the required temperature. Under these conditions the disperse dye molecules transfer to the textile material. The transfer printing process is used mainly on textile materials with at least 65 per cent thermoplastic fibres and invariably disperse dyes are used.

Molecular configuration and characteristics

As a rule disperse dyes have the smallest molecules of all the common dye classes. Tables 6.4 and 6.5 provide an indication of the relative size of disperse dye molecules. Fig. 6.6 is an example of the anthraquinone type of disperse dyes. A feature of disperse dye molecules is their lack of polar groups, evidenced by the insolubility of disperse dyes.

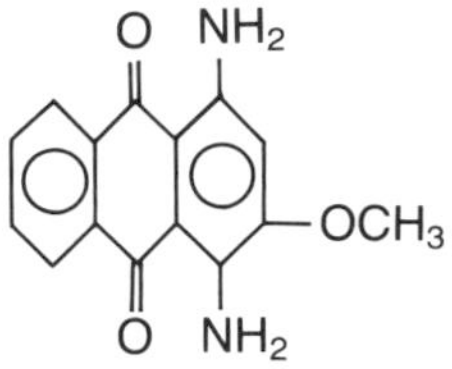

Figure 6.6   The structural formula for C.I. Disperse Red 11, 62015 — a disperse dye

Properties of disperse dyes

Light-fastness

Textile materials which have been coloured with disperse dyes have a fair to good light-fastness. The light-fastness rating is about 4–5. This may be attributed in part to the non-polar nature of the dye molecule which will not readily attract water molecules and other polar agents that may have a degrading effect. Further, the aromatic or benzene structure of disperse dyes gives them a relatively stable structure. Only with prolonged exposure to the ultraviolet component of sunlight will any significant loss of colour occur in a disperse coloured textile material.

Wash-fastness

Textile materials coloured with disperse dyes have a moderate to good wash-fastness. The wash-fastness rating is about 3–4. This is due partly to the insolubility of disperse dye molecules and partly to the hydrophobic nature of the fibres to which disperse dye are usually applied.

Gas-fading

In the presence of nitrous oxide, textile materials dyed with certain blue and violet disperse dyes with an anthraquinone structure will fade.

Nitrous oxide is produced by open gas fires or when nitrogen and oxygen are caused to react by the red hot elements of electric heaters. Nitrous oxide is also present in exhaust fumes from cars.

Fading caused by nitrous oxide can be minimised by treating the textile material with a chemical based on an **azoic thiophene-benzene complex**. The improved resistance to gas-fading occurs because the nitrous oxide will react with this complex in preference to the disperse dye molecule.

Sublimation

Disperse dyes have the ability to undergo sublimation; that is, they can be vaporised without a significant change in their colour, light-fastness or wash-fastness. The ability of disperse dyes to sublime is the result of a stable electron arrangement. This property is used to advantage in transfer printing. The ability of disperse dyes to undergo sublimation may also be a disadvantage. Excessive hot pressing or ironing of disperse dyed or printed textiles may result in colour loss, by the heat applied causing the disperse dye molecules to vaporise or sublime and thus leave the fibres. Fading is apparent after the application of the heat.

Mordant dyes

The term **mordant** is derived from the Latin **mordeo**, which means to bite or to take hold of. The mordant dye is attached to the textile fibre by a mordant, which can be an organic or inorganic substance. The most commonly used mordant is inorganic **chromium**. Other inorganic mordants, such as aluminium, copper, iron and tin, and organic mordants, such as tannic acid, are rarely used. Since chromium is used so extensively, mordant dyes are sometimes called chrome dyes.

Fibres most readily dyed with mordant dyes are the natural protein fibres, particularly wool; and sometimes the synthetic fibres modacrylic and nylon.

Dyeing with mordant dyes

Three methods are used to apply mordant dyes to textile materials.

Chrome mordant method

This method of dye application has two stages. In the first stage, mordanting, the mordant is applied to the textile material. In the second stage the mordanted textile material is put in the dye liquor.

The mordant is applied to the textile from an aqueous medium containing the mordant, sodium or potassium dichromate, and an acid such as acetic acid. Mordanting involves boiling the textile material in the aqueous solution containing the mordant for about half to three quarters of an hour. The mordanted textile is then transferred to the aqueous solution containing the mordant dye and acid and the temperature raised slowly to the boil. This stage of dyeing can take up to about 1½ hours at the boil in order to obtain a level dyeing and achieve adequate exhaustion of the dye. During this stage the dye molecule attaches itself to the mordant which is already in the fibre polymer system and forms complexes which are called **lakes**. The dye is thought to be held in the fibre polymer system by forming a link with the mordant which has formed a link with the fibre polymer. The complex which is formed within the fibre polymer is relatively large and provides dyeings with good wet-fastness. This is due to the presence of van der Waals' forces which bind the larger molecules and the presence of hydrogen bonds within the polymer system of the fibre which prevent the subsequent removal of the dye molecules in aqueous treatments such as laundering.

Metachrome method

This is a one stage process in which the dye and the mordant are applied to the fibre simultaneously. This method can only be used with dyes which do not form the dye mordant complex immediately on coming together; that is, the mordant and the dye anion do not form the complex until they have entered the polymer system of the fibre. In fact, the dye complex can be formed in the dye liquor and care must be taken that this does not occur. (This will give rise to poor rub-fastness.) To minimise the formation of the complex in the dye liquor, the mordant dye is added and the textile material treated with the dye liquor and the temperature is raised to about 50°C. At this point the mordant is added and the temperature of the dye liquor raised to the boil slowly in about 45 minutes and dyeing continued at the boil for about 60 minutes. The method of attachment of the dye to the fibre is the same as for the chrome mordant method.

After-chrome method

This method involves a two-stage process which is the reverse of the chrome mordant method. The after-chrome method involves the application of the dye followed by mordanting. This method involves the use of certain mordant dyes, which are actually acid dyes which can be mordanted. The dyes are applied to the textile material from an aqueous solution which contains the dye and sodium sulphate. The textile material is treated in this liquor by slowly raising the temperature of the dye liquor to the boil where it is kept for about an hour. At this point, the mordant is added and the temperature maintained at the boil for another 45 minutes to one hour. During this period the dye complexes are formed within the fibre polymer system; the mode of attachment of the dye to the fibre is the same as for the chrome mordant method.

Printing with mordant dyes

Mordant dyes are rarely, if ever, used for printing as it is more convenient to print textile materials with other classes of dyes.

Molecular configuration and characteristics

Figure 6.7 is an example of a mordant dye and shows the formation of the dye-mordant complex. The chromium cation in Fig. 6.7 has a valency of 6 (that is, has six bonds) which is represented by the six lines directed toward the chromium atom. The mordant dye is shown to be attached to the chromium cation by three of the six bonds.

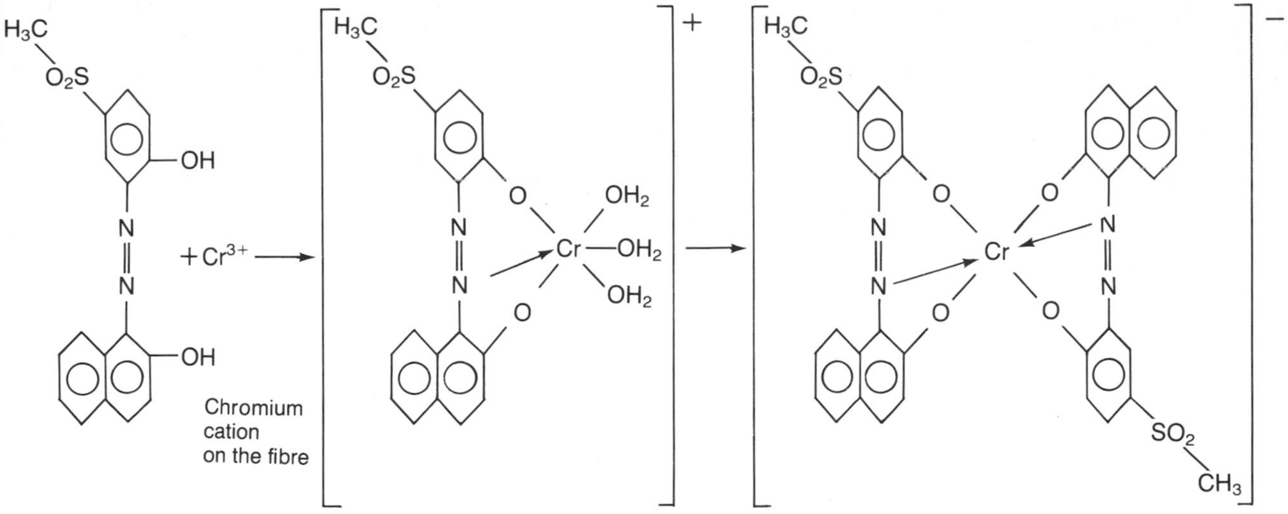

Figure 6.7 The formation of a mordant dye molecule within the fibre. The dye shown is C.I. Acid Violet 78, 12205. It should be noted that, while mordant dye molecules can be synthesised as such, they can also be built up as lakes within the fibre from certain acid and direct dye molecules.
a The dye has slight negative polarity.
b The dye molecules combines with the chromium cation. This is now called a lake or dye complex, which is positively charged because of the chromium cation. It may therefore combine with another dye molecule. (*Note*: This lake can also be regarded as a 1 : 1 metal complex dye molecule.)
c This much larger lake or dye complex is now negatively charged and can, therefore, combine with the smaller, positively charged lake (b) to form an even greater lake. Thus lakes of mordant dyes are built up to provide very good wash-fastness of those coloured textile fabrics dyed with them. *Note*: This lake can also be regarded as a 2 : 1 metal complex dye molecule.

The other three bonds have molecules of water attached to them. It is thought that the three molecules of water are there as an intermediate step only and will gradually be replaced by another mordant dye anion. Thus, two mordant dye molecules form a complex with the chromium cation to form a lake or a dye chromium complex. The formation of these relatively large complexes results in the very good wash-fastness of this class of dye.

Properties of mordant dyes

Light-fastness

The light-fastness rating of mordant dyes is about 5. The presence of the chromium in the dye molecule contributes to the very good light-fastness of mordant dyed textile materials. The presence of the chromium adds to the stability of the chromophores resulting in added resistance to the ultraviolet component of sunlight.

Wash-fastness

The wash-fastness rating of mordant dyes is about 4–5. The very good wash-fastness of textile materials dyed with mordant dyes is due to the large dye molecules or lakes that are formed within the polymer system of the fibre. These molecules, in addition to being large and difficult to remove, are also held by hydrogen bonds and van der Waal's forces.

Dull and limited range of colours

There is a limited range of colours in the mordant dye class and these are also relatively dull. It is thought that it is the presence of the metal chromium which is responsible for the dullness of colour and the limited colour range.

Disadvantages of using mordant dyes

This class of dye is now used to a lesser extent, for the following reasons:

1 Colour matching is difficult as the process of mordanting means that the colour builds up gradually.
2 Lengthy periods of application are both detrimental to protein and polyamide fibres and rather costly.
3 Dichromate salts such as sodium and potassium become pollutants once they are discharged into the sewerage.

   These disadvantages have contributed to the replacement of mordant dyes with the premetallised dyes.

Premetallised dyes

Premetallised dyes are so called because the metal, usually chromium, is already incorporated in the dye molecule during its manufacture. These dyes are also referred to as **metal complex dyes**. The incorporation of the metal into the dye molecule has meant that the dye can be more readily applied to the fibre, thus eliminating part of the lengthy dyeing process.

There are two types of premetallised dyes: **1:1 premetallised dyes**, which have one dye molecule for every metal atom (see Fig. 6.8a); and **2:1 premetallised dyes**, which have two dye molecules for every metal atom (see Fig. 6.8b).

The fibres most readily coloured with premetallised dyes are man-made synthetic nylon and natural protein fibres.

Dyeing with premetallised dyes

1:1 premetallised dyes

The 1:1 premetallised dyes have to be applied in very acid conditions in order to achieve adequate exhaustion, therefore they have largely been replaced by the 2:1 premetallised dyes.

The very acid conditions needed to apply these dyes can detrimentally affect the properties of the textile materials on which they are used. The 2:1 premetallised dyes are more easy to apply and require only slightly acid or neutral dye liquor. Therefore, the 1:1 premetallised dyes are used only in exceptional circumstances.

2:1 premetallised dyes

The 2:1 premetallised dyes are applied from a slightly acid or neutral dye liquor. These dyes are soluble in an aqueous liquor because of the presence of anionic solubil-

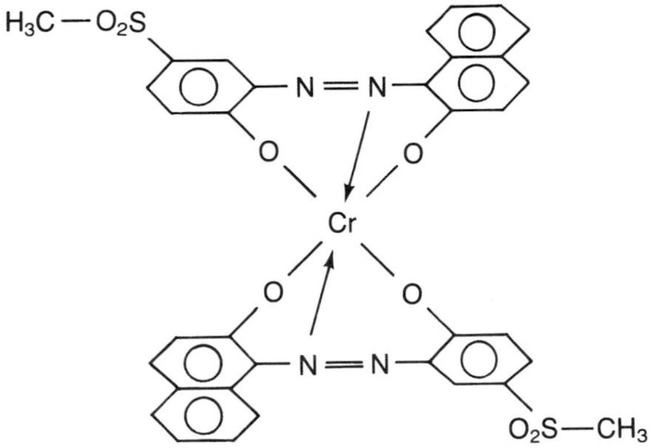

Figure 6.8 Structural formulae for metal complex dyes.
a a 1 : 1 metal complex dye molecule — C.I. Acid Orange 74, 18745
b a 2 : 1 metal complex dye molecule — C.I. Acid Violet 78, 12205

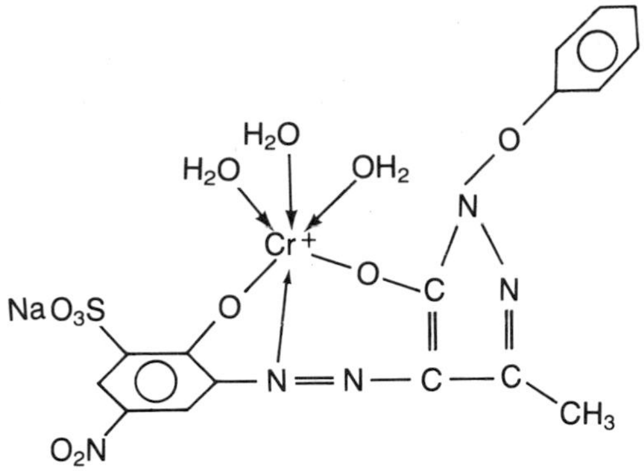

ising groups in the dye molecule. The coloured component of the dye is anionic and is attracted like acid dyes to the positively charged amine groups of protein and polyamide fibres.

wool$-NH_3^+$	+	$^-$Dye	→	wool$-NH_3^+$ $^-$Dye
wool polymer with positively charged amino group		anionic dye radical of a 2:1 premetallised dye molecule		ionic links formed between positively charged amino group on wool polymer and anionic dye radical or a 2:1 premetallised dye molecule

In addition to the ionic link, the large dye molecule means that van der Waals' forces will play a significant role in holding the dye in the fibre polymer system. Because of the large size of the dye molecule and the strong forces holding the dye molecule within the fibre, 2 : 1 premetallised dyes are slow dyeing but have very good wash-fastness.

Printing with premetallised dyes

Like mordant dyes, premetallised dyes are rarely used for printing as other classes of dye can be applied more conveniently to textile materials.

Molecular configuration and characteristics

The formulae in Figs 6.8a and 6.8b show the structure of the two types of premetallised dyes. Little will be said about the 1:1 premetallised dyes as these can be regarded as being obsolete. The 2:1 premetallised dyes, unlike the 1:1 premetallised dyes, have a symmetrical structure with the chromium atom at the centre. This symmetrical structure contributes to the stability of the dye molecule as well as to its resistance to degradation. The aqueous solubility of the 2:1 premetallised dye molecules is due to non-ionic groups, such as the $-SO_2-CH_3$ or methyl sulphone group shown in Fig. 6.8b.

Properties of premetallised dyes

Light-fastness

The light-fastness rating of premetallised dyes is about 5. The reasons for this very good light-fastness are the same as those given for mordant dyes on page 000.

Wash-fastness

The wash-fastness rating of premetallised dyes is about 40–5. This very good wash-fastness is attributed to the ionic link between the dye and fibre. In addition there are van der Waals' forces which occur because of the relatively large dye molecule and make it difficult for the dye molecule to be removed during laundering.

Dull and limited range of colours

There is a limited range of rather dull colours in the premetallised dye class. As with mordant dyes, this is thought to be because of the presence of the metal chromium.

Advantages of premetallised dyes over mordant dyes

The 2:1 premetallised dyes are water soluble, have very good wash-fastness and colour matching is much easier than with the mordant dyes. Premetallised dyes do not have the disadvantages listed for mordant dyes on page 000.

Reactive dyes

Reactive dyes are so called because their molecules react chemically with the fibre polymers of some fibres to form a covalent bond between the dye molecule and fibre polymer.

The fibres most readily coloured with reactive dyes are the man-made and natural cellulose fibres, synthetic nylon, and natural protein fibres.

Dyeing with reactive dyes

The application of reactive dyes involves the formation of a covalent bond between the dye molecule and the polymer of the particular fibre. The process of applying reactive dyes is considered below for cellulosic, protein and nylon fibres.

Man-made and natural cellulosic fibres

The dye liquor is prepared in a manner similar to that for applying direct dyes. The reactive dye is dissolved in water to which an electrolyte is added to assist exhaustion of the dye. The textile material is then introduced to the dye liquor and the dye is exhausted onto the fibres.

For the reaction between dye and fibre to take place, alkali must be added to the dye liquor. With some reactive dyes this reaction with alkali can be carried out at room temperature. However, with most reactive dyes, the temperature of the dye liquor must be increased, in some cases to the boil, to effect the reaction betweeen the dye molecule and the polymer system of the fibre. Reactive dyes have specific temperatures at which reaction between dye and fibre are optimum. In any case the formation of the covalent link requires the addition of an alkali.

The covalent link is formed between the dye molecule and the hydroxyl groups of the cellulosic fibre. Figures 6.9, 6.10 and 6.11 show the formation of the covalent bond between the dye molecule and fibre polymer.

Nylon fibres

The dye liquor is made slightly acid for nylon fibres. Heat is applied to assist the exhaustion of the dye, with the chemical reaction being effected by the addition of alkali. The covalent link is formed between the dye molecule and the terminal amino group of the polyamide fibre polymer (see Fig. 6.9).

Protein fibres

Reactive dyes are applied to protein fibres under slightly acid conditions. Formation of the covalent link between the dye molecule and fibre polymer occurs as the temperature is increased. Once again the optimum temperature depends on the specific reactive

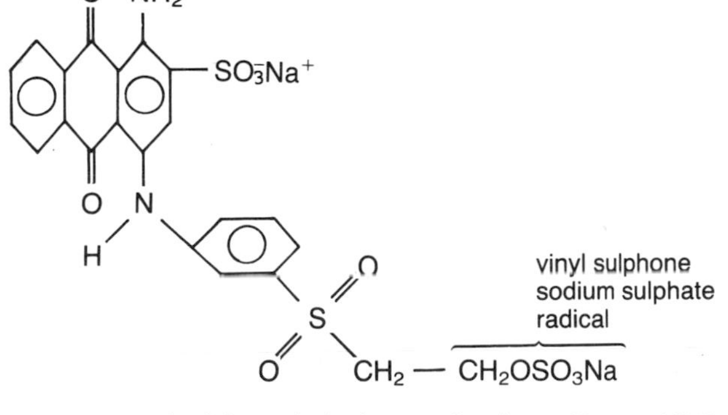

Figure 6.9 Structural formula for a vinyl sulphone derivative reactive dye — Remazol Brilliant Blue, C.I. Reactive Blue 19, 61200

dyes used. The application of heat to the dye liquor serves to increase exhaustion as well as to effect covalent bond formation between dye and fibre. Reaction with further dye fibres can be effected by raising the pH of the dye bath to about 8–8.5 with ammonia.

The reactive dyes used for protein fibres can form covalent bonds with one of the many groups in the protein fibre: the terminal and side chain amino groups, the –SH group of cystein and the hydroxyl group of the tyrosine amino acid residue. However, most of the covalent bonds occur with the amino groups since these are more numerous than the other groups. The reaction between wool and reactive dyes is shown in Fig. 6.10.

Printing with reactive dyes

Reactive dyes can be used for printing textile materials such as cellulosics and wool. The printed materials are wet steamed to ensure dye molecule penetration of the polymer system of the fibre and the formation of the covalent bond.

Molecular configuration and characteristics

The many reactive dyes have one characteristic in common; namely, their ability to form a covalent bond with the fibre to which they are applied. (See Figs 6.10 and 6.11.)

The formulae of the reactive dyes given in Figs 6.10 and 6.11 show a dye molecule which incorporates a group capable of reacting with a fibre polymer to form a covalent bond. The colour component of the reactive dye is somewhat similar to those of acid, direct and disperse dyes. In fact some reactive dyes have been derived from dyes in these other classes.

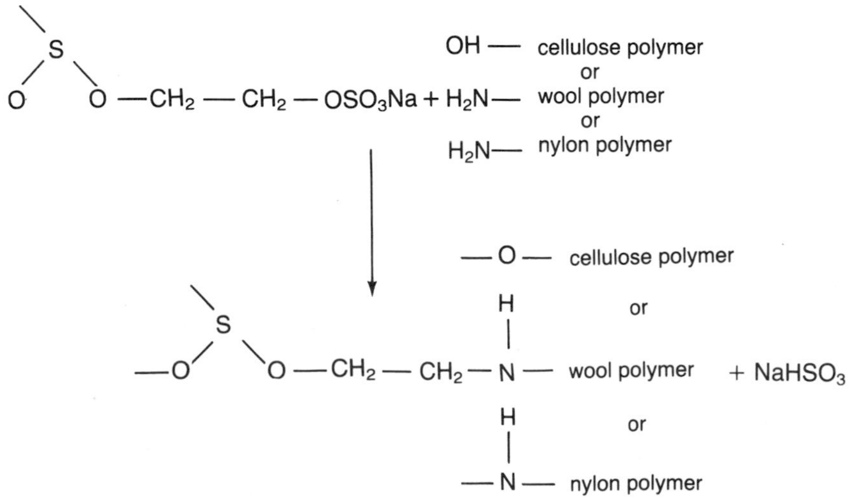

Figure 6.10 The vinyl sulphone sodium sulphate radical of a Remazol-type reactive dye molecule and how it attaches itself, by way of covalent bonding, to fibre polymers

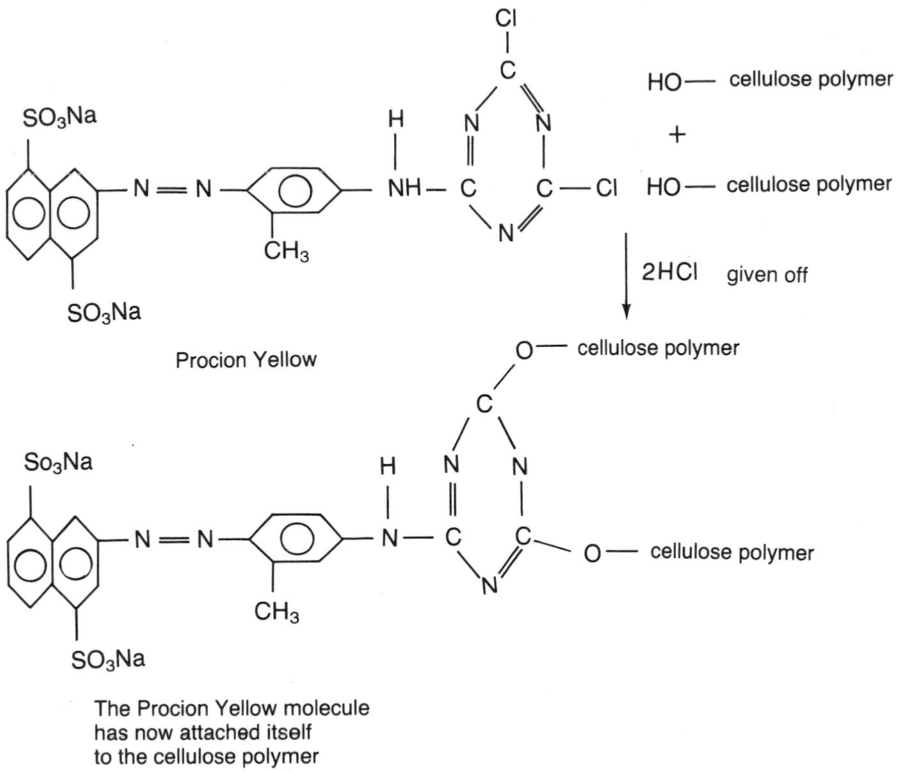

Figure 6.11 How a Procion-type reactive dye molecule attaches itself to cellulose polymers. The dye shown here is Procion Yellow (C.I. Reactive Yellow 3, 13245), a dichlorotriazinyl reactive dye.

Properties of reactive dyes

Light-fastness

In general, textile materials coloured with reactive dyes have very good light-fastness, the light-fastness rating being about 6. These dyes have a very stable electron arrangement and provide very good resistance to the degrading effect of the ultraviolet component of sunlight. There are, however, some reactive dyes with only fair light-fastness.

Wash-fastness

Textile materials coloured with reactive dyes have very good wash-fastness; the wash-fastness rating is about 4–5. This is attributed to the very stable covalent bond that exists between the dye molecule and the fibre polymer. Under the usual laundering and dry-cleaning conditions one finds in the home, there are few chemicals that have an effect on the covalent bond. (See page 156 under 'Effect of chlorine'.)

Washing-off

Textile materials which are coloured with reactive dyes have to be thoroughly rinsed and scoured. Reactive dyes can react with the hydroxyl groups of the water molecule to produce dye molecules with poor substantivity for the fibre. In fact it is these molecules which have to be removed by a washing-off process, involving scouring and rinsing. If these molecules of dye are not removed, poor rub-fastness may result.

Effect of acids

The formation of the covalent bond between dye and fibre occurs under alkaline conditions. The presence of acids may reverse this process. Perspiration and atmospheric pollution which are both slightly acid may affect textile materials coloured with reactive dyes and result in some fading.

Effect of chlorine

When reactive dyes were first introduced it was found that some of them were adversely affected by bleaches which contained chlorine. This is significant when you consider that one out of every ten homes in Australia has a swimming pool which is kept clean by the addition of chlorine. Swimwear, therefore, has to be coloured with dyes resistant to chlorine bleach. This can be achieved if the right reactive dyes are chosen, otherwise the swimwear will fade.

Sulphur dyes

These dyes are so called because they contain sulphur atoms in their molecules.

The fibres most readily coloured with sulphur dyes are the natural and man-made cellulosic fibres.

Dyeing with sulphur dyes

Sulphur dyes are insoluble in water. An aqueous solution of the sulphur dye is effected by reacting some sulphur dyes with sodium sulphide and others with sodium hydrosulphite. The role of sodium sulphide or sodium hydrosulphite is to reduce the sulphur dye to produce the water soluble or leuco form of the dye. In some instances the addition of sodium carbonate may be necessary to achieve the desired alkalinity. In this reduced or leuco form, sulphur dyes are substantive to cellulosic fibres. To achieve adequate exhaustion, it is necessary to add an electrolyte such as sodium chloride to the dye liquor.

To obtain adequate penetration and a satisfactory rate of dyeing, the dye liquor is heated. This increases the energy of the constituents of the dye liquor, increasing the rate of dyeing, and ensures adequate penetration of the fibre polymer system.

Once the dye is within the fibre polymer, the reduced sulphur dye is converted to its original insoluble form. This is achieved by an oxidation treatment with a mild reagent such as sodium perborate.

Printing with sulphur dyes

Sulphur dyes are not used for printing textile materials.

Molecular configuration and characteristics

Little is known about the structure of sulphur dyes. Sulphur dyes are produced by chemically reacting compounds such as *p*-aminophenol and dinitronaphthalene with sulphur. Sulphur dyes are thought to contain a thiazine ring, and to contain sulphur links within their molecules. (See Figs 6.12 and 6.13).

The following equations show how sulphur dyes are reduced to their soluble leuco form and are then oxidised, while in the fibre, back to the insoluble form.

$$Dye-S-S-Dye \quad + \quad 2H \longrightarrow \quad Dye-SH \quad + \quad HS-Dye$$

water insoluble sulphur dye molecule	reducing agent represented here by hydrogen	the di-sulphide bond of sulphur dye molecule has been split, the resultant–SH radicals make the reduced sulphur dye molecule water soluble, this is the leuco form

then

$$Dye-SH + HS-Dye \quad + \quad O \longrightarrow \quad Dye-S-S-Dye \quad + \quad H_2O$$

the water soluble or leuco form of the sulphur dye molecule within the fibre	oxidising agent represented here by oxygen	the insoluble sulphur dye molecule has reformed	water formed from the H and O

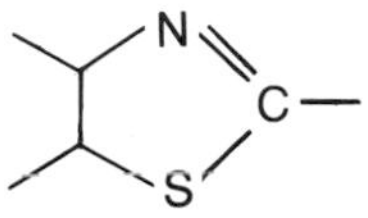

Figure 6.12 The thiazine ring thought to characterise sulphur dye molecules

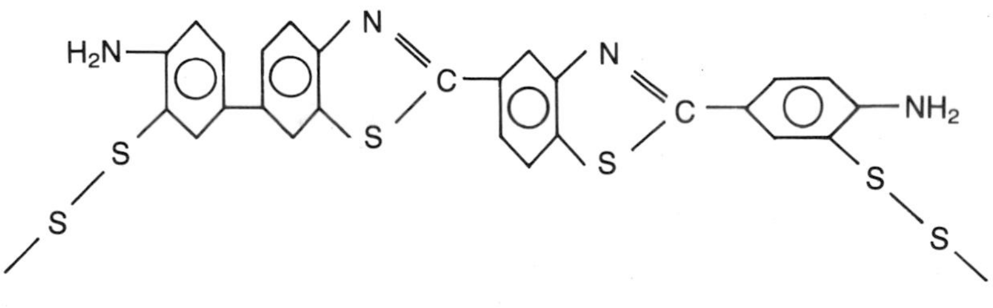

Figure 6.13 Portion of a sulphur dye molecule. This structural formula is incomplete because the complete composition and structure of sulphur dye molecules is not known.

Properties of sulphur dyes

Light-fastness

The light-fastness rating of sulphur dyes is about 4. This fair light-fastness may be improved somewhat by an after-treatment with metallic salts to give a light-fastness of about 5. The fair light-fastness is due to a lack of stability of the dye molecule in the presence of the ultraviolet component of sunlight which degrades the chromophore of the sulphur dye molecule. The improvement in light-fastness with a metallic salt is attributed to the increased stability of the chromophores through the presence of the metal atom.

Wash-fastness

The wash-fastness rating of sulphur dyes is about 3–4. This fair wash-fastness is due partly to the relatively large dye molecule and partly to the aqueous insolubility of the dye molecule. The lack of any significant polar groups in the dye molecule means that the dye is retained within the fibre because of its size, its aqueous insolubility and van der Waals' forces of attraction.

Colour range of sulphur dyes

Sulphur dyes have a colour range which is mainly limited to black, brown, blue and olive. Sulphur dyed textile materials are also dull. No satisfactory explanation can be offered for this.

Bronzing

Sulphur dyed textiles may show a metallic or bronze sheen which is referred to as **bronzing.** This effect is undesirable as it detracts from the aesthetic appeal of the dyed textile material, as well as giving rise to poor rub-fastness. This effect is usually present in heavy or dark shades and can be caused by excessively heavy dyeing, exposure of textile materials to the atmosphere during dyeing causing premature oxidation of the dye, failure to remove excess dye liquor following dyeing, or an insufficient amount of sodium sulphide in the dye liquor to keep the dye in its soluble form. The bronzing effect can be removed by an after-treatment in an aqueous solution of dilute sodium sulphide which will remove the excess dye molecules that are present on the surface of the textile material.

Cost of sulphur dyes

The relatively low cost of sulphur dyes has meant their continued use particularly for dark colours such as navy and black.

Vat dyes

The name **vat** was derived from the large wooden vessel from which vat dyes were first applied. Vat dyes provide textile materials with the best colour-fastness of all the dyes in common use.

The fibres most readily coloured with vat dyes are the natural and man-made cellulosic fibres.

Dyeing with vat dyes

The application of vat dyes to cellulosic materials occurs in five stages.

Aqueous dispersion

The insoluble vat dye is dispersed in water.

Vatting

This step involves the chemical reduction of the vat dye to produce the soluble, re-duced or **leuco** form of the dye. This is achieved by sodium hydrosulphite, sodium hydroxide and water. The sodium hydrosulphite chemically reduces the vat dye in the alkaline conditions created by the presence of sodium hydroxide. *Note*: The vatting stage also temporarily alters the original colour of the dye.

Absorption of dye molecules by the fibre

The vatted dye molecules are substantive to the cellulosic material when this is intro-duced into the dye liquor. To achieve adequate exhaustion, an electrolyte is added to the dye liquor and the temperature may be increased depending on the specific vat dye. The application of the dye molecule to the fibre occurs at temperatures specific to a particular vat dye and occurs in a range from 20° to 60°C. The addition of the electro-lyte alters the equilibrium of the dye liquor so as to increase the substantivity of the dye molecules for the fibre. During this stage of dye application the textile material must be kept immersed in the dye liquor to prevent premature oxidation of the leuco compound.

Re-oxidation of dye molecules within the fibre

Once within the polymer system of the fibre the leuco form of the vat dye has to be oxidised and converted to its original colour and the insoluble form of the dye. Oxida-tion of the leuco compound can be achieved by atmospheric oxygen although this is somewhat slow. In practice, a mild oxidising reagent such as sodium perborate is used to convert the soluble leuco compound into the original insoluble vat dye.

Soaping-off vat dyes

During the previous stage some insoluble vat dye may be deposited on the surface of the textile material. This has to be removed to prevent poor rub-fastness as well as a possible change of shade due to the subsequent removal of this surface deposit. Soap-ing-off, which is the boiling of the dyed material in a liquor containing some suitable detergent, removes this surface dye. The term soaping-off was derived from the fact that before the development of detergents, soap was used to remove the surface dye.

Printing with vat dyes

Printing of textile materials with dyes is achieved through the preparation of a paste with stabilised reduced vat dye. The fabric is printed with the design and dye fixation is obtained by steaming to achieve adequate penetration of the fibre polymer by the dye molecule. The textile material is then oxidised and soaped-off as in the case of dyeing.

Molecular configuration and characteristics

Vat dyes are based on indigo and anthraquinone (see Figs 6.14 and 6.15). The excellent fastness properties of textile materials coloured with vat dyes is attributed in part to the very large size of the vat dye molecule and in part to its aqueous insolubility. In general, vat dyes based on anthraquinone have better fastness properties than vat dyes derived from indigo.

Solubilised forms of vat dyes have been developed (see Fig. 6.16). *Note*: It is the leuco ester part of the dye molecule that is responsible for the aqueous solubility of vat dyes.

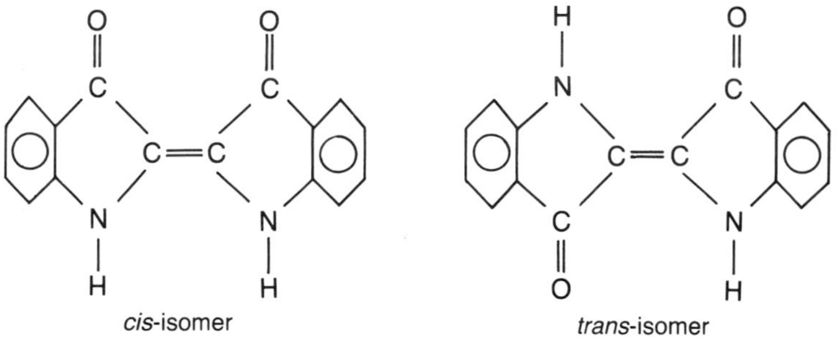

Figure 6.14   Indigo, C.I. Vat Blue 1, 7300 — an indigo type vat dye. The diagram shows the structural formulae of synthetic indigo dye. It always exists as these two isomers, but on dyeing only the co-planar trans-isomer is taken up by the fibre's polymer system. Indigo has a fair light-fastness, moderate wash-fastness, and poor fastness to bleaching.

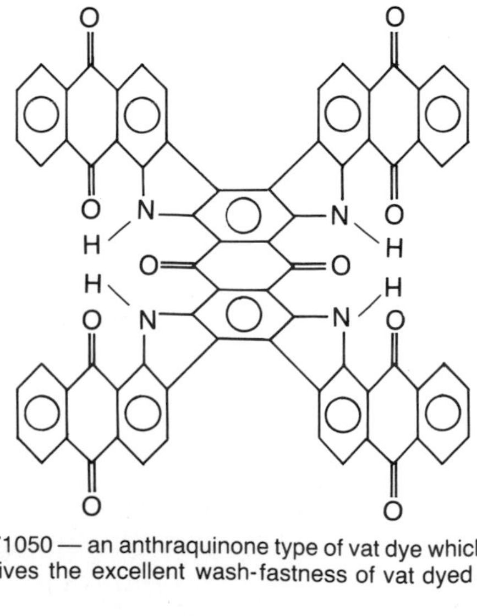

Figure 6.15   C.I. Vat Green 8, 71050 — an anthraquinone type of vat dye which illustrates the enormous size vat dye molecules can have and gives the excellent wash-fastness of vat dyed and printed textiles.

160

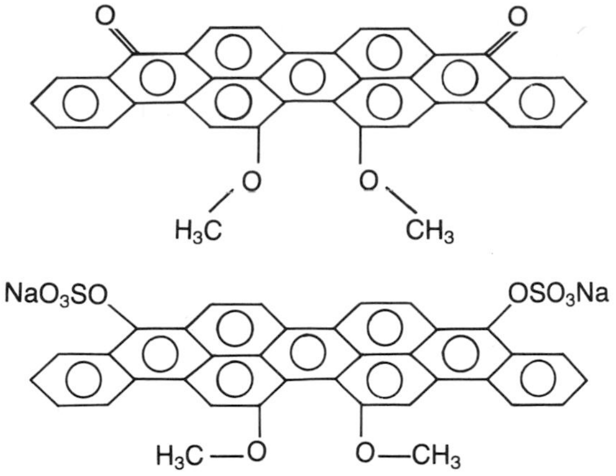

Figure 6.16 Solubilising vat dyes.
a A water insoluble anthroquinone type of vat dye — C.I. Vat Green 1, 59825. By reacting this dye to accept sodium sulphonate groups, it becomes water soluble.
b C.I. solubilised Vat Green 1, 59826. This is the leuco sulphuric ester of C.I. Vat Green 1, 59825; i.e. it is a water-solube vat dye.

Properties of vat dyes

Light-fastness

The light-fastness rating of vat dyes is about 7. The excellent light-fastness of textiles coloured with vat dyes is attributed to the stable electron arrangement in the chromophores of the vat dye molecule. The presence of the numerous benzene rings contributes to the stability of the vat dye molecule.

Wash-fastness

The wash-fastness rating of vat dyes is about 4–5. The excellent wash-fastness of textile materials coloured with vat dyes is attributed to the large vat dye molecule as well as its aqueous insolubility. The large vat dye molecule is trapped within the polymer system of the fibre because of its size and aqueous insolubility and is absorbed within the fibre polymer system by van der Waals' forces.

Cost of vat dyes

Vat dyes have always been very expensive compared with other dye classes and are invariably used when good fastness properties are required.

Solubilised vat dyes

As with sulphur dyes, a solubilised form of the vat dye has been developed. This has made vat dyes easier to handle and results in more level dyeings (see Fig. 6.16).

Fluorescent brighteners

Fluorescent brighteners, which are also known as optical brightening agents (OBAs), are colourless dyes. Fluorescence occurs when the ultraviolet component of sunlight is absorbed and subsequently reflected as additional blue light. When applied to textile materials, OBAs cause the textile material to reflect more blue light which is observed as a whiter, brighter textile material. OBAs are usually used for white textile materials making these appear whiter and brighter. These compounds are *not* bleaches and are only effective when ultraviolet radiation, such as sunlight, is present.

Fibres to which fluorescent brighteners may be applied

Fluorescent brighteners are available for most textile fibres. Domestic laundry detergents usually contain fluorescent brighteners but these are usually only suitable for cellulosic fibre textile materials.

Fluorescence

Molecules of fluorescent brighteners contain conjugated double bonds; that is, molecules which contain alternating single and double covalent bonds. The electrons in the conjugated systems are capable of absorbing the invisible ultraviolet radiation component of sunlight and reflecting this in the visible region of the solar spectrum. Thus, OBAs absorb electromagnetic radiation in the 300–400 nm range (the invisible ultraviolet radiation) and reflect this in the 400–500 nm range (visible blue light).

Application of fluorescent brighteners

OBAs have chemical structures which are similar to dyes and they can be classified in the same way as dyes; that is, according to their application. Details of their application can be obtained from the manufacturers of the compounds. For effective brightening, each type of textile fibre requires its own specific type of OBA.

Molecular configuration and characteristics

Over four-fifths of the commonly available fluorescent brighteners are derived from stilbene (see Fig. 6.17).

Molecules of fluorescent brighteners contain conjugated bonds such as —C = C—C = C—C = C— or —N = C—C = C—C = C—C—N = C—C—C— occurring in aromatic, heterocyclic or linear structures. It is the presence of these conjugated double bonds that enables ultraviolet light from sunlight to be absorbed and re-emitted as visible blue light. Figure 6.18 shows examples of fluorescent brighteners.

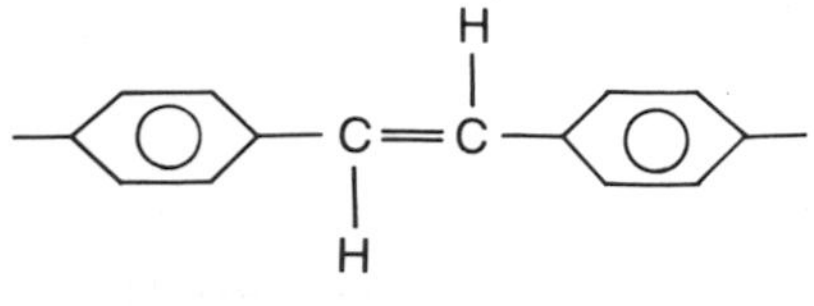

Figure 6.17 Stilbene, the organic radical upon which fluorescent brightening agents are based

162

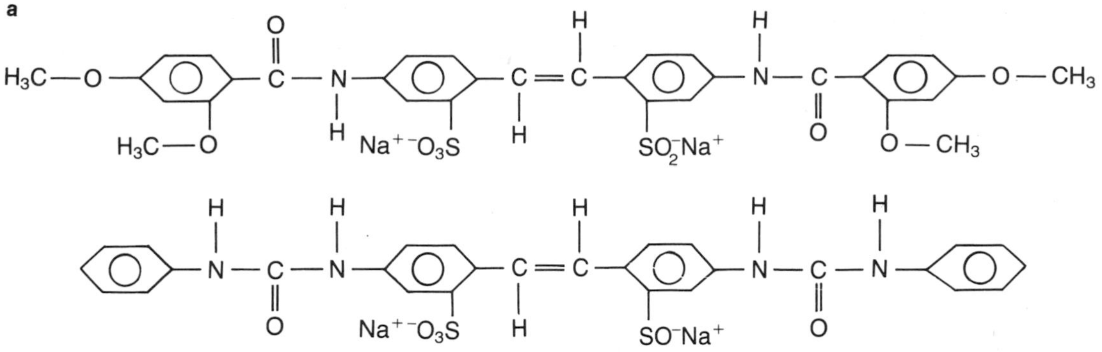

Figure 6.18 Fluorescent brighteners
a A pure blue fluorescent brightener — C.I. Fluorescent Brightener 34, 406055
b A violet fluorescent brightener of the Blankaphor type — C.I. Fluorescent Brightener 30, 40600

Properties of fluorescent brighteners

Whiteners and brighteners

To the trained observer, even bleached or white textile material has a slight yellow tinge. This small amount of yellow can give the impression of slight soiling and may detract from their aesthetic appeal. The presence of a slight amount of blue gives the impression that the textile material is whiter. Before the advent of OBAs, improved whiteness was obtained using a laundry blue, which is a blue pigment.

The development of OBAs has meant that this slight addition of blue can be obtained through the light reflected by the OBAs in the presence of ultraviolet radiation. This makes 'white' textile materials 'whiter' and 'brighter'. Coloured textile materials tend to appear brighter.

OBAs are present in most domestic detergents but these are usually only suitable for cellulosic textile materials.

Light-fastness

There is a large variation in the light-fastness rating of these compounds. When applied to cellulosic and protein fibres their light-fastness ranges from 1 to 2, and in some instances may reach 3. It should be pointed out that this poor light-fastness is not too important in the case of cellulosics, since any loss of the OBA's effect due to sunlight will be replaced in subsequent laundering with domestic detergents.

Fluorescent brighteners on nylon can reach a light-fastness rating of 4 with selected OBAs, a rating as high as 7 for polyesters, and in the case of acrylic fibres a light-fastness of about 4–5.

The poor overall light-fastness of fluorescent brighteners is due to their continuous absorption and emission of light which results in their chemical degradation.

Wash-fastness

The wash-fastness rating of fluorescent brighteners is about 3. The fair wash-fastness of fluorescent brighteners is due partly to their lack of substantivity for textile materials and their gradual degradation by exposure to sunlight. The fair wash-fastness may not be noticeable in cellulosics because of the presence of OBAs in domestic detergents. When fluorescent brighteners are used on other fibres they are applied in the manufacturing situation and brighteners are chosen which will last the expected life of the textile article.

Applying fluorescent brighteners to polyamides and wool

Both wool and nylon fibres yellow when exposed to sunlight over a period of time. Nylon fibres can be treated with selected OBAs to obtain a white which has reasonable fastness to both sunlight and washing. OBAs are not applied to wool. Not only do they have poor fastness properties on wool but they may accelerate the yellowing of wool on exposure to sunlight.

Solvent dyeing of textiles

In recent years, the use of water and its disposal in a non-polluting form has become more expensive. This has led to the development of alternative methods of applying colour to textile materials.

One such method is through the use of organic solvents. The use of organic solvents for the purposes of dyeing is still comparatively expensive, largely due to the cost of recovering the organic solvent which is re-used. The equipment used for this method of dyeing is expensive.

Solvent dyeing is still relatively untried and uneconomic when compared with conventional dyeing techniques. However, this does not preclude its possible use in the future.

7 The chemical finishing of textiles

The chemical finishing of textiles refers to the application of specific compounds in order to improve the physical and/or chemical properties of the textile material.

Handle

Textile materials are subjected to many processes during the transformation of fibre to fabric and during the manufacture of the final product be it garment, upholstery or whatever. During the many stages fibres undergo, they may be damaged and in some cases natural fats may be removed from the fibres resulting in a harsh and undesirable handle. The restoration of a satisfactory handle can be achieved through the addition of suitable chemical compounds.

In the case of cotton and wool oils, waxes and similar substances have frequently been added to achieve a soft handle. Anionic compounds such as sulphated oils and sulphated alcohols have also been used to soften the handle of cotton fabrics. Cationic compounds may be applied to most fibres to soften the handle of their textile materials. Included in this category of compounds are the fatty acids and polyethylene polyamine reaction products and fatty quaternary ammonium compounds (see Table 7.1).

In addition to the compounds referred to above, non-ionic reagents such as condensates of fatty materials with ethylene or propylene oxide have been used to modify and improve the handle of textile articles. These compounds form a fatty film on the fibre surface. This fatty film makes the fibre smoother and more slippery, providing the sensation of greater softness. Thus, when the textile material is handled and/or compressed, its fibres will readily slide past each other, providing a sensation of softness.

In the same way as compounds are applied to textile materials to achieve a softer handle, a compound can be applied to obtain a stiffer, crisper handle as is done, for example, to cotton shirting fabric. Starch was once used domestically, but this has now been largely replaced by spray-on silicon resins, such as Fabulon, which are applied just before ironing.

More durable results can be obtained by impregnating the textile material with a chemical such as alkali soluble ethyl cellulose. The application of these chemicals is usually restricted to cellulosic materials such as cotton and viscose.

Easy-care finishes

Cellulosic textile materials crease readily. To overcome this a number of easy-care finishes have been developed. The first successful one consisted of impregnating the fabric with a urea-formaldehyde condensate. This condensate, when dried and cured with heat, forms a resin. The crease resistance of the fabric improved markedly. The process was developed further and has been applied to other cellulosic materials. (See Fig. 7.1.)

Over the years many resins have been applied to cellulosic materials in an attempt to improve effectiveness of the easy-care finish. The resins which can be used, however, must possess certain characteristics. The resins must be capable of penetrating the fibre, of forming colourless products, and they must be unaffected by the normal conditions to which the textile material may be subjected during manufacture and in the home; for example, pressing, dry cleaning, laundering and bleaching. (*Note*: Some of the resins are affected by hypochlorite bleaching, which causes resin finished fabrics to assume a yellow to tan colouration.)

Urea-formaldehyde resins are rarely used today as there are other resins which are more effective; for example, melamine-formaldehyde. (See Fig. 7.2.)

The wrinkle resistance imparted to cellulosic textile materials is due to the resin

Table 7.1 Examples of chemical softening agents.

Type and general formula	Example
Fatty sulphated alcohol $R-CH_2O-SO_3Na$	Octadecyl sodium sulphate $C_{17}H_{35}-CH_2O-SO_3Na$
Fatty quaternary ammonium compounds $\left[\begin{array}{c} R^1 \\ \mid \\ R-N-R^2 \\ \mid \\ R^3 \end{array}\right]^+ X^-$ where R = high molecular weight alkyl radical R^1, R^2 and R^3 = low molecular weight alkyl radicals X = chloride or bromide ion	Hexadecyl or cetyl trimethyl ammonium bromide $\left[\begin{array}{c} CH_3 \\ \mid \\ C_{16}H_{33}-N^+-CH_3 \\ \mid \\ CH_3 \end{array}\right]^+ Br^-$
Fatty acid polyethylene polyamine $R-CO-NH-[-C_2H_4-NH-]_nH$ where n = usually 2 or 3	Stearamide triethylene amine $C_{17}H_{35}-CO-NH-[-C_2H_4-NH-]_3H$
Non-ionic fatty alcohol ethylene oxide condensate $R-CH_2O-[-CH_2CH_2-O-]_nH$ where n = usually 2 or 3	Octadecyl trioxyethylene $C_{17}H_{35}-CH_2O-[-CH_2CH_2-O]_3H$

Note: there are many more types of chemical softening agents than the ones given here.

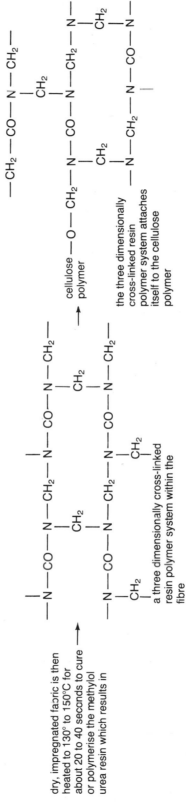

Figure 7.1 The general steps involved in applying urea-formaldehyde resin to achieve a crease-resistant or easy-care finish on cellulosic fibred textile materials. The polymerisation of other easy-care resins, such as melamine-formaldehyde, dihydroxydimethylolethylene-urea (DMDHEU), etc. tends to follow along similar lines. Their chemical formulae, however, lend themselves less readily to representation in this illustrative manner.

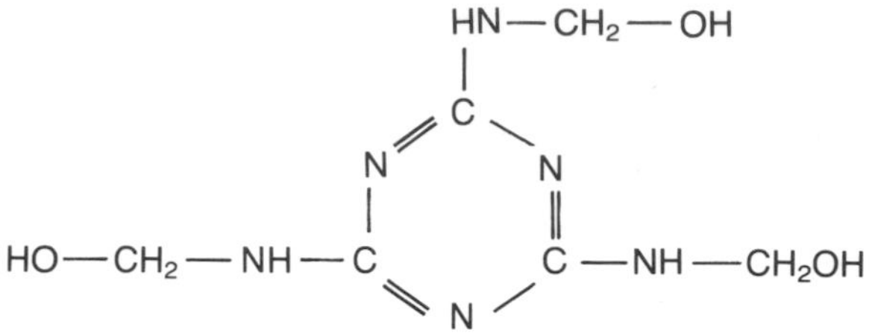

Figure 7.2 Formula of the melamine formaldehyde monomer

entering and enveloping the fibres. The three dimensionally cross-linked polymer system of the resin stiffens the fibres. Being stiffer, the fibre will resist being bent; that is, wrinkled. However, excessive crushing of the resin-treated textile material will result in the breakdown of the resin, and the textile material will tend to wrinkle more readily.

The application of resins to all cotton textile materials is invariably accompanied by a loss in strength and a stiffer handle. The experienced finisher endeavours to counteract this with the addition of other chemicals to improve the handle of the cotton textile material.

The development of easy-care resin finishes, in recent years, has not overcome the loss of strength and abrasion resistance which occurs when they are applied to cotton textile materials. On the other hand, easy-care resin finishes are also applied to polyester/cellulosic blends. The overall performance of the blend is significantly improved by such resin treatment, even though the polyester already has excellent easy-care properties and is not affected by the treatment.

Flame-proofed fabrics

Most textile materials burn readily and rapidly. Whilst wool textile materials tend not to support combustion once the flame is removed, cellulosic textile materials will burn readily once they are ignited. The great danger with cellulosic fibres is afterglow, which may remain if the flame has been incompletely extinguished. Afterglow may often re-ignite a flame in the textile material. Synthetic fibres may melt rather than burn. Acrylics will burn readily. Hot molten thermoplastic fibre will cause severe burns and intense shock to the victim wearing clothes composed of such fibres.

The high flammability of cellulosic fibres, particularly when in the form of loose-fitting garments such as nightdresses, has resulted in research to reduce their ease of ignition and flame propagation. The research has concentrated on preventing the occurrence of afterglow. When any of the cellulose fibres burn, they produce water, carbon-containing char, a tarry substance, and non-flammable vapour as combustion products. If the char is still very hot, even when the fibre has been extinguished, the cellulosic material may re-ignite.

Although many compounds have been developed over the years to minimise the flammability of textile materials, and in particular cotton, the only ones which have achieved commercial success are those based on:

1 THPC—tetrakis-hydroxymethyl-phosphoniumchloride; for example, Proban; and

2 Pyrovatex CP—a phosphonoalkylamide.

Flame-proofing of cellulosic materials can be achieved by the application of certain chemicals. Suggested reasons of the effectiveness of flame-proofing treatments are as follows:

a These chemicals alter the course of decomposition of the cellulose fibres on burning. Less flammable tars and a reduced volume of flammable gases are produced and the amount of non-volatile, non-flammable carbonaceous material produced is increased.

b These chemicals may, on heating, yield inert gases. As these inert gases are non-flammable, they will act as flame retardants by reducing the concentration of atmospheric oxygen around the flame, thus limiting propagation of the flame.

c The heat generated by the burning textile material may be dissipated by endothermic changes in the chemical applied to impart flame resistance. In so doing, these chemicals will conduct the heat away from the fibre. In other words, the chemical can absorb considerable amounts of heat energy without causing its temperature, or that of its surroundings, to rise. The withdrawal of heat limits the propagation of the flame.

There are still problems related to the use of flame-resistant finishes for cellulosic materials. These are:

1 a harshening of fabric handle;

2 a breakdown of the flame-resistant finish by laundering and dry cleaning.

These disadvantages may in part be overcome by the use of specially manufactured, fire-retardant, man-made fibres. The addition of organo-phosphorous compounds to the spinning solution of acrylics, acetates, polynosics, polyesters, polypropylenes and viscose will make them fire retardant. However, a reduction in fibre tenacity, and hence durability, tends to occur more or less in direct proportion to the percentage of organo-phosphorous compound added. This treatment is not applied to nylon.

The presence of chlorine in fibres also acts as a fire retardant, as explained on page 96. Unfortunately, the relatively low softening point of chlorine-containing fibres, which causes them to wrinkle and distort badly, precludes their general use.

The industrial nylon, Nomex, is fire retardant owing to the aromatic groups in its polymer structure and the highly crystalline arrangement of its polymer system.

Finishes impervious to water

Textile fabrics treated with finishes impervious to water fall into two categories: waterproof and water-repellent.

Waterproof finishes

The fabric is coated with a synthetic resin or 'plastic', rubber, wax, fat or oil to prevent any water penetration of the fabric. Such a chemical coating limits the air permeability of the fabric, and adversely affects its comfort.

Water-repellent finishes

The fibres in the fabric become covered with a film of synthetic resin. This repels and delays absorption and penetration of water through the fabric. These finishes allow air to permeate the fabric, and its comfort is largely retained in contrast with the water-proof finishes.

Most of the original waterproof finishes, produced by the application of rubber, waxes and oxidised oils, have been replaced by applying impervious films of polyvinyl chloride—PVC plastic. The low cost of this type of application, associated with the very light weight of the waterproof fabric produced, compensates for the lack of comfort in the garments produced.

Cotton canvas and tarpaulins are usually waterproofed by impregnation with a cuprammonium solution. This causes a slight and partial surface dissolution of the fibres which on drying re-solidifies and at the same time fuses adjacent fibres. The result is a fabric that is nearly impervious to water. Fabrics proofed in this manner are mainly used for covers, tenting and the like where handle and comfort are not important.

If fabrics for clothing are to be comfortable, the finishes must allow air to circulate. These finishes are thus water-resistant rather than waterproof. Various water-resistant finishes have been developed over the years with the first commercially successful product being Velan PF.

Velan PF is a stearamido methyl pyridinium chloride (see Fig. 7.3). Velan PF is applied from a buffered aqueous solution, cured at 125–150°C and rinsed and dried. It is thought that Velan PF is decomposed to methylol stearamide which reacts with the cellulosic material and results in a water-repellent finish (see Fig. 7.3). As each fibre will now be covered with a film of methylol stearamide, a fatty hydrophobic compound, the textile material will be water-resistant. The fatty nature of this water-resistant finish also softens the handle of the textile material to which it has been applied.

The success of this process has led to the development of methylol stearamide as a water-repellent substance, rather than Velan PF. Methylol stearamide is more economical but does not provide as durable a finish as Velan PF. The use of methylol stearamide with partially formed urea–formaldehyde provides excellent water-repellent finishes with adequate fastness properties.

Fabrics can also be made water-repellent with thermo-setting silicone resins. Their application involves the impregnation of the fabric with an aqueous dispersion of partially polymerised monomethyl and dimethyl siloxanes. On curing, the methyl siloxanes polymerise and combine with the cellulose polymers (see Fig. 7.4).

The silicone resin polymers combine most readily with the –OH groups found in cellulose polymers. They are therefore most successfully applied to cellulosic fabrics, reasonably successful on synthetic fabrics, and least successful on wool fabrics.

The silicone resins are hydrophobic because they are 'fatty': they are nearly as 'fatty' as the hydrocarbons, alkanes, or an alkyl radical such as the stearyl radical.

A common use of silicone resins is for fabric stiffening. Fabulon, for example, contains silicone resins. Under the heat of the domestic electric iron, the silicone resins in Fabulon will readily polymerise. The rigidity of the three dimensionally cross-linked,

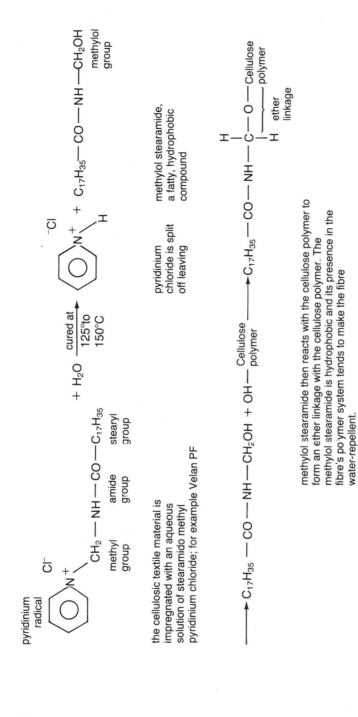

Figure 7.3 Steps in the process of making celulosic textile materials water repellent, using a quaternary ammonium compound. *Note:* The relatively common use of the stearyl radical (i.e. $C_{17}H_{35}$) in water-repellent compounds, chemical softening agents, etc., is due to its ready availability from tallow or animal fat. It is derived from stearic acid, the major constituent of tallow or animal fat.

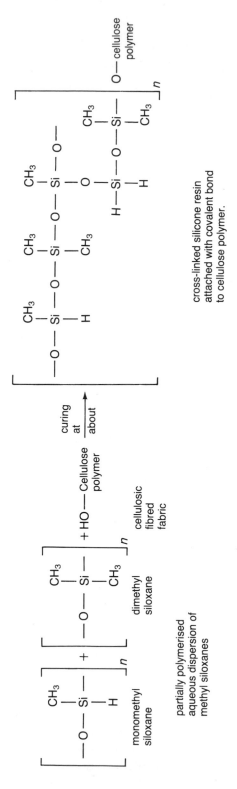

Figure 7.4   Steps in the process of making cellulosic textile materials water repellent by using a silicone resin

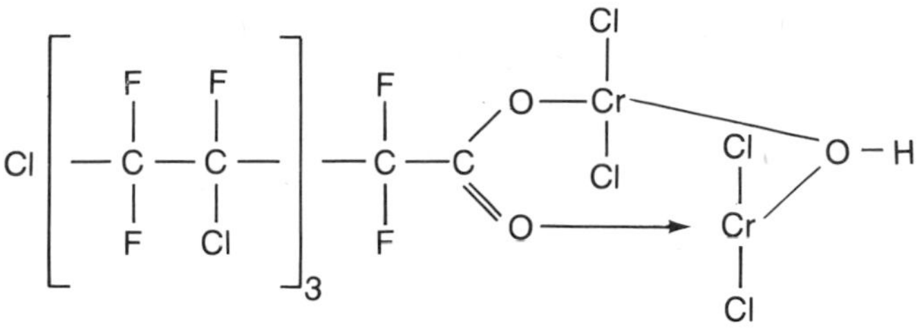

a perfluoro-carbon fatty compound
containing also chlorine and
based upon chromium.

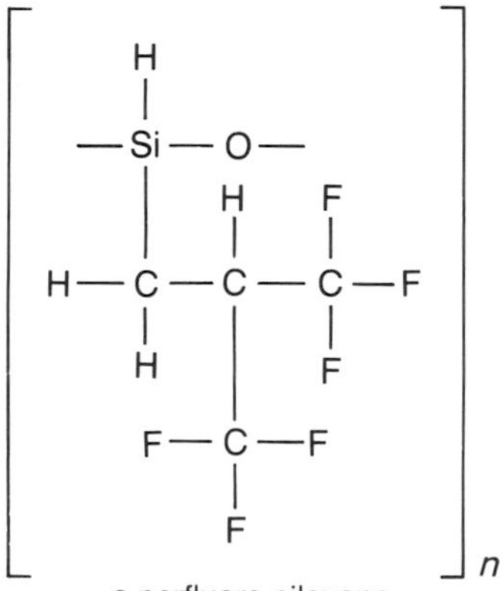

a perfluoro-siloxane
fatty polymer

Figure 7.5 Examples of the finishing compounds used to make textile materials soil and water repellent.
Note: The fluorine and chlorine atoms, being polar, repel the greasy soil molecules, while the fatty carbon chains
(—C—C—C) or fatty siloxane chains (—Si—O—) repel the water molecules.

silicon resin film produced on the fibre's surface imparts a pleasant crisp handle to the ironed article.

Water-repellent finishes can also be obtained by the application of perfluoro fatty compounds; that is, fatty compounds whose molecules contain two or more fluorine atoms. These fatty compounds not only repel water, but the fluorine, and sometimes the chlorine, atoms of their molecules tend to repel greasy soil. This occurs because the strongly ionic nature of the fluorine atoms repels the non-ionic greasy soil molecules. Such water-soil-repellent finishes (for example, Scotchgard) are most successfully applied to cellulosic fabrics because their molecules react most readily with cellulose polymers. (See Fig 7.5.)

Anti-static finishes

The development of anti-static finishes was found necessary with the introduction of synthetic fibres. Because of the hydrophobic nature of synthetic fibres they are likely to develop static electricity. The development of static electricity can be minimised by applying anti-static compounds, such as quarternary ammonium salts, or other hygroscopic compounds. These types of compounds, being ionic or polar, will attract water

173

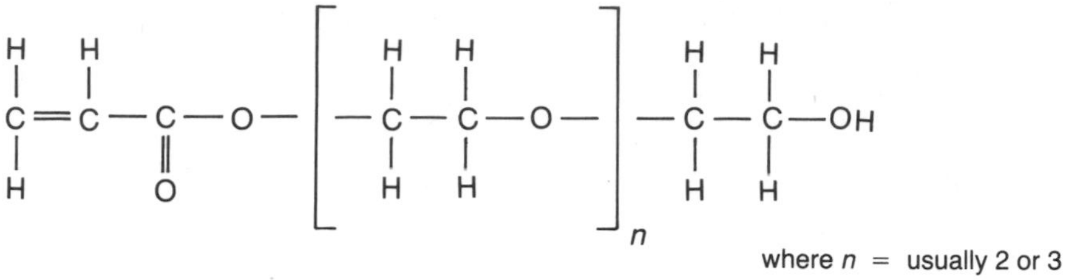

Figure 7.6 An anti-static agent, polyethylene glycol acrylate. As its —OH group is polar, it will attract water molecules.

molecules, minimising or dissipating any static charge which might develop. (See Fig. 7.6.)

Finishes to prevent attack by insects and micro-organisms

Natural and viscose fibres, unlike acetate and synthetic fibres, are prone to be eaten or otherwise detrimentally affected by various insects and micro-organisms.

Wool is the main dietary constituent of sundry species of clothes moth larvae and carpet beetles. Chlorinated hydrocarbon compounds, such as Mitin FF, Eulan U33, and Dieldrin are easily applied to make the wool fibres unpalatable and poisonous to these insects (see Fig. 7.7).

The amount of chlorinated hydrocarbon applied varies from 0.05 per cent for Dieldrin to 1.5 per cent for Eulan U33. The percentages are based upon the mass of wool textile material treated, to provide effective protection for the wool, but to be harmless to the wearer. The chemical stability of these agents is responsible for the durability and effectiveness of their mothproofing finishes; but it is also their chemical stability which tends to make them **non-biodegradable**. This explains their decreasing usage and increasing replacement by such biodegradable, synthetic pyrethroids as **permethrin**. This is the common or generic name for biodegradable, synthetic chlorinated

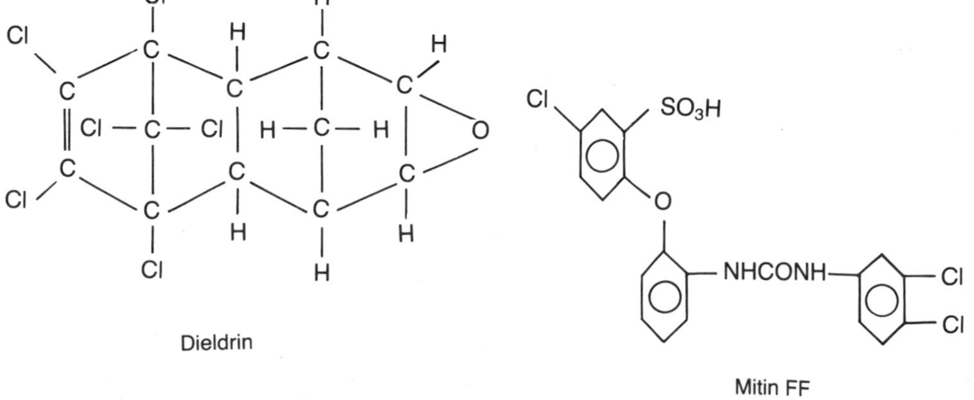

Figure 7.7 Two examples of non-biodegradable, chlorinated hydrocarbons used for mothproofing wool textiles

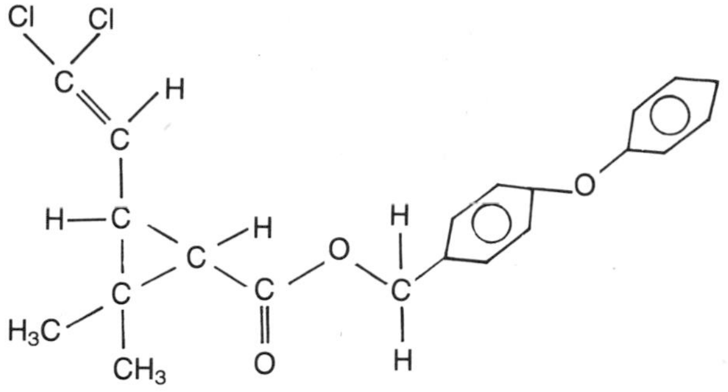

Figure 7.8 Permethrin — an example of a biodegradable, chlorinated hydrocarbon mothproofing agent for wool textiles

hydrocarbon compounds similar to pyrethrin. Pyrethrin is the common, natural, biodegradable, insecticidal component of most fly-sprays; but because pyrethrin is unstable or readily breaks down in the presence of sunlight, it can only be used as a *temporary* mothproofing agent. Permethrin, however, is stable in sunlight and thus provides a durable, effective mothproofing finish. It is applied in amounts varying from 0.1 to 0.2 per cent according to the mass of wool textile to be treated. (See also Fig. 7.8.)

Industrial cotton textile materials may have to be mildew-proofed and/or rot-proofed. Mildew-proofing is to protect the cotton textile against fungi or vegetable micro-organismic growth on the fibres. Rot-proofing protects the cotton against the much more destructive micro-organisms found in soil and decaying vegetable matter. Micro-organisms also create very acidic conditions which are most detrimental to cotton. Cotton textiles can be protected against the detrimental effects of micro-organisms by the following means:

1 applying antiseptic agents, such as salicylanilide, cupric sulphate or bluestone, or cationic agents as shown in Fig. 7.9; these agents give only temporary protection against rot and mildew and need to be regularly reapplied to maintain adequate protection;

2 chemically modifying the cellulose polymers in the cotton fibres. This can be done by reacting them with acrylonitrile, which is vinyl cyanide (see Table 1.1) and which makes the cellulose polymer poisonous to any micro-organism.

Note: Rot- and mildew-proof finishes are not normally applied to cotton textiles intended for apparel use.

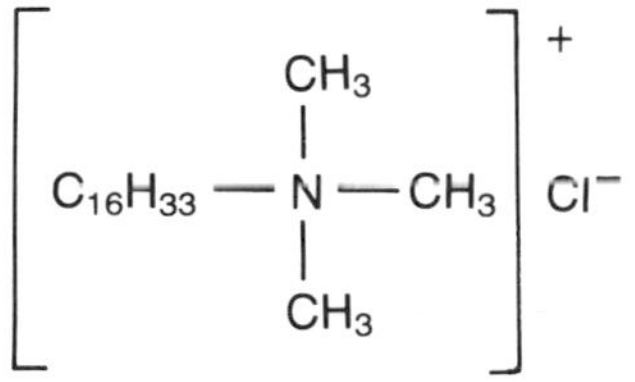

Figure 7.9 Cetyl trimethyl ammonium chloride, a cationic agent used for mildew- and rot-proofing industrial cotton textiles

175

Anti-shrink treatments for wool

Shrink-resistant wool textile materials can be obtained by:

1   modifying the wool fibre surface by partial dissolution of the epithelial cells (scales), and/or
2   coating the wool fibre with a film of resin to mask the epithelial cells.

Both treatments have the same effect; namely, the reduction of the directional friction effect (DFE) caused by the scales and responsible for the felting of wool fibres. In reducing the DFE, fibre migration in a rootward direction is minimised when agitation of the wool textile material occurs, as during normal laundering (see pages 70–72).

Shrink resistance achieved by controlled surface dissolution of the scales is usually carried out with chlorine-containing compounds in an aqueous or gaseous medium, under acid or alkaline conditions. The two methods are called **wet** or **dry chlorination** respectively. Wool textile materials can also be made shrink resistant by applying to them such resins as polyacrylic, polyurethane or polyamide-epichlorhydrin. Knitted wool garments sold under the registered trademark of Superwash Wool have been treated with one of these resins and are therefore machine washable. This shrink-resist treatment used to produce Superwash Wool is very effective because the fibres first undergo wet chlorination; that is, they are treated with a chlorine solution which partially dissolves the epithelial cells. Only then is the polyamide epichlorhydrin resin applied; the cross-linked polymers of the resin attach themselves with covalent bonds to the amine and sulphide groups in the wool polymers on the surface of the fibre.

8 Colour

The importance of colour in textiles and clothing cannot be underestimated. Historically, textile and clothing fashion, as well as lifestyles, can be identified by a colour attributable to a particular period of time. The late 1960s and the 1970s will probably be remembered for the faded blue denim look of jeans and other denim garments.

The study of colour would be incomplete without first studying light.

Light

In order for a dyed or printed material to be seen, light must be reflected from the object and be received by the eye. Light is a form of energy, more specifically radiant energy, and it forms part of the electromagnetic radiation spectrum which is comprised of all radiant energy as shown in Fig. 8.1.

Light travels in waves, which are not coloured or visible. The focusing of light waves on the retina, which is the inner lining of the eye, creates impulses which are transmitted via the optic nerve to the brain. The sensation created by these impulses is perceived as colour.

Light is produced by many sources; these include the sun, electric globes, as well as various flammable substances such as gas, kerosene, candles and so on.

Sunlight is generally accepted as white light, but for standardisation purposes indirect sunlight is used. In the southern hemisphere this is light from the southern sky or south skylight, whilst in the northern hemisphere this is light from the northern sky or north skylight.

The influence of weather and limited sunlight hours mean that the sun is not a suitable source of light if one wants to make comparisons under reliable and standardised conditions. In order to carry out colour comparisons regularly and under standard conditions, a colour matching booth can be used. The artificial light in the matching booth is based upon Xenon and Tungsten lamps which simulate daylight.

Common lighting conditions

Direct sunlight

Direct sunlight has a slight yellow hue, and is not considered a completely suitable source of white light. The light is very intense, and creates extremes in contrasts which tire the eyes rather quickly.

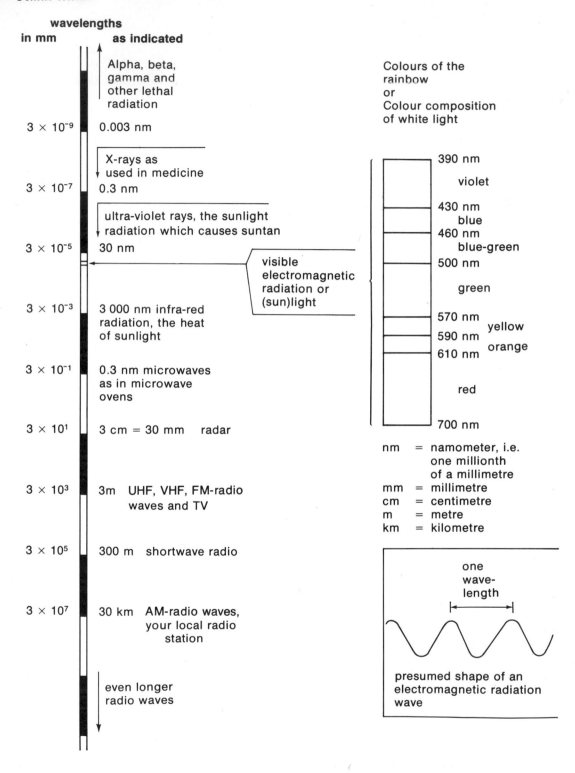

Figure 8.1   The electromagnetic radiation spectrum

Indirect sunlight

This light has a slight blue hue, making the light appear whiter, and is more suitable than direct sunlight. The light is more diffuse and hence is less tiring to the eyes.

Colour-matching booth light

A colour-matching booth provides light which simulates various other types of light, including direct sunlight, indirect sunlight and fluorescent light. This provides a consistent light source and has the least tiring effect on the eyes.

Composition of sunlight

Sunlight is radiant energy reaching the earth from the sun by means of light waves. Sunlight is seen because the radiant energy or electromagnetic radiation of sunlight causes a photochemical reaction in the retina of the eye, which is perceived by the brain as light and colour. Sunlight provides warmth, and this is attributed to the infrared waves of the solar spectrum. It is the ultraviolet component of sunlight which burns skin.

At times if you look at sunlight from a specific angle or in a particular direction, you will see a rainbow. This is because the sunlight is shining on falling raindrops and it is refracted, or scattered, to produce a spectrum consisting of seven distinct colours—the colours of the rainbow: *violet, blue, blue-green, green, yellow, orange* and *red*. These seven visible colours, as well as the invisible infrared waves and ultraviolet waves, are important for their effect on textiles.

Ultraviolet light

The ultraviolet (UV) component of the solar spectrum is essentially invisible, and it has a shorter wavelength than violet light (ultraviolet means *beyond* violet; See Table 8.1). An alternative name is *black light*. Ultraviolet light causes certain substances to fluoresce, and it is this effect which is utilised to make optical brightening agents. These are chemicals which, when applied to textiles and subjected to the ultraviolet

Table 8.1 The solar spectrum.

Colour	Wavelength in nanometres (nm)[1]
Ultraviolet	30 to 390
Violet	390 to 430
Blue	430 to 460
Blue-green	460 to 500
Green	500 to 570
Yellow	570 to 590
Orange	590 to 610
Red	610 to 700
Infrared	700 to 3 000

[1] 1 nm = one millionth of a millimetre.

component of sunlight, absorb the ultraviolet light and convert it to light in the blue region of the solar spectrum. This reflected blue light makes white textiles look whiter.

The detrimental effects on the polymer system of a fibre and on dye molecules during prolonged exposure to sunlight may be mainly attributed to ultraviolet light waves. This is borne out by the fact that fibres and dyes have a better resistance to the effects of sunlight if they are exposed to it behind glass; glass filters out or absorbs most of the incident ultraviolet waves from sunlight.

Infrared radiation

The term *infra* means below or further on. In other words, the infrared waves are at the 'red' end of the visible light spectrum (see Fig. 8.1 and Table 8.1). Although essentially invisible, infrared waves extend the heat energy radiated by the visible light band. In fact, a significant portion of the heat experienced during exposure to sunlight is due to the invisible infrared radiation. Infrared waves, like ultraviolet, also penetrate clouds. Thus, even on overcast days, outdoor exposure of textiles subjects them to the effects of ultraviolet light assisted by the heat energy provided by infrared radiation.

What is colour?

Colour is a sensation which occurs when light enters the eyes. Light waves enter the eye and are focused on the retina by the lens of the eye. A photochemical reaction occurs which results in impulses that are transmitted along the optic nerve to the brain. The colour which is observed, perceived or experienced by the brain is dependent on the particular wavelength or combination of wavelengths of the light source.

If a textile material is examined in white light the material has a particular colour. This colour occurs because the textile material will absorb all the light falling upon it, and reflect only the wavelengths of its colour. Thus, a white fabric appears white in white light because it reflects all the light waves. However, a green fabric appears green in white light because the dye on the fabric absorbs most of the light and reflects only light with wavelengths which appear green to the eye. There are different greens because the reflected light is composed of different wavelengths which depend on the type of dye, amount of dye and structure of the textile material.

The green fabric when viewed under green light will appear green because most of the incident green light is reflected. On the other hand, if the green fabric is viewed under any light source other than white or green the fabric will appear black. This occurs because the green fabric will absorb nearly all the light that is incident on it and since the light is not white or green, very little light will be reflected and the fabric will be seen as black. Any coloured fabric which is viewed under light which is *not* white or the particular colour of the fabric will also appear black.

Specifying colour

There are three terms which are used to describe and specify colour.

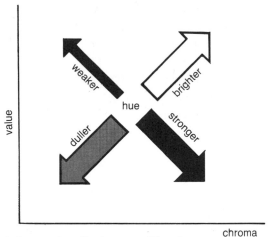

Figure 8.2   The relationship between a hue, its chroma and its value

1   **Hue** is the common name of the colour; for example, pink, mauve, scarlet, beige, tan.

2   **Value** is the term used to describe lightness, darkness, tone or shade of the hues. A colour is termed light in value when it approaches white and dark in value when it has a deep colour or approaches black.

3   **Chroma** is the term used to describe depth of colour; that is, the dullness, brightness, saturation, intensity, vividness or purity of the colour. A bright, intense colour is said to have much chroma whereas a dull colour is said to have little chroma. (*Note*: Chroma is from the Greek for colour.)

Figure 8.2 illustrates the relationship between a hue and its value and chroma. These terms and Fig. 8.2 will be easier to understand if you can examine the colour cards available from most paint manufacturers. The pastel colours of the brilliant gloss paints will be placed toward the top-right of Fig. 8.2 as they are very bright, light colours. The dark colours of the brilliant gloss paints will be placed in the lower right-hand corner of Fig. 8.2 as these are very bright, strong colours.

The pastel colours of the flat plastic paints would be placed toward the top left corner of the figure as these colours are dull and tend toward white. The darker colours of the flat plastic paints will be placed in the lower left hand corner as these colours are strong but dull.

Perception of colour

The perception of light and colour is part of one of the five human senses and occurs when light focuses on the retina and initiates a photo-chemical reaction in the retina. This reaction results in the sensation of colour.

The retina has two distinct types of nerve cells which are called cones and rods (see Fig. 8.3).

Cones are nerve cells which convey the sensation of colour to the brain. Cones are

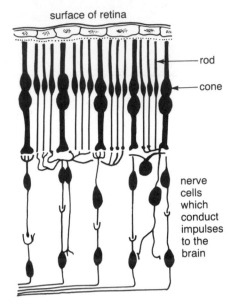

surface of retina

rod

cone

nerve
cells
which
conduct
impulses
to the
brain

Figure 8.3 A section through the retina

affected by or respond to bright daylight or strong artificial light. Cones are not sensitive to low illumination. Cones occur in the greatest concentration in the centre of the retina. This is the area of the retina upon which most light falls.

Rods are nerve cells which become more prolific as the retina curves forward towards the lens of the eye. Rods come into play during the evening when there is low illumination or little light and therefore insufficient energy to stimulate the cones. Rods are responsible for night vision, where little colour is perceived but where differences in greys and blacks are important, as occurs between dusk and dawn.

Cones are the nerve cells responsible for vision during the day or in artificial light when colours are perceived according to their hue, value and chroma. Rods enable vision at dusk or at night and enable differentiation between greys and blacks.

The theory of colour vision

There is no theory of colour vision which has been universally accepted. However, the Young–Helmholtz theory of colour vision is probably the most accepted theory.*

This theory proposed that the many cones in the retina are of three different types. This has now been physiologically confirmed and the three types are:

1 cones that respond largely to the wavelengths responsible for the red colour sensation in the brain;

2 cones that respond largely to the wavelengths responsible for the green colour sensation in the brain;

*See also 'Development of the CIE system', page 195.

3 cones that respond largely to the wavelengths responsible for the blue colour sensation in the brain.

The three types of cones are thought to analyse the light entering the eye and, depending on the composition of the incident light, initiate certain photo-chemical reactions within the cones. These photochemical reactions alter the electrical field within the cones and send new electrical impulses via the optic nerve to the brain where they are perceived as colour.

Under normal circumstances, the photochemically sensitive substance in the cones, which is a vitamin A aldehyde, responds in milliseconds to changes in the incident light. The sensitivity of this substance enables changes in light to be observed even with slight changes in the composition of incident light.

The more intense the light, the more intense and longer the photochemical reaction. The intensity of the photochemical reaction may cause the eye to continue to see light or colour for a brief period even after the eye is no longer exposed to the incident light.

The subjective nature of colour vision

Instruments such as the spectrophotometer, developed to measure colour, have shown that each colour is composed of specific wavelengths. The eye, however, is unable to view colours consistently. The inability of the eye to view colour consistently means that colour vision is subjective and the differences seen by the eye at different times may be due to all or some of the following factors:

Tiredness of the eyes

This occurs when the eyes are made to concentrate too long on one or a combination of coloured objects. One of the following may result.

Positive after-image

Prolonged exposure to a coloured object may result in the colours being seen for a few seconds even after the object has been removed from view. This effect is called positive after-image. The effect is due to excessive stimulation of the photo-chemical substance. The excessive stimulation temporarily prevents the photo-chemical substance from regeneration making the retina momentarily insensitive to light.

Successive contrast

This occurs when, having concentrated upon a coloured object, the eyes are turned away and see the complementary colour(s) of the colour(s) just viewed. Successive contrast is the commonest type of after-vision. There is no simple explanation for this phenomenon.

Simultaneous contrast

Sometimes an object being observed appears to be surrounded by a halo, or tinged with its complementary colours. This effect is called simultaneous contrast.

It is important to rest one's eyes regularly when making colour comparisons to prevent any of the effects described above.

Emotional state of the observer

The emotional state or past experiences involving colours can cause an observer to perceive colours differently.

Type of illumination

Different sources of illumination will greatly influence the colours perceived by people.

Poor illumination

Provides inadequate light energy to stimulate the cones to perceive the actual colour of the material being observed. With poor illumination, only the rods of the retina may be stimulated and the colours observed will be restricted to shades of grey, black and faint green.

Direct sunlight

Is characterised by a slightly yellow white light (see Fig. 8.4). This source of light tends to impart a slight yellow tinge to all colours. The observer tends to ignore the slight yellow tinge of direct sunlight and white paper appears white to the eye despite the yellow component of direct sunlight.

Indirect sunlight

This is also referred to as southlight or northlight, and is a blue-white light. (See Fig. 8.5.) This light tends to impart a slight blue tinge to all hues. The observer tends to discount the slight blueing effect of indirect sunlight.

Note: As a general rule blue-white is considered a whiter white than a yellow-white. Yellow-white materials give the impression of being somewhat soiled. The practice of 'blueing' white laundry is still quite common, although this is more frequently and more effectively carried out using optical brighteners which are found in most domestic laundry detergents.

Incandescent light

This lacks blue light waves (see Fig. 8.6). It has a distinctly yellow-red appearance and has a similar effect on colours to direct sunlight.

Fluorescent light

This light lacks yellow light waves (see Fig. 8.7). It has a distinct blue-white appearance, particularly when compared with incandescent light. The blueness of this light brightens any colours exposed to it.

Intensity of illumination

The retina of the eye needs time to adapt to varying levels of illumination. It takes time for the eye to adjust when one goes from a brightly lit area to one with little light and vice versa.

Contrast

Perception of colours can be influenced by the background against which the coloured object is viewed. A yellow textile material when viewed against a grey background will

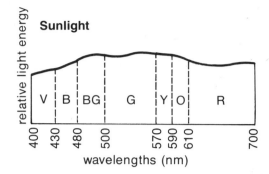

Figure 8.4 In any source of light each wavelength has a certain amount of light energy. With sunlight this energy is similar for each wavelength. However, the colours yellow, orange and red represent over 40 per cent of the sun's colour spectrum. The white colour of sunlight, therefore, has a very slight yellow-red hue.

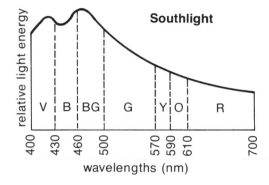

Figure 8.5 Southlight (i.e. light reflected from the southern sky during daylight hours) contains an excess of blue light energy, because the molecules of the air scatter the blue light waves more than waves of the other colours.

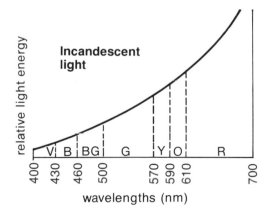

Figure 8.6 An electric light bulb emits incandescent light. This contains an excess of yellow and red light energy. Thus incandescent light is yellowish, although the eyes still perceive it as white light, until it is compared with fluorescent light.

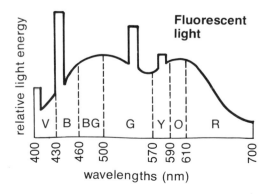

Figure 8.7 Fluorescent light. This contains an excess of blue and green light energy and a deficiency of red. Fluorescent light thus has a distinct blue colour, although the eyes will perceive it as white light.

result in the yellow hue having more value and chroma; that is, it will appear brighter than if it were viewed against a yellow background.

Age of the observer

The natural ageing process of the human body will reduce one's ability to respond to various stimuli. Ageing yellows the lens of the eye and increases the yellow pigment in the central region of the retina. This results in older people seeing more yellow in colours, a fact which is often not accepted.

Defective colour vision

Approximately 8 per cent of the male population and about 2 per cent of the female population have defective colour vision in one or more forms. Defective colour vision can be described as the inability to see primary colours correctly and, in some instances, the inability to see colour at all. The latter form of defective colour vision results in the individual being able to see only white, black and a range of greys. A person with this defect would sit in front of a colour television set and would see the program in black and white only. Defective colour vision is a sex-linked hereditary characteristic.

Colour mixing

The rainbow

Sunlight is generally accepted as the source of white light and it consists of the seven colours of the rainbow. These are violet, blue, blue-green, green, yellow, orange and red. A colour wheel is a circle divided into seven equal segments, each coloured with one of these hues. If the disc is rotated rapidly, the seven colours will combine and white will be observed. White can also be produced if blue, green and red are painted in equal proportions on a disc which is rotated rapidly. White can be produced if pure blue, green and red light are projected onto a white screen. Where the lights overlap, white is produced. The violet, blue-green, yellow and orange colours of the rainbow are each made up of a combination of two of blue, green and red.

Additive colour mixing

As described above, blue, green and red light waves when mixed will add together to produce white light. At present there is no satisfactory explanation for this phenomenon. Because of this red, blue and green are called the *primary additive colours* (see Fig. 8.8). Figure 8.9, a colour triangle, also illustrates the additive nature of coloured light.

Examples of the additive effect of coloured light

1 part or **red** + 1 part of **blue** + 1 part of **green** = **white**
1 part of **red** + 1 part of **green** = **yellow**

1 part of **red** + 1 part of **blue**	= **magenta**
1 part of **blue** + 1 part of **green**	= **cyan**

Projecting coloured light onto a white screen will confirm the following:

1 1 part of **blue** + 2 parts of **yellow** = **white**
since, two parts of **yellow** equal 1 part of **red** plus 1 part of **green**.

2 1 part of **green** + 2 parts of **magenta** = **white**
since, 2 parts of **magenta** equal 1 part of **red** plus 1 part of **blue**.

3 1 part of **red** + 2 parts of **cyan** = **white**
since, 2 parts of **cyan** equal 1 part of **green** plus 1 part of **blue**.

The additive nature of primary colours is utilised in colour television. The colours one sees on a colour television screen are obtained by projecting blue, green and red dots onto the screen. The colours on the screen are varied by varying the concentration of the different dots. Stage lighting is another situation where additive colour mixing is used.

A knowledge of additive colour mixing is necessary to understand subtractive colour mixing which is utilised in textile dyeing and printing. The primary additive colours are also the basis of colour specification.

Subtractive colour mixing

The mixing of dyes, printing pastes, paints and pigments is called subtractive colour mixing. The term subtractive is used as colour is *subtracted* or *removed* from each colour to produce black. The three subtractive primary colours are in fact secondary colours shown in Figs 8.8 and 8.9—yellow, cyan and magenta. Figure 8.10 illustrates how the primary subtractive colours can be combined to produce black. The production of black by mixing the three subtractive colours in equal proportions can be explained as follows.

Yellow	=	1 part of **green** + 1 part of **red**
Magenta	=	1 part of **blue** + 1 part of **red**
Cyan	=	1 part of **blue** + 1 part of **green**

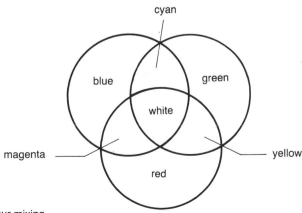

Figure 8.8 Additive colour mixing

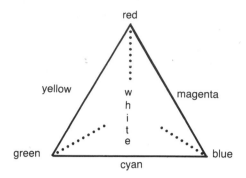

Figure 8.9 Colour triangle

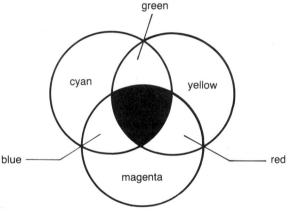

Figure 8.10 Subtractive colour mixing

So, as yellow contains no blue, it would absorb any blue incident on it and reflect green. This would be absorbed by the magenta, as it contains no green. Only the red would be reflected by the overlap of yellow and magenta, but with the overlap of cyan, the red is absorbed by the cyan. Simultaneously, the green of the cyan would be absorbed by the magenta and the blue of cyan absorbed by the yellow. Thus, as all the light waves are absorbed by the overlapping secondary colours, the resultant colour is black (see also Fig. 8.10).

Colour specification and colour specifying systems

Many names are given to the different colours. For example, blue can be called sky blue, aquamarine, navy blue, delft blue, azure, etc. The extensive list of names for colours makes it difficult for designers, dyers, printers and the consumer (1) to name a specific colour, so that it can be readily identified, and (2) to provide a formula, or recipe, which would enable a particular hue to be reproduced consistently.

For a colour to be identified and reproduced consistently, it must be possible to specify it accurately. The object of colour specification is not just to give a description of a colour, but to specify that particular colour accurately. Consider, for example, the many hues of red there are—scarlet, ruby, crimson, etc.—and you will realise the need for colours to be specified accurately.

Of the systems developed to specify colour, the Munsell and CIE systems are the ones most frequently used. The Ostwald system, which was developed by the German physical chemist Wilhelm Ostwald in the 1920s, enjoyed some early success, but it was superseded by the Munsell system. The deficiency of the Ostwald system was its inability to add new or different colours to those on which it was based.

Today, most of the subjective colour order systems, such as the colour atlases of the dye and paint manufacturers, colour codes used by architects, etc. are based essentially on the Munsell system. This system describes colours using charts which display a large range of hues, ordered according to value and chroma.

The CIE system describes colours in numerical proportions. These numerical pro portions refer to the amounts of the primary colours—blue, green and red—which are required to produce a particular colour.

The Munsell system

The Munsell system is a subjective colour ordering system which was developed by an American called Albert Munsell. In 1915 he completed his first determined attempt to provide a precise nomenclature for colours. Using water colours, he painted many hues on small squares of white paper and arranged these in the order that became known as the Munsell system.

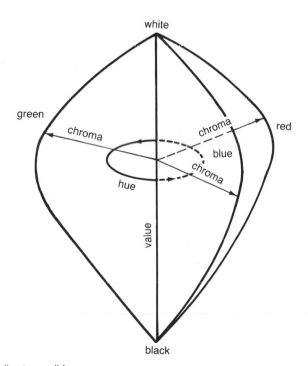

Figure 8.11 The Munsell colour solid

Munsell used a three-dimensional colour solid to plan his colour system (see Fig. 8.11). The solid, which is shaped like a top, is pure black at the bottom and pure white at the top, with pure red, blue and green at equal intervals around the circumference. Going around the solid horizontally left to right, blue tends to purple and then to red; red tends to yellow which becomes green; and the green tends to blue-green which becomes blue. As the colours approach the top of the solid, they become lighter and finally white. As they move out from the axis of the solid they become more pure and intense.

Thus each colour in the Munsell system has three parameters—hue, chroma and value—which are represented by the three dimensions of the solid.

A Munsell colour chart is made up of hundreds of small coloured rectangles, called colour chips, which are arranged according to their hue, value and chroma. Each chip represents one specific colour. Munsell judged the difference in colour (or the colour interval) between any two adjacent chips to be the same. (*Note*: Munsell's colour perception was so accurate that subsequent objective measurement of his charts resulted in relatively little modification.) Any colour can be specified easily and quickly according to the three Munsell parameters of hue, chroma and value.

The advantage of the Munsell system over any other subjective ordering system is that it can accommodate and specify every colour in existence and any new colours which may be developed in the future. Its advantage over the objective CIE system is that the Munsell charts allow visual examination of the numerous colours.

Munsell value

The Munsell value refers to the lightness or darkness of a colour and it is represented by the vertical axis of the Munsell solid. The Munsell value scale, shown in Fig. 8.12, ranges from black to white in eleven equal intervals with black being zero, white being 10 and with various shades of grey in between. The intervals along the vertical scale are such that the visual difference between any adjacent values is the same. The value scale is also referred to as the trunk of the Munsell solid or tree.

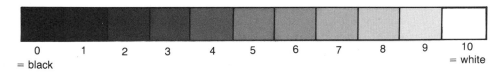

Figure 8.12 Munsell value scale

Munsell hue

This second parameter specifies the many hues shown in Fig. 8.11. From his practical experience as an artist, Munsell decided to base his charts on ten hues, five principal hues and five hues which fall between the principal hues and are known as intermediate hues. Although these divisions are technically hues, they are known in common usage as the Munsell colours.

Figure 8.13 is a disc whose ten equal divisions represent the ten Munsell colours, namely:

1 **Principal Munsell colours**—red, yellow, green, blue and purple.

2 **Intermediate Munsell colours**—yellow-red, green-yellow, blue-green, purple-blue and red-purple.

Each of the ten areas on Fig. 8.13 is sub-divided into ten equal parts, each representing a colour. The sub-divisions numbered one to ten represent the principal and the intermediate Munsell colours.

Munsell chroma

The third parameter of the Munsell system is chroma which refers to the purity, intensity, vividness, saturation or brightness of a particular colour. The closer a colour is to the neutral axis, or the value scale, the duller it becomes.

When represented on a disc such as Fig. 8.14, chroma radiates outwards from the centre in equal steps of two. Munsell chose a chroma difference of two because this is more readily perceived than a chroma difference of one, which cannot always be seen.

Specifying colour using the three Munsell parameters

In order to describe the Munsell hue and chroma scales clearly, they have been depicted separately in Figs 8.13 and 8.14. They have then been combined on one diagram, Fig. 8.15, which shows the numerous colours which are possible, at least in theory, for any one of the value intervals ranging from 1 to 9. *Note*: On the value scale 0 = black and 10 = white.

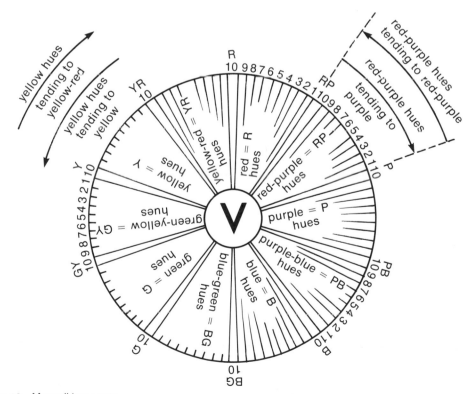

Figure 8.13 Munsell hue scale

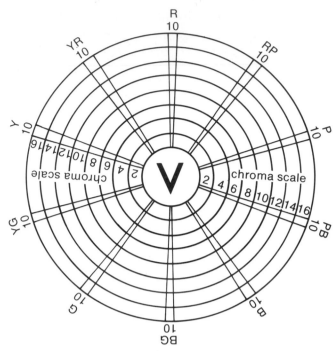

Figure 8.14 Munsell chroma scale

An examination of the Munsell solid (Fig. 8.11) shows that the discs found along the value scale do not all have equal diameters. The diameter of a disc depends on its position on the vertical axis which is the value scale. Figure 8.16, which is a cut-away section of the Munsell solid, illustrates this more clearly.

The following steps specify a colour using the Munsell colour system. The example used is a slightly dark, bright, purple-blue colour indicated by the asterisk in Fig. 8.17.

1 The hue number is quoted first; for example, **5**.

2 This is followed by the capital letter(s) which stand for the principal or intermediate Munsell colour; for example, **PB** = purple blue.

3 Next the value step is quoted to indicate the lightness/darkness of the colour; for example, **4**.

4 Lastly the chroma number is quoted to indicate the brightness/dullness of the colour; for example, **8**.

Thus, the slightly dark, bright, purple-blue colour has been specified as the colour **5PB/8**.

Munsell colour charts

In Fig. 8.15 you will notice that those hues near the value scale are represented by smaller and smaller wedge-shaped blocks. Munsell did not develop his colour system using a solid but arranged his colour chips in the form of charts.

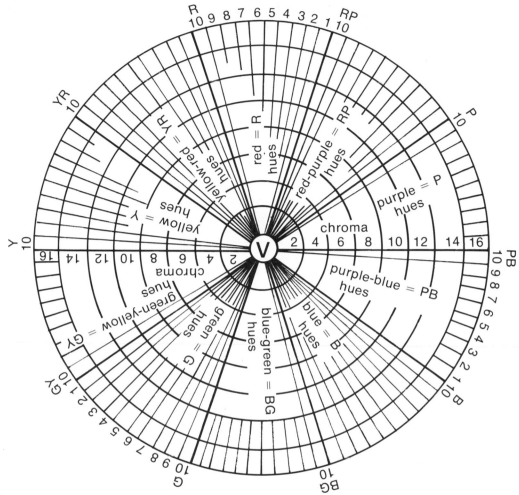

Figure 8.15   Combined Munsell hue and chroma scales

Figure 8.17 is a black and white representation of a Munsell colour chart which has been produced as follows. Consider a sheet of paper, held standing on its edge, passing through any one of the diameters such as R to BG, G to RP, B to YR, Y to PB, or P to GY as shown in Fig. 8.18. Consider that this sheet of paper extends the length of the value scale from 0 to 10. Figure 8.17 shows the hues of two Munsell colours— purple-blue and yellow. The representation of two Munsell colours on each chart has the advantages of being economical as well as indicating the hues that are opposite each other in the Munsell system.

In Fig. 8.17, some of the rectangles have dotted lines and represent hues which may be developed in the future. The rectangles with solid lines represent hues which have already been developed. The columns of rectangles represent the chroma scale and the rows of rectangles or colour chips represent the value scale.

The Munsell system usually consists of about twenty charts which together are known as The Munsell Colour Atlas. Each of the charts has two Munsell colours which lie on the same diameter—see Figs 8.15 and 8.17. For example; purple-blue and yellow lie on the same diameter. The twenty charts are at 2.5, 5.0, 7.5 and 10.0 on the hue scale for each of the Munsell colours. There are, therefore, about 960 different colour chips in the atlas.

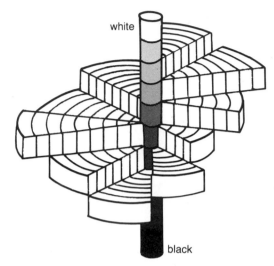

Figure 8.16 Three-dimensional representation of the Munsell colour solid

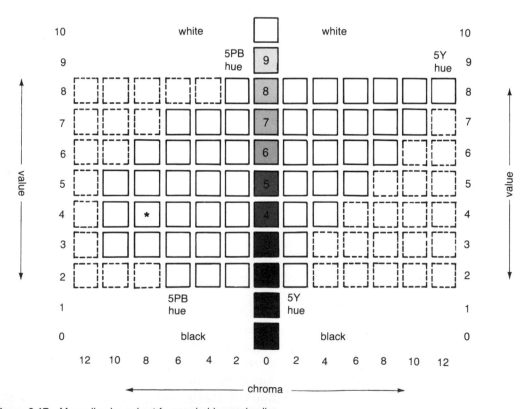

Figure 8.17 Munsell colour chart for purple-blue and yellow

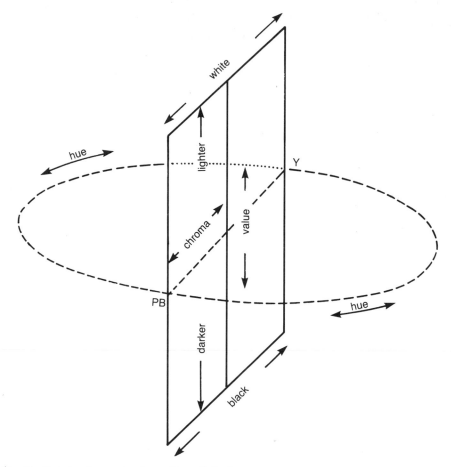

Figure 8.18 The first step in constructing a Munsell chart

The CIE system

The CIE system is named after the Commission Internationale de L'Eclairage (the International Commission of Illumination) which developed it. The Commission was set up by a number of countries in order to arrive at an objective means of specifying colour. The CIE system specifies colour in terms of the proportion of the primary additive colours (blue, green and red) required to produce a particular colour.

The development of computers has enabled the CIE system to be utilised and applied more effectively for the colour matching of textile materials, dyes and other coloured materials.

Development of the CIE system

In 1802, Thomas Young, an English physician, postulated that the human eye has three basic colour receptors: one each for blue, green and red. Young's contemporaries rejected his theory of colour vision. However, in 1867, Hermann von Helmholtz, a German physicist and physiologist, extended Young's theory. In 1871, the Scottish physicist James Maxwell, using the theories of Young and Helmholtz, developed them further to arrive at the principles of colour photography. The theory which resulted is known by one of the following names: (1) Young–Helmholtz theory of colour vision, (2) Young–Helmholtz–Maxwell theory of colour vision, (3) Trichromatic theory of colour vision, and (4) Tristimulus theory of colour reception, the last name being preferred.

Young's original concepts have, in part, been confirmed physiologically. The cones in the retina have been found to be particularly sensitive to lightwaves of about 450 nm (blue), 540 nm (green) and about 575 nm (yellow). As the Tristimulus theory of colour reception is based on blue, green and red, it may be necessary to review this theory on the basis of the colours to which cones are sensitive.

In 1931, the Commission Internationale de L'Eclairage developed the CIE system of colour specification which was based on the Tristimulus theory of colour reception.

The basic principles of the CIE system

The three primary additive colours add together to give white; that is:

blue + green + red = white

⅓ blue + ⅓ green + red = white

0.33′ blue + 0.33′ green + 0.33′ red = 1.0 white

Since any hue depends on the amounts of red, green and blue it contains, the above equations can be re-written in general terms as follows.

Let x = amount of red
X = red
y = amount of green
Y = green   Then $xX + yY + zZ = C.$
z = amount of blue
Z = blue
C = desired hue

This is the basic equation used by colour physicists to specify hue or to define the chromaticity of a dyed or printed textile material—using the CIE system. The chromaticity of a coloured textile refers to how much of X, Y and Z are required to produce its particular hue. Thus, as stated earlier, equal amounts of red, green and blue produce white and the equation is written:

$$\tfrac{1}{3}X + \tfrac{1}{3}Y + \tfrac{1}{3}Z = \text{white}$$

The sum of the coefficients of X, Y and Z are always equal to unity in the CIE system. A red hue may be expressed mathematically as follows:

$$\tfrac{2}{3}X + \tfrac{1}{4}Y + \tfrac{1}{12}Z = \text{a red hue}$$

Note that $\tfrac{2}{3} + \tfrac{1}{4} + \tfrac{1}{12} = 1$

A green hue may be expressed as follows:

$$0.19X + 0.68Y + 0.13Z = \text{a green hue}$$

Note that $0.19 + 0.68 + 0.13 = 1$

The chromaticity diagram

As the terms x, y and z are related mathematically (i.e. $x + y + z = 1$) the colour physicist can depict this graphically. The x, y and z of the equation $xX + yY + zZ = C$ are known as the chromaticity co-ordinates and a graph of these points is called the chromaticity diagram. As $x + y + z = 1$, the chromaticity diagram need only show two of the three co-ordinates as the third can always be deduced by subtracting the sum of the other two from 1. See Fig. 8.19, where x is the horizontal axis and and y is the vertical axis.

The way in which this graph is plotted is beyond the scope of this text and a knowledge of how it is plotted is not necessary to understand the CIE system. It is more important to understand how the chromaticity diagram is used to specify colour.

A detailed chromaticity diagram is shown in Fig. 8.22 but before examining it, look at Fig. 8.20 which shows the basic triangular shape of the chromaticity diagram. Examine Fig. 8.21 which is the same as Fig. 8.20 but to which graduated scales have been added along the x and y axes, as well as along the perimeter of the chromaticity graph. The graduated scales along the x and y axes give the values of x and y. The graduated scale along the perimeter of the chromaticity graph represents the wavelengths as given in Table 8.1 and Fig. 8.1. This graduated scale is in nanometers (nm). These measure each colour's wavelength in millions of a millimetre.

Note: Purple does not occur in the visible light spectrum. It is not a natural colour and its wavelength is not known. Because of this the purple line on the chromaticity graph is not graduated.

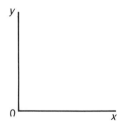

Figure 8.19

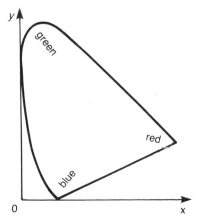

Figure 8.20

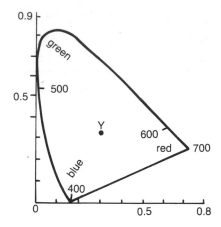

Figure 8.21 The point Y is the location of white. White corresponds to the point here $x = 0\ 33'$ and $y = 0.33'$. Therefore, $z = 0.33'$ as $x + y + z = 1$.

Basic specification using the CIE system

A reflectance spectrophotometer is an instrument used to measure the hue of a textile material. This form of objective colour measurement is called colorimetry.

The reflectance spectrophotometer is able to measure reflected light and to translate this measurement electronically to produce values for x, y and z. For example, say the reflectance spectrophotometer measures the dominant wavelength of reflected light

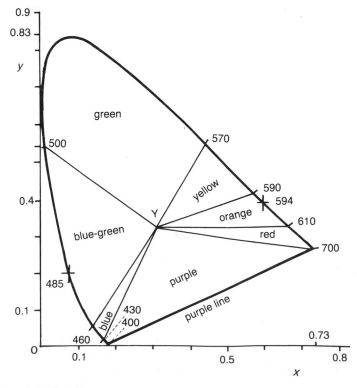

Figure 8.22 The chromaticity diagram

from a coloured textile material as 594 nm. This wavelength is essentially the wavelength of orange light and on the chromaticity graph (Fig. 8.22) the x and y co-ordinates for orange light are about 0.6 and 0.4 respectively; z, therefore, will equal zero.

A hue which has a dominant wavelength of 485 nm will cause the reflectance spectrophotometer to print out automatically that $x = 0.075$, $y = 0.200$ and $z = 0.725$. A z value of 0.725 indicates a blue hue. This can be confirmed by looking at the location of 485 nm on the chromaticity graph.

Chromaticity values can also be expressed as percentages. Thus, for example, if $x = 0.075$, $y = 0.200$ and $z = 0.725$, then the hue with these co-ordinates would be made up of 7.5 per cent red, 20.0 per cent green and 72.5 per cent blue.

Complete colour specification using the CIE system

The chromaticity co-ordinates specify the hue of a coloured object such as textile material but they do not indicate the luminosity of the colour; that is, they do not specify how light or dark the colour is, or how much grey it possesses?

The luminosity of a hue is represented by adding a third dimension to the chromaticity diagram. This is obtained by projecting a third axis, the luminosity axis, upward from the point where white is located on the chromaticity diagram. This axis is called the Y axis and luminosity is measured in percentage terms along it. The resultant figure is called the CIE colour solid—see Fig. 8.23. One can think of it as a triangular pyramid with one straight and two curved sides. No light (i.e. black) equals zero luminosity, and white, which has 100 per cent luminosity, is at the top of the scale.

To specify a colour completely using the CIE system, one requires a value for x, which cannot be greater than about 0.73 (see Fig. 8.22), a value for y which cannot exceed about 0.83 (see Fig. 8.22), and a luminosity value expressed as a percentage between 0 and 100 per cent, where the greater the percentage of Y, the lighter the hue.

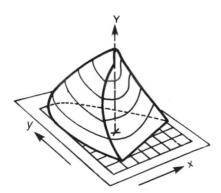

Figure 8.23   Three-dimensional representation of the CIE system's chromaticity diagram

Metamerism

When a dyed or printed textile material is examined under different lighting conditions, a marked change in its colour may be observed. This phenomenon is known as metamerism. Two textile materials may appear to have the same colour under one type of illumination but will appear different in colour when viewed under another type of illumination. If this occurs the textile materials are said to be a **metameric match**.

The problem of metameric matches may arise when two fibres of different chemical composition, such as cotton and polyester for instance, have to be dyed the same colour. Because the fibres are of different chemical composition, they invariably cannot be dyed successfully with the same dye. Rather, a different dye is required for each fibre to achieve the same colour. Then, in all likelihood, the similarly appearing colours achieved with the two different dyes will have different spectral reflectance curves. Thus the fibres will appear similar under one type of illumination, but different under another type of illumination.

To avoid metamerism, the reflectance curves of the two or more coloured textile materials must coincide at all wavelengths. Thereby the same colour is obtained under any type of illumination, and metamerism will not occur.

Should metamerism occur, it may present problems for the textile dyer or printer, manufacturer and consumer. A metameric textile material may appear, say, green under one type of illumination, whilst, under another type of illumination it may appear nearly brown, as can occur with certain khaki coloured items.

Optical properties of textile materials

A textile material can reflect, absorb or transmit the light falling on it (see Fig. 8.24). The hue of a textile material will depend on the extent to which the light is reflected, absorbed or transmitted. Thus, the optical properties of textile materials must be considered when considering dyeing, printing and colour matching.

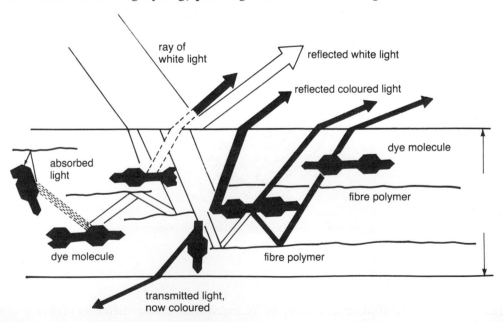

Figure 8.24 An attempt to depict how one ray of white light is reflected, absorbed and transmitted by a dyed fibre

The optical properties of textile materials are influenced by one or more of the following:

type of fibre used
type of yarn
fabric construction
other factors described below.

The optical properties of fibres

Lustrous and translucent fibres

As a rule, these two characteristics are interdependent and occur together. Fibres in this category include the bright lustred man-made fibres and silk. The lustrous effect is due to the high proportion of light which is reflected very evenly by the smooth, regular surface of the fibre. The irregular surface of viscose rayon or that of the acetate fibres seems to have little effect on the extent of the lustre.

The greater the lustre, or the more light reflected, the lighter the appearance of the hue of the fibre. The reflected light stimulates the rods of the retina which differentiate shades of grey, lightness or darkness. This causes the brain to perceive more white and thus a lighter colour. In addition, the fibre's translucency allows partial transmission of light and enables the eyes to 'see through' the fibre. This reduces the amount of hue actually seen and adds to the sensation of seeing a lighter hue.

The hue of the coloured textile material is also affected by the background against which it is examined. The fibre's translucent characteristic together with the colour of the background may affect the chroma and/or value of the colour that is seen.

Delustred fibres

These man-made fibres are delustred with titanium dioxide, a white, very finely powdered pigment. These very fine particles scatter the light being reflected, thereby imparting a subdued lustrous appearance to the fibre. The colours of dyed or printed delustred fibres are brighter than those of lustrous fibres, as the incident white light is scattered and hence cannot dilute or lighten the colour reflected by the dye molecule.

Opaque and dull fibres

These are the cotton and wool fibres. Both fibres reflect little, if any, light. They tend to absorb most of the light which falls on them. Thus, the lack of lightness and brightness of dyed and printed cotton and wool textile materials compared with their man-made fibre equivalents is due to this light absorption.

Most cotton fabrics are bleached before colour is applied, which makes them appear lighter and brighter than if they were not bleached. Wool, on the other hand, is not bleached as much and tends to dull gradually owing to atmospheric oxidation.

Effect of fibre fineness

Dyeing equal masses of fine and coarse fibres, each with the same quantity of dye, will result in the coarse fibres dyeing darker than the fine fibres. This is because there are fewer coarse fibres and more fine fibres per unit mass. Hence, each coarse fibre can take up more dye than can each fine fibre, under identical dyeing conditions. This fact must be considered when attempts are made to colour materials containing fibres with different diameters. The above is not applicable in printing as the dye/pigment is applied per unit surface area of the fabric.

Mercerised cotton

The process of mercerising cotton improves the dye uptake. This enables deeper colours (that is, colours with more chroma) to be obtained with mercerised cotton.

The colours of cottons which are stretched or tension mercerised appear lighter and brighter than colours of unmercerised cottons. This is because this process results in more light being reflected from the surface of the fibre; in other words, the value of the colour is increased.

Optical properties of yarns

Filament and staple spun yarns

Filament yarns are much smoother than staple spun yarns. They therefore reflect more light, which makes them more lustrous. If this lustre is significant, the yarn can be perceived as having a colour of higher value and less chroma than is actually present.

Staple spun yarns have little, if any, lustre and appear darker (that is, they have a lower value) than comparably coloured filament yarns. This occurs because staple spun yarns have a more irregular surface than fiilament yarns and are unable to reflect light to the same extent as the smooth filament yarns.

High twist (hard spun) yarns and low twist (soft spun) yarns

High twist yarns have a smooth, more regular surface compared with soft spun yarns. Soft spun yarns have a more hairy, less regular surface. Hard spun yarns, with their comparatively smoother surface, reflect more light, giving them some lustre. Thus, hard spun yarns will have a more lustrous, lighter, brighter appearance compared with an equivalently coloured soft spun yarn.

Thick yarns and thin yarns

Thick yarns tend to appear duller and darker compared with an equivalently coloured thin yarn. The structure of the thicker yarn results in more light being absorbed and results in a darker colour. Thicker yarns will have a lower value and lower chroma compared with an equivalently coloured thin yarn.

Textured yarns

The irregular surface of textured yarns absorbs much light and scatters most of the reflected light. This produces a colour with lower value than an equivalently coloured yarn which is not textured.

The optical properties of fabrics

There are many factors which influence both the structure and surface characteristics of knitted, woven and the newer fabric forms. The explanations given above for fibres and yarns and those that follow for fabrics should provide some explanation of the optical properties of fabrics.

Smooth and irregular fabric surface structures

Smooth fabrics reflect some light from their regular and even surfaces. Though such surfaces may not be lustrous, they will lighten the colour of the dyed or printed textile material.

The colour of smooth fabrics will have a lighter value and chroma compared with fabrics with a raised, brushed, napped or other irregular surface. Fabrics with an irregular surface absorb more light than those with smoother surfaces and result in a duller appearance. These fabrics have a lower value and chroma compared with an equivalent but smooth surfaced fabric.

The optical properties of lustrous fabrics are the same as those given above for lustrous, translucent fibres and filament yarns. The colour of a particular form of fabric will be affected by the surface of the fabric as well by the optical properties of the fibres and yarns from which it is produced.

Opaque and translucent fabrics

Opaque fabrics have a duller/darker colour; that is, less value and less chroma, since these fabrics absorb most of the incident light. Translucent fabrics have a lighter colour than an equivalent opaque fabric. The colour of a garment made from a translucent fabric will be influenced by the colour and optical properties of the fabric as well as by the colour of the skin against which the fabric is worn.

Glossary

Reference: *The Penguin Dictionary of Science* by E.B. Uvarov et al. (Fifth Edition), Penguin Books, 1979

acetylate   To introduce an acetyl group (CH_3CO-) into an organic compound. In textile chemistry this may be the reaction between the $-OH$ group(s) of cellulose with acetic acid and/or acetic anhydride (CH_3COOH and/or $(CH_3CO)_2O$ respectively).

acid   A compound which liberates hydrogen ions (H^+) when dissolved in water. An aqueous solution is acidic when it contains an excess of H^+ over hydroxyl radicals (OH^-).

alcohol   Organic compounds containing one or more $-OH$ groups. Alcohols react with organic acids to form esters.

aliphatic   Of organic compounds having open chains of carbon atoms, in contradistinction to the closed rings of carbon atoms of the aromatic compounds.

alkali   A compound which liberates hydroxyl radicals (OH^-) when dissolved in water. An aqueous solution is alkaline when it contains an excess of OH^- over H^+.

alkanes   Hydrocarbons conforming to the general formula C_nH_{2n+2}, where $n = 1$ or more. Alkanes are saturated hydrocarbons, and therefore generally stable and relatively unreactive. The liquid and solid alkanes are hydrophobic and water repellent.

alkyl radical   The radical of an alkane, e.g. methyl radical

amide group   Has the formula $-CONH-$. When found in nylon polymers it is called the amide group; when found in wool polymers it is called the peptide group.

amino group   A radical with the formula $-NH_2$

angstrom (Å)   One ten millionth of one millimetre (0.000 000 1 mm), or one ten thousandth of one micrometre. The angstrom is no longer a preferred metric unit.

anion   A negatively charged ion or radical; e.g., Cl^-, OH^-

aromatic   Of organic molecules containing one or more benzene rings: ⬡ or C_6H_6

atom   The smallest particle of an element

catalyst   A substance — compound or element — the presence of which influences the rate of a chemical reaction, but which remains chemically unchanged at the end of the reaction

cation   A positively charged ion on radical; e.g. Na^+, NH_4^+

Colour Index (C.I.)   An authoritative, descriptive catalogue of natural and synthetic dyes and dye auxiliaries published by the Society of Dyers and Colourists, England

coplanar   In the one plane. A coplanar molecular structure is one in which all the atoms are in the one plane.

cover factor   The area covered by a yarn's thickness when resting on a surface. A hairy yarn, for example, has a greater cover factor than a smooth yarn. Cover factor usually refers to yarns, but fibres also have a cover factor. A fibre with an oval cross-section has a greater cover factor than a fibre with a circular cross-section.

curing   The application of heat, usually to polymerise and/or set resins applied to textile materials

degree of polymerisation (DP)   The number of monomers or repeating units in one polymer. More specifically, it is the average molecular weight.

detergent   A cleaning agent belonging to the class of chemicals known as surface-active agents

easy-care   Any garment of textile material may be described as being easy-care if it does not shrink out of fit and requires little or no ironing after laundering or dry-cleaning.

elasticity   The ability of a material or fibre to resume its original form, size or shape after forces which caused its deformation have been removed; the ability to return from stretch

electrolyte   A compound which, in aqueous solution or in the molten state, conducts an electric current and is simultaneously decomposed by it into ions; compounds which dissociate into ions and/or radicals in aqueous solution

electrons   The negatively charged particles which surround the positive nucleus of an atom

endothermic   Describes a chemical or other reaction which absorbs heat energy.

energy   The capacity to work. There are various forms of energy; e.g. mechanical, electrical, heat, atomic, chemical, potential. *See also* **kinetic energy**.

ester   The organic compound formed from the reaction between an alcohol and an organic acid. An ester has the general formula $R-COO-R$, where R, in the case of textile polymers, is a polymer radical.

exhaust   The absorption of dye molecules from the dye liquor by the fibres being dyed

heat   Energy possessed by a substance in the form of kinetic eneryg (q.v.) of atomic or molecular vibration, rotation or translation

heterocyclic   Describes organic compounds whose molecules are ring structures which include atoms of elements other than carbon and hydrogen, e.g. pyridine (C_5H_5N). *Note:* such compounds are not necessarily aromatic.

hydrocarbons   Organic compounds whose molecules are composed only of carbon and hydrogen

hydrolysis   The chemical decomposition of a substance by the action of water, the water itself being also decomposed. Acids and alkalis often catalyse hydrolysis. The destructive effect of hydrolysis upon fibre polymers will then also result in the rupture of inter-polymer forces of attraction.

hydrophilic   Having a strong affinity for water; water or moisture absorbent

hydrophobic   Having an aversion to water; non-absorbent or water-repellent

hygroscopic   Describes the ability of a fibre or substance to absorb moisture from the atmosphere.

imino group   Has the formula $-NH-$. The hydrogen atom of this group is known as the **imino hydrogen.**

incident light   Light rays which fall on the surface of a body, such as a fibre surface

inorganic   Of mineral or non-living origin; the opposite to organic (q.v.). Examples of inorganic substances are concrete, mineral ores, rocks, etc. Examples of inorganic compounds are sodium chloride, sulphuric acid, potassium dichromate, calcium carbonate, etc.

ion   A positively or negatively charged atom, e.g. Na^+, Cl^-

isomerism   The existence of two or more compounds which have the same chemical formula but different properties because of a different spatial arrangement of the atoms within their molecules. Each such compound is called an **isomer.** (*cis–trans* isomerism is illustrated on page 160.)

joule   Unit of energy, e.g. heat

kinetic energy   The energy a body possesses by virtue of its motion. Heating a fibre raises its kinetic energy because the increase in temperature increases the atomic vibration of the polymers of the fibre.

leuco   White, colourless. The leuco compound of a dye is its chemically reduced form which does not display the correct hue of the dye.

light-fastness   The fastness to sunlight of the colours of dyed or printed textiles. Light-fastness ratings are as follows in Table G1 below:

Table G1 Light-fastness ratings

Rating number	Description
1	very poor light-fastness
2	poor
3	moderate
4	fair
5	good
6	very good
7	excellent
8	maximum light-fastness (textile material may break down before colour begins to fade)

linear   In line; e.g. a linear polymer is like a line, having no branches or long side-groups.

liquor   A term applied to water-based solutions used in textile processing. A liquor may contain several dissolved, suspended, and undissolved substances.

methyl radical   The radical $-CH_3$, which is derived from methane (CH_4). Methyl radicals are found in many dye molecules.

methylene radical   The radical $-CH_2-$, which is found in many fibre polymers

micrometre (μm)   One millionth of a metre, or one thousandth of a millimetre (i.e. 0.001 mm); previously called a micron

moisture content   The amount or mass of water contained in the fibre or textile material, expressed as a percentage of the 'as is' or air-dry mass of the fibre or textile

moisture regain   The amount or mass of water contained in the fibre or textile, expressed as a percentage of the oven-dry weight of the fibre or textile

mole   The molecular weight of a substance expressed in grams

molecule   The smallest part of any substance still possessing the properties of that substance. Molecules are composed of atoms. Polymers (see page 8) are the molecules of fibres.

morphology   With reference to textile fibres, it is the study of the size, shape, structure and composition of the fibre, and their influence on fibre properties and fibre end-uses.

nanometre (nm)   One millionth of a millimetre (0.000 001 mm); officially, one hundred millionth of a metre (0.000 000 001 m)

oleophilic   Having a strong affinity for oil; readily absorbs oil, grease, wax, etc.

oleophobic   Having an aversion to oil; repels oil, grease, wax, etc.

organic   The term used to describe substances composed essentially of carbon and hydrogen, often also with oxygen and nitrogen. All the commonly used textile fibres are organic.

pH scale   An acidity–alkalinity scale ranging from 1 to 14. A pH of 1 is most acid; a pH of 14 is most alkaline; and a pH of 7 is neutral.

photochemical reaction   A chemical reaction initiated by light, usually sunlight

plasticity   The property of a material or fibre to remain deformed when the forces which caused its deformation have been removed. A **plastic** fibre will tend to remain stretched and distorted, while fabric made from such a fibre will tend to wrinkle and distort on wearing.

polar group   A group of atoms which are charged either negatively or positively

polarity   The positive or negative charge of an atom or group of atoms

radical   A group of atoms, present in a compound, which retain their identity as a group throughout any chemical changes which affect the rest of the compound. Examples of radicals are the sulphate radical $-SO_4^=$, sulphonate radical $-SO_3^-$, carboxyl radical $-COO^-$, amide group $-CONH-$, etc,

relative humidity   A measurement of the amount of moisture or water vapour present in one cubic metre of air, expressed as a percentage of the maximum amount of water vapour the one cubic metre of air could hold at the temperature when the measurement was taken.

resiliency   A term considered to have the same meaning as elasticity. Usually applied in textiles, however, to mean the ability of a fibre or fabric to spring back, recoil, or return to its original form or shape after compression; e.g. the pile of a carpet is usually expected to be resilient.

saponification   Alkaline hydrolysis. In textiles this often refers to hydrolysis of the ester groups of polyester and acetate polymers during laundering, which is usually under alkaline conditions.

saturated covalent bond   A single covalent or valence bond which does not take part in addition reactions; represented in structural formulae of compounds by a short, single line between the letters or symbols signifying atoms. In textile chemistry saturated covalent bonds occur most frequently between two carbon atoms, and/or between one carbon atom and an atom of hydrogen, oxygen and/or nitrogen; less frequently between other atoms. Saturated covalent bonds are generally stable, unreactive and strong.

soap   A cleaning agent manufactured by reacting natural oils or fats, usually with sodium hydroxide. Soap is a surface-active agent (q.v.).

sublimate   A solid obtained by the direct condensation of a vaporised solid without passing through the liquid state

substantivity   The attraction between fibre polymers and dye molecules

surface-active agent (also called **surfactant**)   Usually an organic compound which, when added to aqueous solutions, reduces the surface tension of water. This allows the water to wet fibres and other materials more efficiently and quickly. The three types of surfactants most commonly used in textiles are **anionic**, e.g. soaps and anionic synthetic detergents; **cationic**, e.g. fabric conditioners and softeners; **non-ionic**, e.g. the non-ionic synthetic detergents. A fourth type, called **amphoteric**, is as yet less commonly used.

synthetic detergent   A cleaning agent synthesised from by-products of petroleum refining. Synthetic detergents are surface-active agents (q.v.).

tenacity (also called **tensile strength** or **specific strength**) The tensile (pulling) stress that has to be applied to break a material — the maximum specific stress that is developed in a tensile test to rupture the textile material or fibre. For textile fibres tenacity is measured or expressed in grams per tex, i.e. g/tex, as explained at the foot of page 212.

tex   The mass in grams of 1000 metres of fibre, filament, sliver, roving or yarn. It is the universal system of describing linear density, mass per unit length of fibres, filaments, slivers, rovings, or yarns. *See also* footnote 1, page 212.

thermo-set resins   Resins which do not become plastic when heated

unsaturated covalent bond (also called an **unsaturated valence bond**) A double or triple bond. Unsaturated covalent bonds can undergo addition reactions and in general are more reactive than saturated covalent bonds (q.v.).

wash-fastness   The fastness to laundering of the colours of dyed or printed textile materials. Wash-fastness is rated in numbers from 1 to 5 as shown in Table G2 below:

Table G2 Wash-fastness ratings

Rating number	Description
1	very poor wash-fastness
2	poor
3	moderate
3–4	fair
4	good
4–5	very good
5	excellent, or no fading at all

wetting agent   A specific surface-active agent primarily formulated to assist water to wet out more efficiently. A wetting agent is not a cleaning agent.

wrinkle-resistant (or **crease-resistant**) Describes a textile material or garment which resists being winkled, but will wrinkle when crushed and then tend to remain wrinkled. *See also* **easy-care.**

wrinkle-shedding   Describes a textile material or garment which may wrinkle when crushed, but when allowed to relax will tend to shed or lose the imposed wrinkles and recover its former unwrinkled appearance. *See also* **easy-care.**

Appendix
Physical properties of fibres

	Acetate	Acrylic	Cotton	Elastomeric
Polymer				
Chemical composition	Secondary cellulose acetate	At least 85% polyacrylonitrile	Cellulose	85% segmented polyurethane, polyether type
Dimensions (approximate)	Short	Very long	Extremely long	Long
Approximate length	160 nm	500 nm	5 000 nm	Unavailable
Approximate thickness	2.3 nm	0.3 to 0.53 nm	0.8 nm	0.7 nm
Degree of polymerisation	130	2 000	5 000	Unavailable
Polymer system	Very amorphous	Very crystalline	Crystalline	Extremely amorphous, when not stretched, to extremely crystalline, when fully extended
Estimated amorphous region	60%	30 to 20%	35 to 30%	—
Estimated crystalline region	40%	70 to 80%	65 to 70%	—
Tenacity	Very weak	Fair to strong	Strong	Very weak
Dry[1]	12 to 27 g/tex[1]	20 to 27 g/tex	27 to 44 g/tex	5 to 7 g/tex
Wet	8 to 24 g/tex	16 to 24 g/tex	27 to 46 g/tex	5 to 7 g/tex
Wet/dry	60 to 70%	80 to 90%	100 to 105%	100%
Elastic-plastic nature	Plastic	Slightly more plastic than elastic	Inelastic	Extremely elastic
Elongation[2]	2% 5% 10% 15% 20%[2]	2% 4% 5% 8% 10%	1% 2% 3% 5%	5% 10% 20% 50%
Elastic recovery[2]	94% 73% 39% 27% 23%[2]	97% 84% 81% 75% 72%	91% 74% 66% 45%	100% 100% 100% 95%
Handle	Very soft, limp	Soft, waxy	Medium to hard, crisp	Medium waxy
Hygroscopic nature	Slightly absorbent	Hydrophobic	Absorbent	Hydrophobic
Moisture regain percentage[3]				
At 65% RH	6.5 to 9.0%[3]	1.2 to 2.0%	7.0 to 8.5%	0.4 to 1.3%
At 95% RH	13.0 to 16.0%	1.5 to 3.0%	18.8 to 19.6%	Unavailable
At 100% RH	18.0%	4.0%	23.6%	3.0%

Flax	Nylon	Polyester	Silk	Viscose	Wool
Cellulose	Polyhexamethylene diaminoadipate	Polyethylene glycol terephthalate	Fibroin	Regenerated cellulose	Keratin
Extremely long	Short	Short	Short	Short	Short
18 000 nm	90 to 140 nm	120 to 150 nm	140 nm	180 nm	140 nm
0.8 nm	0.3 nm	0.6 nm	0.9 nm	0.8 nm	1 nm
18 000	50 to 80	115 to 140	Not known	175	Not known
Crystalline	Very crystalline	Extremely crystalline	Very crystalline	Very amorphous	Extremely amorphous
Less than cotton	35 to 15%	35 to 15%	35 to 20%	65 to 60%	70 to 75%
More than cotton	65 to 85%	65 to 85%	65 to 70%	35 to 40%	30 to 25%
Very strong	Strong to very strong	Strong to very strong	Strong	Fair	Weak
59 g/tex	36 to 65 g/tex	29 to 50 g/tex	30 to 41 g/tex	14 to 45 g/tex	9 to 18 g/tex
64 g/tex	32 to 55 g/tex	29 to 50 g/tex	23 to 32 g/tex	7 to 24 g/tex	7 to 16 g/tex
108%	82 to 89%	100%	77 to 78%	50 to 53%	78 to 89%
Very inelastic	Elastic	More elastic than plastic	More plastic than elastic	Plastic	Elastic
1% 2% 3%	2% 5% 10% 15% 20%	2% 4% 5% 8% 10%	1% 2% 4% 10% 15%	2% 3% 10% 15% 20%	2% 5% 10% 15% 20%
90% 70% 60%	100% 98% 90% 82% 75%	97% 90% 87% 89% 77%	99% 92% 70% 51% 40%	82% 52% 40% 34% 30%	99% 98% 90% 82% 75%
Hard, very crisp	Medium to hard, waxy	Medium to hard waxy	Medium, warm	Medium to soft, limp	Medium to soft, warm
Absorbent	Not absorbent	Completely hydrophobic	Very absorbent	Extremely absorbent	Very absorbent
7.0%	4.0 to 4.5%	0.1 to 0.3%	8.9 to 10.1%	12.0 to 14.0%	14.0 to 16.3%
Unavailable	6.0%	0.4%	21.5 to 23.0%	25.0 to 30.0%	25.6 to 27.9%
Unavailable	8.0%	0.4%	30.0%	45.0%	33.3%

	Acetate	Acrylic	Cotton	Elastomeric
Thermal properties	Extremely heat sensitive	Very heat sensitive	Very heat resistant	Extremely heat sensitive
Softening range	175 to 190°C	235°C	150°C begins to discolour	110 to 120°C
Melting point	260°C	Does not melt	Does not melt	230°C
Decomposition begins	Unavailable	280 to 330°C	240°C	Unavailable
Ignition temperature	520°C	560°C	390°C	Unavailable

[1] The dry tenacity of acetate is 12 to 17 g/tex. This means a load of mass 12 grams to 17 grams is required to break the acetate filament or staple fibre if 1 000 metres of it weighed 1 gram. Tex is the mass in grams of 1 000 metres of fibre, filament or yarn.

[2] If acetate filament or staple fibre is stretched 2% of its original length, it will recover 94% of this elongation of 2%. Were it to be stretched 20%, that is, one-fifth of its original length, it would recover only 23% of this one-fifth elongation and, hence, remain considerably distorted. Therefore, the greater the elastic recovery percentage, the more elastic is the fibre, and vice versa.

[3] Moisture regain percentage is the amount of moisture or water contained in the fibre and expressed as a percentage of the oven dry weight of the fibre. Triacetate has a moisture regain of 4.5% at 65% RH and 20°C. This increases to about 16% at 100% RH and 20°C. On heat setting of triacetate its moisture regain is permanently reduced to 2.5% to 3.0% at 65% RH and 20°C and to about 10% at 100% RH and 20°C.

Flax	Nylon	Polyester	Silk	Viscose	Wool
Very heat resistant	Heat sensitive	Heat sensitive	Very heat sensitive	Heat sensitive	Heat sensitive
280°C begins to discolour	220 to 230°C	220 to 240°C	100°C begins to yellow	130°C begins to yellow	100°C handle harshens
Does not melt	250 to 260°C	250 to 260°C	Does not melt	Does not melt	Does not melt, 130°C begins to yellow
310°C	315°C	Unavailable	170°C	230°C	180°C
Unavailable	520°C	Unavailable	420°C	430°C	590°C

Index